VINTAGE THURBER

VINTAGE THURBER

A COLLECTION, IN TWO VOLUMES,

OF THE BEST WRITINGS AND DRAWINGS OF

JAMES THURBER

WITH AN INTRODUCTION BY

HELEN THURBER

VOLUME I

HAMISH HAMILTON
LONDON

Printed in Great Britain
by W. S. Cowell Ltd, Butter Market, Ipswich

Contents

NOTE

A number of the pieces appearing in this volume were originally published in slightly different versions. These are 'A Sort of Genius', from *My World and Welcome to It*, 'Am Not I Your Rosalind ?', 'The Lady on the Bookcase' and 'The Ordeal of Mr Matthews', all from *The Beast in Me*, and 'My Own Ten Rules for a Happy Marriage' and 'The Interview', both from *Thurber Country*, all of which were altered when they reappeared in *Alarms and Diversions;* and 'Memorial', from *My World and Welcome to It*, which was slightly rewritten when it appeared in *Thurber's Dogs*. The later versions are followed here in each case.

'Mr Punch', from *My World and Welcome to It*, was originally entitled 'Backward and Downward with Mr Punch', and 'The French Far West', from *Let Your Mind Alone*, was originally entitled 'Wild Bird Hickok and His Friends'.

The original captions for 'My wife always has me shadowed on Valentine's Day' and 'It's a strange mood she's in, kind of a cross between Baby Doll and Elizabeth Barrett Browning', both in *Men, Women and Dogs*, were 'My wife had me arrested one night last week' and 'She says she's burning with a hard, gemlike flame. It's something they learn in school, I think'.

Introduction

It is difficult to know what to say in introducing such a huge and all-inclusive collection of one man's work as you will find in these two volumes of *Vintage Thurber*. I don't want to be pompous about it (for to sound pompous in England is to be a parody of something tolerated but unloved); on the other hand, I must not be irreverent, since I learned, to my sorrow (in one brief skirmish with the London theatre critics), that you British take your humorists very, very seriously. I lost that tiny battle, thoroughly, unequivocally and, what is worse, at the box office, and anyone crossing my path in the cool wet spring of 1961 could have heard me snarling, all the way from St James's to the Strand, 'Why do the British insist on keeping Thurber locked up in the library, perched on a cold marble pedestal on top of the bookcase, like a bust of Homer!' And that's a pretty long snarl.

Anyway, here he is back, where (you say) he belongs, between the covers of a book.

James Thurber, writer and artist, has been described by many people in as many ways. Peter De Vries once called him 'a storyteller, mimic, fantasist, realist, running commentator and mine of information on every subject under the sun.' You'll find all those Thurbers in this collection, but there are still others that I prefer: the analyzer, and the rememberer. He used those words himself once to describe a character in a story ('One is a Wanderer'), and to me they express more than anything else his greatest gifts. If he had not been a rememberer, these volumes would be thin indeed. If he had not been an analyzer, there would be no Thurber on the printed page.

Perhaps a few of the pieces appearing here would have been left out and others put in if the author himself had put together his own definitive collection. My husband had a way of scorning his early 'short funny pieces' as juvenilia, and rating far higher his later, more complex and literary ones. One or two of these, incidentally, almost didn't get printed in the magazine where for many years the greater part of Thurber's work appeared. When Harold Ross, the late editor of the *New Yorker*, first read 'A Call on Mrs Forrester', for example, he puzzled over it for a long time and left it, day after day after day, lying dejectedly on his desk. When I finally cornered him in the hall and demanded a decision, he blurted out, 'It's *literary*. I don't understand a goddam word of it.' Never shy with Ross, I followed him down to the water cooler, told him that just because he didn't understand the story was no reason to think it wasn't good, and pointed out that it was a brilliant pastiche of both Willa Cather and Henry James. He stared at me blankly for a minute, then went scowling back to his office, where he put a surly 'R' on the manuscript and sent it through. I've always wondered if it was 'pastiche' that did the trick. It was the kind of word he skirted around cautiously, not knowing what it meant and probably (I hope I'm not misjudging him) connecting it with a kind of ice cream served in fluted paper cups at children's birthday parties.

And then there are the drawings, scattered like salt and pepper through these two volumes. Oh, those drawings! E. B. White has remarked that in them 'one finds not only the simple themes of love and misunderstanding, but also the rarer and tenderer insupportabilities.' Sterner critics, usually the parents of young children, have written that their four-year-old daughter could do better, and some have even proved it by enclosing a few childish drawings that bore the unmistakable mark (I can hardly call it promise) of a mature Thurber.

James Thurber himself has confessed, 'My drawings have been described as pre-intentionalist, meaning that they were finished before the ideas for them had occurred to me. I shall not argue the point.' Again he wrote, 'I went back over the drawings in the wistful hope that I could find evidence on which to base a fond belief that my work, or fun, somehow improved after this "first phase." The only change I could find, however, in comparing old and recent scrawls, was a certain tightening of my lack of technique over the eras, the inevitable and impure result of constant practice. In the case of a man who cannot draw, but keeps on drawing anyway, practice pays in meagre coin for what it takes away.'

As for the imaginary animals that make up 'A New Natural History', the artist once admitted that they had come from 'the shameless breeding ground of the idle mind' and were 'obviously going nowhere in particular.' Who cares? To me at least, the members of this unreal bestiary are very real: the Peeve, or Pet Peeve, whose puffed-up plumage brings to mind the petulance of your own husband (or wife, if you are a husband); the Hopeless Quandary, with that so large and obviously phony tear on his cheek; the Goad, who could double for that nasty man you got stuck with at last night's party; the Barefaced Lie and the White Lie, two widely distributed rodents; a rare and deadly blossom called simply the Stepmother's Kiss; and my own favourites, derived from your country, the Scone and the Crumpet peering out of the Tiffin. Not real indeed! Just watch, the next time you go to an outdoor tea party in the English countryside.

But why do I go on like this when the Thurber drawings have been so gloriously described by Dorothy Parker, twice in this collection, and anything I might say would be pale compared to her eloquence? It was she who pointed out that Thurber people 'have the outer semblance of unbaked cookies.' So all right, think of something. Do you know a better way to describe them?

In one of his faintly crotchety moments, my husband once remarked that 'Humour isn't considered one of the major arts. I guess books of humour don't last because, like the passions, humour is a changing thing.' But another time, when he was not, to quote E. B. White again, 'trailing a thin melancholy,' he wrote 'A thing that cannot stand laughter is not a good thing.' I happen to think he was right the second time. And I hope that you will find in these pages of Thurber, along with many other things – sad, witty, ironic, lonely, bitter, strange, beautiful and wise – his gift to you of laughter, laughter that will make this distillation of his writing and drawing 'a good thing.'

Vintage Thurber is perhaps a dangerous title. I can hear certain critical phrases about old wine in new bottles, and dregs settling, and on and on like that. But after all, nothing in these pages goes back, like your famous laid-down Port, to Victorian days. The oldest bottle in this cellar is vintage 1929 – a good year for wine and humour, incidentally, if not for stocks and bonds – and has hardly had time to age. My advice is: don't be professional wine-tasters about this collection; don't roll it around on your tongue and spit it out. Sniff the bouquet as long as you like, sip here and there if you want to, and then, for Thurber's sake, drink up. If you get a little drunk in the process, so much the better. If he were here, you can be sure he would be filling your glass, over and over again.

HELEN THURBER

West Cornwall, Conn.
July, 1963

My World—and Welcome to It

FOR

NORMA AND ELLIOTT NUGENT

What Do You Mean It *Was* Brillig?

I WAS sitting at my typewriter one afternoon several weeks ago, staring at a piece of blank white paper, when Della walked in. 'They are here with the reeves,' she said. It did not surprise me that they were. With a coloured woman like Della in the house it would not surprise me if they showed up with the toves. In Della's afternoon it is always brillig; she could outgrabe a mome rath on any wabe in the world. Only Lewis Carroll would have understood Della completely. I try hard enough. 'Let them wait a minute,' I said. I got out the big Century Dictionary and put it on my lap and looked up 'reeve.' It is an interesting word, like all of Della's words; I found out that there are four kinds of reeves. 'Are they here with strings of onions?' I asked. Della said they were not. 'Are they here with enclosures or pens for cattle, poultry, or pigs; sheepfolds?' Della said no sir. 'Are they here with administrative officers?' From a little nearer the door Della said no again. 'Then they've got to be here,' I said, 'with some females of the common European sandpiper.' These scenes of ours take as much out of Della as they do out of me, but she is not a woman to be put down by a crazy man with a dictionary. 'They are here with the reeves for the windas,' said Della with brave stubbornness. Then, of course, I understood what they were there with: they were there with the Christmas wreaths for the windows. 'Oh, *those* reeves!' I said. We were both greatly relieved; we both laughed. Della and I never quite reach the breaking point; we just come close to it.

Della is a New England coloured woman with nothing of the South in her accent; she doesn't say 'd' for 'th' and she pronounces her 'r's. Hearing her talk in the next room, you might not know at first that she was coloured. You might not know till she said some such thing as 'Do you want cretonnes in the soup tonight?' (She makes wonderful cretonnes for the soup.) I have not found out much about Della's words, but I have learned a great deal about her background. She told me one day that she has three brothers and that one of them works into a garage and another works into an incinerator where they burn the refuge. The one that works into the incinerator has been working into it since the Armitage. That's what Della does to you; she gives you incinerator perfectly and then she comes out with the Armitage. I spent most of an hour one afternoon trying to figure out what was wrong with the Armitage; I thought of Armistead and armature and Armentières, and when I finally hit on Armistice it sounded crazy. It still does. Della's third and youngest brother is my favourite; I think he'll be yours, too, and everybody else's. His name is Arthur and it seems that he has just passed, with commendably high grades, his silver-

3

service eliminations. Della is delighted about that, but she is not half so delighted about it as I am.

Della came to our house in Connecticut some months ago, trailing her glory of cloudiness. I can place the date for you approximately: it was while there were still a great many fletchers about. 'The lawn is full of fletchers,' Della told me one morning, shortly after she arrived, when she brought up my orange juice. 'You mean neighbours?' I said. 'This early?' By the way she laughed I knew that fletchers weren't people; at least not people of flesh and blood. I got dressed and went downstairs and looked up the word in the indispensable Century. A fletcher, I found, is a man who makes arrows. I decided, but without a great deal of conviction, that there couldn't be any arrow-makers on my lawn at that hour in the morning and at this particular period in history. I walked cautiously out the back door and around to the front of the house – and there they were. I don't know many birds but I do know flickers. A flicker is a bird which, if it were really named fletcher, would be called flicker by all the coloured cooks in the United States. Out of a mild curiosity I looked up 'flicker' in the dictionary and I discovered that he is a bird of several aliases. When Della brought my toast and coffee into the dining room I told her about this. 'Fletchers,' I said, 'are also golden-winged woodpeckers, yellowhammers, and high-holders.' For the first time Della gave me the look that I was to recognize later, during the scene about the reeves. I have become very familiar with that look and I believe I know the thoughts that lie behind it. Della was puzzled at first because I work at home instead of in an office, but I think she has it figured out now. This man, she thinks, used to work into an office like anybody else, but he had to be sent to an institution; he got well enough to come home from the institution, but he is still not well enough to go back to the office. I could have avoided all these suspicions, of course, if I had simply come out in the beginning and corrected Della when she got words wrong. Coming at her obliquely with a dictionary only enriches the confusion; but I wouldn't have it any other way. I share with Della a form of escapism that is the most mystic and satisfying flight from actuality I have ever known. It may not always comfort me, but it never ceases to beguile me.

Every Thursday when I drive Della to Waterbury in the car for her day off, I explore the dark depths and the strange recesses of her nomenclature. I found out that she had been married for ten years but was now divorced; that is, her husband went away one day and never came back. When I asked her what he did for a living, she said he worked into a dove-wedding. 'Into a what?' I asked. 'Into a dove-wedding,' said Della. It is one of the words I haven't figured out yet, but I am still working on it. 'Where are you from, Mr Thurl?' she asked me one day. I told her Ohio, and she said, 'Ooooh, to be sure!' as if I had given her a clue to my crazy definitions, my insensitivity to the ordinary household nouns, and my ignorance of the commoner migratory birds. 'Semantics, Ohio,' I said. 'Why, there's one of them in Massachusetts, too,' said Della. 'The one I mean,' I told her, 'is bigger and more confusing.' 'I'll bet it is,' said Della.

Della told me the other day that she had had only one sister, a beautiful girl who died when she was twenty-one. 'That's too bad,' I said. 'What was the matter?' Della had what was the matter at her tongue's tip. 'She got tuberculosis from her teeth,' she said, 'and it went all through her symptom.' I didn't know what to say to that except that my teeth were all right but that my symptom could probably be easily gone all through. 'You work too much with your brain,' said Della. I knew she was trying to draw me out about my brain and what had happened to it so that I could no longer work into an office, but I changed the subject. There is no doubt that Della is considerably worried about my mental condition. One morning when I didn't get up till noon because I had been writing letters until three o'clock, Della told my wife at breakfast what was the matter with me. 'His mind works so fast his body can't keep up with it,' she said. This diagnosis has shaken me not a little. I have decided to sleep longer and work less. I know exactly what will happen to me if my mind gets so far ahead of my body that my body can't catch up with it. They will come with a reeve and this time it won't be a red-and-green one for the window, it will be a black one for the door.

The Whip-Poor-Will

THE NIGHT had just begun to get pale around the edges when the whip-poor-will began. Kinstrey, who slept in a back room on the first floor, facing the meadow and the strip of woods beyond, heard a blind man tapping and a bugle calling and a woman screaming 'Help! Police!' The sergeant in grey was cutting open envelopes with a sword. 'Sit down there, sit down there, sit down there!' he chanted at Kinstrey. 'Sit down there, cut your throat, cut your throat, whip-poor-will, whip-poor-will, whip-poor-will!' And Kinstrey woke up.

He opened his eyes, but lay without moving for several minutes, separating the fantastic morning from the sounds and symbols of his dream. There was the palest wash of light in the room. Kinstrey scowled through tousled hair at his wristwatch and saw that it was ten minutes past four. 'Whip-poor-will, whip-poor-will, whip-poor-will!' The bird sounded very near – in the grass outside the window, perhaps. Kinstrey got up and went to the window in his bare feet and looked out. You couldn't tell where the thing was. The sound was all around you, incredibly loud and compelling and penetrating. Kinstrey had never heard a whip-poor-will so near at hand before. He had heard them as a boy in Ohio in the country, but he remembered their call as faint and plaintive and faraway, dying before long somewhere between the hills and the horizon. You didn't hear the bird often in Ohio, it came back to him, and it almost never ventured as close to a house or barn as this brazen-breasted bird murdering sleep out there along the fence line somewhere. 'Whip-poor-will, whip-poor-will, whip-poor-will!' Kinstrey climbed back into bed and began to count; the bird did twenty-seven whips without pausing. His lungs must be built like a pelican's pouch, or a puffin or a penguin or pemmican or a paladin. . . . It was bright daylight when Kinstrey fell asleep again.

At breakfast, Madge Kinstrey, looking cool and well rested in her white piqué house coat, poured the coffee with steady authority. She raised her eyebrows slightly in mild surprise when Kinstrey mentioned the whip-poor-will the second time (she had not listened the first time, for she was lost in exploring with a long, sensitive finger an infinitesimal chip on the rim of her coffee cup).

'Whip-poor-will?' she said, finally. 'No, I didn't hear it. Of course, my room is on the front of the house. You must have been slept out and ready to wake up anyway, or you wouldn't have heard it.'

'Ready to wake up?' said Kinstrey. 'At four o'clock in the morning? I hadn't slept three hours.'

'Well, I didn't hear it,' said Mrs Kinstrey. 'I don't listen for night noises; I don't even hear the crickets or the frogs.'

'Neither do I,' said Kinstrey. 'It's not the same thing. This thing is loud as a fire bell. You can hear it for a mile.'

'I didn't hear it,' she said, buttering a piece of thin toast.

Kinstrey gave it up and turned his scowling attention to the headlines in the *Herald Tribune* of the day before. The vision of his wife sleeping quietly in her canopied four-poster came between his eyes and the ominous headlines. Madge always slept quietly, almost without moving, her arms straight and still outside the covers, her fingers relaxed. She did not believe anyone had to toss and turn. 'It's a notion,' she would tell Kinstrey. 'Don't let your nerves get the best of you. Use your will power.'

'Um, hm,' said Kinstrey aloud, not meaning to.

'Yes, sir?' said Arthur, the Kinstrey's coloured butler, offering Kinstrey a plate of hot blueberry muffins.

'Nothing,' said Kinstrey, looking at his wife. 'Did you hear the whip-poor-will, Arthur?'

'No, sir, I didn't,' said Arthur.

'Did Margaret?'

'I don't think she did, sir,' said Arthur. 'She didn't say anything about it.'

The next morning the whip-poor-will began again at the same hour, rolling out its loops and circles of sound across the new day. Kinstrey, in his dreams, was beset by trios of little bearded men rolling hoops at him. He tried to climb up onto a gigantic Ferris wheel whose swinging seats were rumpled beds. The round cop with wheels for feet rolled toward him shouting, 'Will power will, will power will, whip-poor-will!'

Kinstrey opened his eyes and stared at the ceiling and began to count the whips. At one point the bird did fifty-three straight, without pausing. I suppose, like the drops of water or the bright light in the third degree, this could drive you nuts, Kinstrey thought. Or make you confess. He began to think of things he hadn't thought of for years: the time he took the quarter from his mother's pocketbook, the time he steamed open a letter addressed to his father; it was from his teacher in the eighth grade. Miss – let's see – Miss Willpool, Miss Whippoor, Miss Will Power, Miss Wilmott – that was it.

He had reached the indiscretions of his middle twenties when the whip-poor-will suddenly stopped, on 'poor', not on 'will.' Something must have frightened it. Kinstrey sat up on the edge of the bed and lighted a cigarette and listened. The bird was through calling all right, but Kinstrey couldn't go back to sleep. The day was as bright as a flag. He got up and dressed.

'I thought you weren't going to smoke cigarettes before breakfast any more,' said Madge later. 'I found four stubs in the ashtray in your bedroom.'

It was no use telling her he had smoked them before going to bed; you couldn't fool Madge; she always knew. 'That goddam bird woke me up again,' he said, 'and this time I couldn't get back to sleep.' He passed her his empty coffee cup. 'It did fifty-three without stopping this morning,' he added. 'I don't know how the hell it breathes.'

His wife took his coffee cup and set it down firmly. 'Not three cups,' she said. 'Not with you sleeping so restlessly the way it is.'

'You didn't hear it, I suppose?' he said.

She poured herself some more coffee. 'No,' she said, 'I didn't hear it.'

Margaret hadn't heard it, either, but Arthur had. Kinstrey talked to them in the kitchen while they were clearing up after breakfast. Arthur said that it 'wuk' him but he went right back to sleep. He said he slept like a log – must be the air off the ocean. As for Margaret, she always slept like a log; only thing ever kept her awake was people a-hoopin' and a-hollerin'. She was glad she didn't hear the whip-poor-will. Down where she came from, she said, if you heard a whip-poor-will singing near the house, it meant there was going to be a death. Arthur said he had heard about that, too; must have been his grandma told him, or somebody.

If a whip-poor-will singing near the house meant death, Kinstrey told them, it wouldn't really make any difference whether you heard it or not. 'It doesn't make any difference whether you see the ladder you're walking under,' he said, lighting a cigarette and watching the effect of his words on Margaret. She turned from putting some plates away, and her eyes widened and rolled a little.

'Mr Kinstrey is just teasin' you, Mag,' said Arthur, who smiled and was not afraid. Thinks he's pretty smart, Kinstrey thought. Just a little bit too smart, maybe. Kinstrey remembered Arthur's way of smiling, almost imperceptibly, at things Mrs Kinstrey sometimes said to her husband when Arthur was just coming into the room or just going out – little things that were none of his business to listen to. Like 'Not three cups of coffee if a bird keeps you awake.' Wasn't that what she had said?

'Is there any more coffee?' he asked, testily. 'Or did you throw it out?' He knew they had thrown it out; breakfast had been over for almost an hour.

'We can make you some fresh,' said Arthur.

'Never mind,' said Kinstrey. 'Just don't be so sure of yourself. There's nothing in life to be sure about.'

When, later in the morning, he started out the gate to walk down to the post office, Madge called to him from an upstairs window. 'Where are you going?' she asked, amiably enough. He frowned up at her. 'To the taxidermist's,' he said, and went on.

He realized, as he walked along in the warm sunlight, that he had made something of a spectacle of himself. Just because he hadn't had enough sleep – or enough coffee. It wasn't his fault, though. It was that infernal bird. He discovered, after a quarter of a mile, that the imperative rhythm of the whip-poor-will's call was running through his mind, but the words of the song were new: fatal bell, fatal bell, fa-tal bell. Now, where had that popped up from? It took him some time to place it; it was a fragment from 'Macbeth'. There was something about the fatal bellman crying in the night. 'The fatal bellman cried the livelong night' – something like that. It was an owl that cried the night Duncan was murdered. Funny thing to call up after all these years; he hadn't read the play since college. It was that fool Margaret, talking about the whip-poor-will and the old superstition that if you hear the whip-poor-will singing near the house, it means there is going to be a death. Here it was 1942, and people still believed in stuff like that.

The next dawn the dream induced by the calling of the whip-poor-will was longer and more tortured – a nightmare filled with dark perils and heavy hopelessness. Kinstrey woke up trying to cry out. He lay there breathing hard and listening to the bird. He began to count: one, two, three, four, five . . .

Then, suddenly, he leaped out of bed and ran to the window and began yelling and pounding on the windowpane and running the blind up and down. He shouted and cursed until his voice got hoarse. The bird kept right on going. He slammed the window down and turned away from it, and there was Arthur in the doorway.

'What is it, Mr Kinstrey?' said Arthur. He was fumbling with the end of a faded old bathrobe and trying to blink the sleep out of his eyes. 'Is anything the matter?'

Kinstrey glared at him. 'Get out of here!' he shouted. 'And put some coffee on. Or get me a brandy or something.'

'I'll put some coffee on,' said Arthur. He went shuffling away in his slippers, still half asleep.

'Well,' said Madge Kinstrey over her coffee cup at breakfast, 'I hope you got your tantrum over and done with this morning. I never heard such a spectacle – squalling like a spoiled brat.'

'You can't hear spectacles,' said Kinstrey, coldly. 'You see them.'

'I'm sure I don't know what you're talking about,' she said.

No, you don't, thought Kinstrey, you never have; never have, nev-er have, nev-er have. Would he ever get that damned rhythm out of his head? It struck him that perhaps Madge had no subconscious. When she lay on her back, her eyes closed; when she got up, they opened, like a doll's. The mechanism of her mind was as simple as a cigarette box; it was either open or it was closed, and there was nothing else, nothing else, nothing else . . .

The whole problem turns on a very neat point, Kinstrey thought as he lay awake that night, drumming on the headboard with his fingers. William James would have been interested in it; Henry, too, probably. I've got to ignore this thing, get adjusted to it, become oblivious of it. I mustn't fight it, I mustn't build it up. If I get to screaming at it, I'll be running across that wet grass out there in my bare feet, charging that bird as if it were a trench full of Germans, throwing rocks at it, giving the Rebel yell or something, for God's sake. No, I mustn't build it up. I'll think of something else every time it pops into my mind. I'll name the Dodger infield to myself, over and over: Camilli, Herman, Reese, Vaughan, Camilli, Herman, Reese . . .

Kinstrey did not succeed in becoming oblivious of the whip-poor-will. Its dawn call pecked away at his dreams like a vulture at a heart. It slowly carved out a recurring nightmare in which Kinstrey was attacked by an umbrella whose handle, when you clutched it, clutched right back, for the umbrella was not an umbrella at all but a raven. Through the gloomy hallways of his mind rang the Thing's dolorous cry: nevermore, nevermore, nevermore, whip-poor-will, whip-poor-will...

One day, Kinstrey asked Mr Tetford at the post office if the whip-poor-wills ever went away. Mr Tetford squinted at him. 'Don't look like the sun was brownin' you up none,' he said. 'I don't know as they ever go away. They move around. I like to hear 'em. You get used to 'em.'

'Sure,' said Kinstrey. 'What do people do when they can't get used to them, though – I mean old ladies or sick people?'

'Only one's been bothered was old Miss Purdy. She darn near set fire to the whole island tryin' to burn 'em out of her woods. Shootin' at 'em might drive 'em off, or a body could trap 'em easy enough and let 'em loose somewheres else. But people get used to 'em after a few mornings.'

'Oh, sure,' said Kinstrey. 'Sure.'

That evening in the living room, when Arthur brought in the coffee, Kinstrey's cup cackled idiotically in its saucer when he took it off the tray.

Madge Kinstrey laughed. 'Your hand is shaking like a leaf,' she said.

He drank all his coffee at once and looked up savagely. 'If I could get one good night's sleep, it might help,' he said. 'That damn bird! I'd like to wring its neck.'

'Oh, come, now,' she said, mockingly. 'You wouldn't hurt a fly. Remember the mouse we caught in the Westport house? You took it out in the field and let it go.'

'The trouble with you—' he began, and stopped. He opened the lid of a cigarette box and shut it, opened and shut it again, reflectively. 'As simple as that,' he said.

She dropped her amused smile and spoke shortly. 'You're acting like a child about that silly bird,' she said. 'Worse than a child. I was over at the Barrys' this afternoon. Even their little Ann didn't make such a fuss. A whip-poor-will frightened her the first morning, but now she never notices them.'

'I'm not frightened, for God's sake!' shouted Kinstrey. 'Frightened or brave, asleep or awake, open or shut – you make everything black or white.'

'Well,' she said, 'I like that.'

'I think the bird wakes you up, too,' he said. 'I think it wakes up Arthur and Margaret.'

'And we just pretend it doesn't?' she asked. 'Why on earth should we?'

'Oh, out of some fool notion of superiority, I suppose. Out of – I don't know.'

'I'll thank you not to class me with the servants,' she said coldly. He lighted a cigarette and didn't say anything. 'You're being ridiculous and childish,' she said, 'fussing about nothing at all, like an invalid in a wheel chair.' She got up and started from the room.

'Nothing at all,' he said, watching her go.

She turned at the door. 'Ted Barry says he'll take you on at tennis if your bird hasn't worn you down too much.' She went on up the stairs, and he heard her close the door of her room.

He sat smoking moodily for a long time, and fell to wondering whether the man's wife in 'The Raven' had seen what the man had seen perched on the pallid bust of Pallas just above the chamber door. Probably not, he decided. When he went to bed, he lay awake a long while trying to think of the last line of 'The Raven.' He couldn't get any farther than 'Like a demon that is dreaming,' and this kept running through his head. 'Nuts,' he said at last, aloud, and he had the oddly disturbing feeling that it wasn't he who had spoken but somebody else.

Kinstrey was not surprised that Madge was a little girl in pigtails and a play suit. The long grey hospital room was filled with poor men in will chairs, running their long, sensitive fingers around the rims of empty coffee cups. 'Poor Will, poor Will,' chanted Madge, pointing her finger at him. 'Here are your spectacles, here are your spectacles.' One of the sick men was Arthur, grinning at him, grinning at him and holding him with one hand, so that he was powerless to move his arms or legs. 'Hurt a fly, hurt a fly,' chanted Madge. 'Whip him now, whip him now!' she cried, and she was the umpoor in the high chair beside the court, holding a black umbrella over her head; love thirty, love forty, forty-one, forty-two, forty-three, forty-four. His feet were stuck in the wet concrete on his side of the net and Margaret peered over the net at him, holding a skillet for a racquet. Arthur was pushing him down now, and he was caught in the concrete from head to foot. It was Madge laughing and counting over him: refer-three, refer-four, refer-five, refer-will, repoor-will, whip-poor-will, whip-poor-will, whip-poor-will...

The dream still clung to Kinstrey's mind like a cobweb as he stood in the kitchen in his pyjamas and bare feet, wondering what he wanted, what he was looking for. He turned on the cold water in the sink and filled a glass, but only took a sip, and put it down. He left the water running. He opened the breadbox and took out half a loaf wrapped in oiled paper, and pulled open a drawer. He took out the bread knife and then put it back and took out the long, sharp carving knife. He was standing there holding the knife in one hand and the bread in the other when the door to the dining room opened. It was Arthur. 'Who do you do first?' Kinstrey said to him, hoarsely....

The Barrys, on their way to the beach in their station wagon, drove into the driveway between the house and the barn. They were surprised to see that, at a quarter to eleven in the morning, the Kinstrey servants hadn't taken in the milk. The bottle, standing on the small back porch, was hot to Barry's touch. When he couldn't rouse anyone, pounding and calling, he climbed up on the cellar door and looked in the kitchen window. He told his wife sharply to get back in the car....

The local police and the state troopers were in and out of the house all day. It wasn't every morning in the year that you got called out on a triple murder and suicide.

It was just getting dark when Troopers Baird and Lennon came out of the front door and walked down to their car, pulled up beside the road in front of the house. Out in back, probably in the little strip of wood there, Lennon figured, a whip-poor-will began to call. Lennon listened a minute. 'You ever hear the old people say a whip-poor-will singing near the house means death?' he asked.

Baird grunted and got in under the wheel. Lennon climbed in beside him. 'Take more'n a whip-poor-will to cause a mess like that,' said Trooper Baird, starting the car.

The Macbeth Murder Mystery

'IT WAS a stupid mistake to make,' said the American woman I had met at my hotel in the English lake country, 'but it was on the counter with the other Penguin books – the little sixpenny ones, you know, with the paper covers – and I supposed of course it was a detective story. All the others were detective stories. I'd read all the others, so I bought this one without really looking at it carefully. You can imagine how mad I was when I found it was Shakespeare.' I murmured something sympathetically. 'I don't see why the Penguin-books people had to get out Shakespeare's plays in the same size and everything as the detective stories,' went on my companion. 'I think they have different-coloured jackets,' I said. 'Well, I didn't notice that,' she said. 'Anyway, I got real comfy in bed that night and all ready to read a good mystery story and here I had "The Tragedy of Macbeth" – a book for high-school students. Like "Ivanhoe." ' 'Or "Lorna Doone",' I said. 'Exactly,' said the American lady. 'And I was just crazy for a good Agatha Christie, or something. Hercule Poirot is my favourite detective.' 'Is he the rabbity one?' I asked. 'Oh, no,' said my crime-fiction expert. 'He's the Belgian one. You're thinking of Mr Pinkerton, the one that helps Inspector Bull. He's good, too.'

Over her second cup of tea my companion began to tell the plot of a detective story that had fooled her completely – it seems it was the old family doctor all the time. But I cut in on her. 'Tell me,' I said. 'Did you read "Macbeth"?' 'I *had* to read it,' she said. 'There wasn't a scrap of anything else to read in the whole room.' 'Did you like it?' I asked. 'No, I did not,' she said, decisively. 'In the first place, I don't think for a moment that Macbeth did it.' I looked at her blankly. 'Did what?' I asked. 'I don't think for a moment that he killed the King,' she said. 'I don't think the Macbeth woman was mixed up in it, either. You suspect them the most, of course, but those are the ones that are never guilty – or shouldn't be, anyway.' 'I'm afraid,' I began, 'that I –' 'But don't you see?' said the American lady. 'It would spoil everything if you could figure out right away who did it. Shakespeare was too smart for that. I've read that people never *have* figured out "Hamlet," so it isn't likely Shakespeare would have made "Macbeth" as simple as it seems.' I thought this over while I filled my pipe. 'Who do you suspect?' I asked, suddenly. 'Macduff,' she said, promptly. 'Good God!' I whispered, softly.

'Oh, Macduff did it, all right,' said the murder specialist. 'Hercule Poirot would have got him easily.' 'How did you figure it out?' I demanded. 'Well,' she said, 'I didn't right away. At first I suspected Banquo. And then, of course, he was the second person killed. That was good right in there, that part. The

13

person you suspect of the first murder should always be the second victim.' 'Is that so?' I murmured. 'Oh, yes,' said my informant. 'They have to keep surprising you. Well, after the second murder I didn't know *who* the killer was for a while.' 'How about Malcolm and Donalbain, the King's sons?' I asked. 'As I remember it, they fled right after the first murder. That looks suspicious.' 'Too suspicious,' said the American lady. 'Much too suspicious. When they flee, they're never guilty. You can count on that.' 'I believe,' I said, 'I'll have a brandy,' and I summoned the waiter. My companion leaned toward me, her eyes bright, her teacup quivering. 'Do you know who discovered Duncan's body?' she demanded. I said I was sorry, but I had forgotten. 'Macduff discovers it,' she said, slipping into the historical present. 'Then he comes running downstairs and shouts, "Confusion has broke open the Lord's anointed temple" and "Sacrilegious murder has made his masterpiece" and on and on like that.' The good lady tapped me on the knee. 'All that stuff was *rehearsed*,' she said. 'You wouldn't say a lot of stuff like that, offhand, would you – if you had found a body?' She fixed me with a glittering eye. 'I—' I began. 'You're right!' she said. 'You wouldn't! Unless you had practised it in advance. "My God, there's a body in here!" is what an innocent man would say.' She sat back with a confident glare.

I thought for a while. 'But what do you make of the Third Murderer?' I asked. 'You know, the Third Murderer has puzzled "Macbeth" scholars for three hundred years.' 'That's because they never thought of Macduff,' said the American lady. 'It was Macduff, I'm certain. You couldn't have one of the victims murdered by two ordinary thugs – the murderer always has to be somebody important.' 'But what about the banquet scene?' I asked, after a moment. 'How do you account for Macbeth's guilty actions there, when Banquo's ghost came in and sat in his chair?' The lady leaned forward and tapped me on the knee again. 'There wasn't any ghost,' she said. 'A big, strong man like that doesn't go around seeing ghosts – especially in a brightly lighted banquet hall with dozens of people around. Macbeth was *shielding somebody!*' 'Who was he shielding?' I asked. 'Mrs Macbeth, of course,' she said. 'He thought she did it and he was going to take the rap himself. The husband always does that when the wife is suspected.' 'But what,' I demanded, 'about the sleepwalking scene, then?' 'The same thing, only the other way around,' said my companion. 'That time *she* was shielding *him*. She wasn't asleep at all. Do you remember where it says, "Enter Lady Macbeth with a taper"?' 'Yes,' I said. 'Well, people who walk in their sleep *never carry lights!*' said my fellow-traveller. 'They have second sight. Did you ever hear of a sleepwalker carrying a light?' 'No,' I said, 'I never did.' 'Well, then, she wasn't asleep. She was acting guilty to shield Macbeth.' 'I think,' I said, 'I'll have another brandy,' and I called the waiter. When he brought it, I drank it rapidly and rose to go. 'I believe,' I said, 'that you have got hold of something. Would you lend me that "Macbeth"? I'd like to look it over tonight. I don't feel, somehow, as if I'd ever really read it.' 'I'll get it for you,' she said. 'But you'll find that I am right.'

*

I read the play over carefully that night, and the next morning, after break-fast, I sought out the American woman. She was on the putting green, and I came up behind her silently and took her arm. She gave an exclamation. 'Could I see you alone?' I asked, in a low voice. She nodded cautiously and followed me to a secluded spot. 'You've found out something?' she breathed. 'I've found out,' I said, triumphantly, 'the name of the murderer!' 'You mean it wasn't Macduff?' she said. 'Macduff is as innocent of those murders,' I said, 'as Macbeth and the Macbeth woman.' I opened the copy of the play, which I had with me, and turned to Act II, Scene 2. 'Here,' I said, 'you will see where Lady Macbeth says, "I laid their daggers ready. He could not miss 'em. Had he not resembled my father as he slept, I had done it." Do you see?' 'No,' said the American woman, bluntly, 'I don't.' 'But it's simple!' I exclaimed. 'I wonder I didn't see it years ago. The reason Duncan resembled Lady Macbeth's father as he slept is that *it actually was her father!*' 'Good God!' breathed my com-panion, softly. 'Lady Macbeth's father killed the King,' I said, 'and, hearing someone coming, thrust the body under the bed and crawled into the bed him-self.' 'But,' said the lady, 'you can't have a murderer who only appears in the story once. You can't have that.' 'I know that,' I said, and I turned to Act II, Scene 4. 'It says here, "Enter Ross with an old Man." Now, that old man is never identified and it is my contention he was old Mr Macbeth, whose am-bition it was to make his daughter Queen. There you have your motive.' 'But even then,' cried the American lady, 'he's still a minor character!' 'Not,' I said, gleefully, 'when you realize that he was also *one of the weird sisters in disguise!*' 'You mean one of the three witches?' 'Precisely,' I said. 'Listen to this speech of the old man's. "On Tuesday last, a falcon towering in her pride of place, was by a mousing owl hawk'd at and kill'd." Who does that sound like?' 'It sounds like the way the three witches talk,' said my companion, reluctantly. 'Pre-cisely!' I said again. 'Well,' said the American woman, 'maybe you're right, but—' 'I'm sure I am,' I said. 'And do you know what I'm going to do now?' 'No,' she said. 'What?' 'Buy a copy of "Hamlet",' I said, 'and solve *that!*' My companion's eyes brightened. 'Then,' she said, 'you don't think Hamlet did it?' 'I am,' I said, 'absolutely positive he didn't.' 'But who,' she demanded, 'do you suspect?' I looked at her cryptically. 'Everybody,' I said, and dis-appeared into a small grove of trees as silently as I had come.

Mr Punch

LOOKING for a Roman coin I had dropped on the library floor of the house I rented for the winter, I found, on a shelf behind a sofa, two dozen immense bound volumes of *Punch*. They contained all the copies of the famous British weekly from the year it was founded until 1891, exactly half a century later. I picked out three volumes at random and began idly turning the pages of first one and then another. When the following Tuesday found me still at it, I realized what I was up to: I was getting ready to make some kind of report on Mr Punch of the nineteenth century. If it has been done before, all I can say is that I am doing it again.

Let us begin, then, with the tome which contains the issues from July, 1889, to July, 1891, and work our way back toward the Civil War. This volume, like all the others, contains some rather heavy introductory notes summarizing what was going on in the world at the time. In this two-year period quite a lot was going on, if you have forgotten. The 'young and impetuous' Kaiser Wilhelm was rattling his sabre and already disturbing the peace of mind of Europe. The volume falls open easily at the double page containing Tenniel's famous cartoon 'Dropping the Pilot' – for it was at this time that Wilhelm got rid of Bismarck. Socialism was raising its troublesome head, so terrifying Mr Punch that he had Tenniel draw a cartoon of a serpent (Socialism) wrapped about the body of an eagle (Trade) and striving to crush the bird's wings (Capital and Labour). The brief, sad romance of Parnell and Captain O'Shea's wife shocked the British Isles and formed a dark foil for the decorous private life of Mr Gladstone, who, past eighty years old, celebrated his golden-wedding anniversary. Tennyson, the poet laureate, became an octogenarian in his turn, and Browning died two years short of the mark. A potato famine was predicted in Ireland and an epidemic of influenza held the world in what I am sure *Punch*, somewhere or other, must have called its grip. A young pianist whom *Punch* laughingly alluded to as 'Paddy Rewski from Irish Poland' gave a concert in London, but *Punch* could not appraise the young man's talents because *Punch* did not attend the concert. *Punch* could report, however, that the life in Marion Crawford's latest novel was real life and that Mr Ibsen's 'A Doll's House' was 'unutterably loathsome' and should be removed from the stages of the world.

The harsh effects on the feminine complexion of that new invention, the electric light, gave *Punch* a hundred whimsical ideas, and so did the new and wonderful Eiffel Tower. (One proud London paper wrote, 'The Eiffel Tower is 1,000 feet high; the Forth bridge, if stood on end, would be 5,280 feet in height.') Mr Edison's phonograph was received with proper respect, *Punch* calling up the spirit of Faraday, who solemnly approved of the device. Montana, the Dakotas, and Washington were admitted to the Union and the government breathed more easily when Sitting Bull was shot dead. Barnum was in London with his great show and Millet's 'The Angelus' was sold to an American. A hydrophobia scare led to the muzzling of all the dogs in England and *Punch* came out for the much-abused Pasteur in a drawing with this dialogue between a husband and wife:

'Oh, Joseph! Teddy's just been bitten by a strange dog! Doctor says we'd better take him over to Pasteur *at once*!'

'But, my love, I've just written and published a violent attack upon M. Pasteur, on the score of his cruelty to rabbits! And at *your instigation*, too!'

'Oh, Heavens! Never mind the rabbits *now*! What are all the rabbits in the world compared to *our only child*.'

Among the minor objects of Mr Punch's annoyance during these years were Mr Pinero for an attack on the London music halls, newfangled barbed wire fences for interfering with fox-hunting, the Americans for coining so much money and so many new words, and Count Tolstoi for a savage assault on tobacco smokers. Of this last *Punch* rhymed, in part:

> Tolstoi knew a man who said
> He cut off a woman's head;
> But, when half the deed was done,
> Lo, the murderer's courage gone!
> And he finished, 'tis no joke,
> Only by the aid of smoke.

Unhorrified by murderers who got a lift from nicotine, Mr Punch could not approve of the use of the weed by ladies, some of whom were apparently going in for cigars:

> You're beautiful, but fairer far
> You'd be – if only you would let
> Your male friends smoke that big cigar
> And yield them, too, that cigarette.

Most of the jokes in this volume are about bad cooks, worse painters, errant nursemaids, precocious children, insolent cab-drivers, and nonchalant young blades in ballrooms. I found, somewhat to my surprise, that a great many of these young blades were named Gus. I found, also to my surprise, that the expression 'I'm nuts on,' meaning 'I'm crazy about,' was used in 1891. And that the Irate-Voice-from-Upstairs joke began fifty years ago (unless what I ran across was just a revival of it):

STERN VOICE (*from first-floor landing, temp. 12.10 p.m.*): Alice!

ALICE (*softly*): Yes, 'Pa'!

VOICE (*with threatening ring in it*): Does that young man in the front parlour take tea or coffee for his breakf—!!?

('*Door*' – *and he was gone!*)

During the eighties and nineties Mr Henry James (of whom I could find no mention anywhere in *Punch*) was in the midst of his elaborate and delicate examinations of American ladies abroad, but Mr Punch lashed out at them in a simpler manner:

SIR JAMES: And were you in Rome?

AMERICAN LADY: I guess not. (*To her daughter*.) Say, Bella, did we visit Rome?

FAIR DAUGHTER: Why, Ma, certainly! Don't you remember? It was in Rome we bought the lisle-thread stockings!

(*American lady is convinced*)

The American male comes in for it, too:

YOUNG BRITISHER: Your father's not with you, then, Miss Van Tromp?

FAIR NEW YORK MILLIONAIRESS (*one of three*): Why, no – Pa's much too vulgar! It's as much as we can do to stand Ma!

Sometimes *Punch* had at our damsels in verse:

THE AMERICAN GIRL

She 'guesses' and she 'calculates,' she wears all sorts o' collars,
    Her yellow hair is not without suspicion of a dye;
Her 'páppa' is a dull old man who turned pork into dollars,
    But everyone admits that she's indubitably spry.

She did Rome in a swift two days, gave half the time to Venice,
    But vows that she saw everything, although in awful haste;
She's fond of dancing, but she seems to fight shy of lawn tennis,
    Because it might endanger the proportions of her waist.

Her manner might be well defined as elegantly skittish;
    She loves a Lord as only a Republican can do;
And quite the best of titles she's persuaded are the British,
    And well she knows the Peerage, for she's read it through and through.

She's bediamonded superbly and shines like a constellation,
    You scarce can see her fingers for the multitude of rings;
She's just a shade too conscious, as it seems, of admiration,
    With irritating tendencies to wriggle when she sings.

She owns she is 'Amur'can,' and her accent is alarming;
    Her birthplace is an awful name you pray you may forget;
Yet, after all, we own 'La Belle Américaine' is charming,
    So let us hope she'll win at last her long-sought coronet.

Phil May, the great caricaturist, came back to London in the early nineties after a long stay in Australia, but his work does not appear in this volume. It could have used some. Before I leave this engrossing period of history and humour I must quote a typical Foreigner-in-the-English-Home joke. This one, with its evidence of the nineteenth-century Englishman's fine ear for the German accent, is my favourite of several hundred:

HOSTESS: Won't you try some of that jelly, Herr Silbermund?

HERR SILBERMUND (*who has just been helped to pudding*): Ach, zank you, no. I voot 'rahzer pear viz ze ills ve haf zan vly to ozzers ve know not of.'

In the years 1869 to 1871 (our second volume), Mr Punch had a wealth of subjects for his little punning pieces and his big political posters. The Fenians in Ireland and America were raising hell on behalf of the freedom of Erin, and the Alabama claims case was still a sore point between England and America. Harriet Beecher Stowe, having freed the slaves, nosed about in the private life of the late Lord Byron and provided the great scandal of the day in a magazine article revealing the love story of the poet and his half sister, Augusta Leigh. General Dan Sickles, hero of the Peach Orchard at Gettysburg, who was god-damming up and down the American chancellery in Madrid as our ambassador, informed his government that the Spaniards were sore about our friendly attitude toward the Cuban insurrectionists and might do something about it. On the eighteenth of July, 1870, the Infallibility of the Pope was declared. On the next day France declared war on Prussia and rushed headlong to defeat, the French *mitrailleuse* proving less deadly than the Prussian needle gun. Disraeli published a novel called 'Lothair' and made Bartlett's 'Quotations' with a crack about critics being people who have failed in literature and the arts. Oxford beat Harvard in the first crew race ever rowed between the two universities and a small, resolute band of women began to clamour for the right to vote. Darwin's 'The Descent of Man' was pie for the wits of *Punch*, and the magazine cried out against the deplorable fact that the word 'reliable', which it described as 'a new and unnecessary American adjective,' was creeping into the inviolable English tongue. On top of everything the women of England were affecting the 'Grecian bend,' which *Punch* called 'an exaggerated forward inclination of the body, an absurd fashion of the hour.'

I devoted a great deal of my research to hunting down seventy-year-old versions of jokes which are still going the rounds, and I offer my most cherished discovery:

THE CURATE: O dear, O dear! Drunk again, Jones! *Drunk* again! And in broad daylight, too!
JONES: Lorsh (*hic*)! Whatsh the oddsh! Sh–Sh–Sho am *I*!

You will remember this one, too:

TICKET COLLECTOR: Now, then, make haste! Where's your ticket?
BANDSMAN (*refreshed*): Aw've lost it!
TICKET COLLECTOR: Nonsense! Feel in your pockets. Ye cannot hev lost it!
BANDSMAN: Aw cannot? Why, man, Aw've lost the *big drum*!

Throughout this volume there runs a series of drawings of cute kiddies above the most distressingly cute captions. If the researcher rapidly tires of the pen-and-ink drawings of the famous George Louis Palmella Busson Du Maurier ('the gentle, graceful satirist of modern fashionable life'), it is perhaps mainly because of the gags he is given to illustrate. I select the ickiest of them. A mother is about to give a dose of medicine to a two-year-old girl:

MASTER GEORGE (*whispers*): I say! Kitty! Has mamma been telling you she'd give you 'a lovely spoonful of delicious currant jelly, O so nice, so very nice'?

KITTY: Ess! Cullen' jelly! O so ni', so welly ni'!
MASTER GEORGE: THEN DON'T TAKE IT!

Du Maurier husbands and wives are pictured engaged in what are surely the most depressing conversations ever recorded in the history of civilized man. I quote the first, but not necessarily the worst, of those I come to in my grim notes:

'Well, Dearest, where have you been tonight? "Monday Pops" again?'
'No, Celia, I have spent a most instructive evening with the "Anthropological Society".'
'The "Anthropohowmuch," Darling?'
'The "Anthropo*logi*cal," Celia! Are you deaf?'
'How nice! And where do they "Anthropo*lodge*," Duckums?'

I shall end my discussion of this fond old volume with a caption that, for its simplicity and point, rose out of these fusty yellow pages like a little cool wind. I like to think this is one the author of 'Trilby' thought up himself. It appears under a drawing of a dowager in a carriage drawn by two horses and surmounted by a coachman and a footman. The lady has just given alms to a poverty-stricken woman whose ragged children are gathered about her knees:

GRATEFUL RECIPIENT: Bless you, my lady! May we meet in Heaven!
HAUGHTY DONOR: Good Gracious! Drive on, Jarvis!

It grieves me to report that *Punch* was unable to let it go at that. In parentheses and italics there follows this explanatory line: 'She had evidently read Dr Johnson, who "didn't care to meet certain people *any*where".' Just in case you hadn't caught on.

In the year 1863 (our third and last volume runs from July, '63, to July, '65) the newly married Edward and Alexandra were cheered everywhere they went. The great Blondin was walking the tightrope in the Crystal Palace and a young woman who imitated him at a small-town carnival fell and broke her neck. The Russians were beating up the Poles, and Schleswig-Holstein was the Czecho-Slovakia of the year – and of the next. Louis Napoleon announced that 'the improvements brought about by civilization would render war still more destructive.' Disraeli said, 'The condition of Europe is one of very grave character. Let us be sure, if we go to war, first of all that it is a necessary and just war.' The Japanese killed an Englishman named Richardson and 'committed a savage assault' on an English woman and two friends. Garibaldi visited London and the three-hundredth anniversary of Shakespeare's birthday was celebrated. *Punch* was irritated by the clamour in the streets caused by organ-grinders and hurdy-gurdy men and hucksters selling watercress and prawns. There is no mention in the volume of what must have been to *Punch* one of the minor events of the early sixties: the battle of Gettysburg.

Mr Punch's snipes and jibes at Abraham Lincoln and the cause of the North are too well known to call for an extended examination, but the researcher will cite two because he wants to append some notes of his own to them:

Instead of *Habeas Corpus* in the United States, which has been suspended, it is now, in the case of the prisoner who is arbitrarily arrested, ABE who has *corpus*. [Researcher's Note: The English government, which was apparently unswayed by *Punch*, suspended the right of habeas corpus in Ireland in 1866.]

LATEST AMERICAN TELEGRAMS (1864)

Grant reduced to grunt.
Sheridan's Rivals successful.
Hunter hunted.
Pillow on Sherman's rear.

[Researcher's Note: The Encyclopedia Americana on Pillow, Gideon, J., American soldier: 'After 1861 he did not figure in any battle save Murfreesboro, in which he had a courtesy command.' Murfreesboro was fought some twenty months before *Punch's* little crack.]

You might also be interested in a diatribe printed January 21, 1865, and headed 'To the Yankee Braggarts':

This American crisis is one which is only to be met by the most unmitigated Swagger, and Mr Punch, hastily constituting himself Head Swaggerer to the English Nation, hereby answers the Yankee journals 'with shouts as loud and shrieks as fierce as their own.' [Researcher's Note: Somebody had got off some remarks in America about our being able to lick England.] War with England, indeed, you long-faced, wizened, ugly, ignorant Occidentals! Defy the flag that has braved a thousand years the battle and the breeze? Laugh at the Lion and give umbrage to the Unicorn? Bah! Bosh! Shut-up! Tremble!

It goes on to say that one Sir Hugh Rose could go over and lick the whole United States. This happened to be the first time I had ever heard of Sir Hugh, but maybe Grant and Lee knew who he was.

The end to all this is well known: Tenniel drew a touching cartoon showing Britannia laying a wreath on Lincoln's bier and Tom Taylor wrote an equally famous and equally touching poem eating all of *Punch's* nasty words and all of Tenniel's nasty drawings. (This, incidentally, was the year that 'Alice in Wonderland' was published, the book that gave Mr Tenniel something really important to do. I find no mention of it in *Punch*.)

Lincoln and the North might be forgiven, but America's pernicious invention of new words wasn't. 'If the pure well of English is to remain undefiled,' said Mr Punch, 'no Yankee should be allowed henceforth to throw mud into it. It is a form of verbal expectoration that is most profane, most detestable.' He gives you an idea of what he has in mind a few pages farther on. Two American ladies are pictured at a dance, with a young beau standing by. Says one of the ladies (under the heading 'Yet Another Americanism'): 'Here, Maria, hold my coat while I have a fling with the stranger.'

American ladies were invariably represented as pretty and well shaped in spite of Mr Punch's purple anger at one Nathaniel Hawthorne, sometime American consul at Liverpool, who had brought out a book about England 'thoroughly saturated with what seems ill-nature and spite' and making a 'savage onslaught upon our women.' Excerpts are quoted, but I have space for only one: 'English girls seemed to me all homely alike. They seemed to be country lasses, of sturdy and wholesome aspect, with coarse-grained, cabbage-rosy cheeks. . . . How unlike the trim little damsels of my native land!' Mr Punch hopes that Mr Hawthorne will go on to write an autobiography, for Mr Punch is 'very partial to essays on the natural history of half-civilized animals.'

I will close this survey with a typical illustrated joke of those years of pain and sorrow. It is labelled 'Gentle Rebuke' and the caption will give you some idea of what the drawing is like:

OLD GENTLEMAN: How charmingly that young lady sings! Pray, who composed the beautiful song she has just favoured us with?
LADY OF THE HOUSE: Oh, it is by Mendelssohn.
OLD GENTLEMAN: Ah! One of his famous 'Songs without Words,' I suppose.
(Moral – Young ladies, when you sing, pronounce your words carefully, and then you will not expose unmusical old gentlemen to making such ridiculous mistakes as the above.)

Has anybody got any bound copies of old almanacs?

The Man Who Hated Moonbaum

AFTER they had passed through the high, grilled gate they walked for almost a quarter of a mile, or so it seemed to Tallman. It was very dark; the air smelled sweet; now and then leaves brushed against his cheek or forehead. The little, stout man he was following had stopped talking, but Tallman could hear him breathing. They walked on for another minute. 'How we doing?' Tallman asked, finally. 'Don't ask me questions!' snapped the other man. 'Nobody asks me questions! You'll learn.' The hell I will, thought Tallman, pushing through the darkness and the fragrance and the mysterious leaves; the hell I will, baby; this is the last time you'll ever see me. The knowledge that he was leaving Hollywood within twenty-four hours gave him a sense of comfort.

There was no longer turf or gravel under his feet; there was something that rang flatly: tile, or flagstones. The little man began to walk more slowly and Tallman almost bumped into him. 'Can't we have a light?' said Tallman. 'There you go!' shouted his guide. 'Don't get me screaming! What are you trying to do to me?' 'I'm not trying to do anything to you,' said Tallman. 'I'm trying to find out where we're going.'

The other man had come to a stop and seemed to be groping around. 'First it's wrong uniforms,' he said, 'then it's red fire – red fire in Scotland, red fire three hundred years ago! I don't know why I ain't crazy!' Tallman could make out the other man dimly, a black, gesturing blob. 'You're doing all right,' said Tallman. Why did I ever leave the Brown Derby with this guy? he asked himself. Why did I ever let him bring me to his house – if he has a house? Who the hell does he think he is?

Tallman looked at his wristwatch; the dial glowed wanly in the immense darkness. He was a little drunk, but he could see that it was half past three in the morning. 'Not trying to do anything to me, he says!' screamed the little man. 'Wasn't his fault! It's never anybody's fault! They give me ten thousand dollars' worth of Sam Browne belts for Scotch Highlanders and it's nobody's fault!' Tallman was beginning to get his hangover headache. 'I want a light!' he said. 'I want a drink! I want to know where the hell I am!' 'That's it! Speak out!' said the other. 'Say what you think! I like a man who knows where he is. We'll get along.' 'Contact!' said Tallman. 'Camera! Lights! Get out that hundred-year-old brandy you were talking about.'

The response to this was a soft flood of rose-coloured radiance; the little man had somehow found a light switch in the dark. God knows where, thought Tallman; probably on a tree. They were in a courtyard paved with enormous

flagstones which fitted together with mosaic perfection. The light revealed the
dark stones of a building which looked like the Place de la Concorde side of the
Crillon. 'Come on, you people!' said the little man. Tallman looked behind
him, half expecting to see the shadowy forms of Scottish Highlanders, but
there was nothing but the shadows of trees and of oddly shaped plants closing
in on the courtyard. With a key as small as a dime, the little man opened a door
that was fifteen feet high and made of wood six inches thick.

Marble stairs tumbled down like Niagara into a grand canyon of a living
room. The steps of the two men sounded sharp and clear on the stairs, died in
the soft depths of an immensity of carpet in the living room. The ceiling
towered above them. There were highlights on dark wood medallions, on burnished shields, on silver curves and edges. On one wall a forty-foot tapestry
hung from the ceiling to within a few feet of the floor. Tallman was looking at
this when his companion grasped his arm. 'The second rose!' he said. 'The
second rose from the right!' Tallman pulled away. 'One of us has got to snap
out of this, baby,' he said. 'How about that brandy?' 'Don't interrupt me!'
shouted his host. 'That's what Whozis whispers to What's-His-Name –
greatest love story in the world, if I do say so myself – king's wife mixed up in
it – knights riding around with spears – Whozis writes her a message made out
of twigs bent together to make words: "I love you" – sends it floating down a
stream past her window – they got her locked in – goddamnedest thing in the
history of pictures. Where was I? Oh – "Second rose from the right," she says.
Why? Because she seen it twitch, she seen it move. What's-His-Name is bending over her, kissing her maybe. He whirls around and shoots an arrow at the
rose – second from the right, way up high there – down comes the whole tapestry, weighs eleven hundred pounds, and out rolls this spy, shot through the
heart. What's-His-Name sent him to watch the lovers.' The little man began
to pace up and down the deep carpet. Tallman lighted a fresh cigarette from
his glowing stub and sat down in an enormous chair. His host came to a stop in
front of the chair and shook his finger at its occupant.

'Look,' said the little man. 'I don't know who you are and I'm telling you
this. You could ruin me, but I got to tell you. I get Moonbaum here – I get
Moonbaum himself here – you can ask Manny or Sol – I get the best arrow shot
in the world here to fire that arrow for What's-His-Name—'

'Tristram,' said Tallman. 'Don't prompt me!' bellowed the little man. 'For
Tristram. What happens? Do I know he's got arrows you shoot bears with?
Do I know he ain't got caps on 'em? If I got to know that, why do I have
Mitnik? Moonbaum is sitting right there – the tapestry comes down and out
rolls this guy, shot through the heart – only the arrow is in his stomach. So
what happens? So Moonbaum laughs! That makes Moonbaum laugh! The
greatest love story in the history of pictures, and Moonbaum laughs!' The little
man raced over to a large chest, opened it, took out a cigar, stuck it in his mouth,
and resumed his pacing. 'How do you like it?' he shouted. 'I love it,' said Tallman. 'I love every part of it. I always have.' The little man raised his hands
above his head. 'He loves it! He hears one – maybe two – scenes, and he loves

every part of it! Even Moonbaum don't know how it comes out, and you love every part of it!' The little man was standing before Tallman's chair again, shaking his cigar at him. 'The story got around,' said Tallman. 'These things leak out. Maybe you talk when you're drinking. What about that brandy?'

The little man walked over and took hold of a bell rope on the wall, next to the tapestry. 'Moonbaum laughs like he's dying,' he said. 'Moonbaum laughs like he's seen Chaplin.' He dropped the bell rope. 'I hope you really got that hundred-year-old brandy,' said Tallman. 'Don't keep telling me what you hope!' howled the little man. 'Keep listening to what I hope!' He pulled the bell rope savagely. 'Now we're getting somewhere,' said Tallman. For the first time the little man went to a chair and sat down; he chewed on his unlighted cigar. 'Do you know what Moonbaum wants her called?' he demanded, lowering his heavy lids. 'I can guess,' said Tallman. 'Isolde.' 'Birds of a feather!' shouted his host. 'Horses of the same colour! Isolde! Name of God, man, you can't call a woman Isolde! What do I want her called?' 'You have me there,' said Tallman. 'I want her called Dawn,' said the little man, getting up out of his chair. 'It's short, ain't it? It's sweet, ain't it? You can say it, can't you?' 'To get back to that brandy,' said Tallman, 'who is supposed to answer that bell?' 'Nobody is supposed to answer it,' said the little man. 'That don't ring, that's a fake bell rope; it don't ring anywhere. I got it to remind me of an idea Moonbaum ruined. Listen: Louisiana mansion – guy with seven daughters – old-Southern-colonel stuff – Lionel Barrymore could play it – we open on a room that looks like a million dollars – Barrymore crosses and pulls the bell rope. What happens?' 'Nothing,' said Tallman. 'You're crazy!' bellowed the little man. 'Part of the wall falls in! Out flies a crow – in walks a goat, maybe – the place has gone to seed, see? It's just a hulk of its former self, it's a shallows!' He turned and walked out of the room. It took him quite a while.

When he came back he was carrying a bottle of brandy and two huge brandy glasses. He poured a great deal of brandy into each glass and handed one to Tallman. 'You and Mitnik!' he said, scornfully. 'Pulling walls out of Southern mansions. Crows you give me, goats you give me! What the hell kind of effect is that?' 'I could have a bad idea,' said Tallman, raising his glass. 'Here's to Moonbaum. May he maul things over in his mind all night and never get any spontanuity into 'em.' 'I drink nothing to Moonbaum,' said the little man. 'I hate Moonbaum. You know where they catch that crook – that guy has a little finger off one hand and wears a glove to cover it up? What does Moonbaum want? Moonbaum wants the little finger to *flap!* What do I want? I want it stuffed. What do I want it stuffed with? Sand. Why?' 'I know,' said Tallman. 'So that when he closes his hand over the head of his cane, the little finger sticks out stiffly, giving him away.' The little man seemed to leap into the air; his brandy splashed out of his glass. 'Suitcase!' he screamed. 'Not cane! Suitcase! He grabs hold of a suitcase!' Tallman didn't say anything; he closed his eyes and sipped his brandy; it was wonderful brandy. He looked up presently to find his host staring at him with a resigned expression in his eyes. 'All right, then, suitcase,' the little man said. 'Have it suitcase. We won't fight about details. I'm trying to tell you my story. I don't tell my stories to everybody.' 'Richard Harding Davis stole that finger gag – used it in "Gallegher",' said Tallman. 'You could sue him.' The little man walked over to his chair and flopped into it. 'He's beneath me,' he said. 'He's beneath me like the dirt. I ignore him.'

Tallman finished his brandy slowly. His host's chin sank upon his chest; his heavy eyelids began to close. Tallman waited several minutes and then tiptoed over to the marble stairs. He took off his shoes and walked up the stairs, carefully. He had the heavy door open when the little man shouted at him. 'Birds of a feather, all of you!' he shouted. 'You can tell Moonbaum I said so! Shooting guys out of tapestries!' 'I'll tell him,' said Tallman. 'Good night. The brandy was wonderful.' The little man was not listening. He was pacing the floor again, gesturing with an empty brandy glass in one hand and the unlighted cigar in the other. Tallman stepped out into the cool air of the courtyard and put on one shoe and laced it. The heavy door swung shut behind him with a terrific crash. He picked up the other shoe and ran wildly toward the trees and the oddly shaped plants. It was daylight now. He could see where he was going.

The Secret Life of Walter Mitty

W E'RE going through!' The Commander's voice was like thin ice breaking. He wore his full-dress uniform, with the heavily braided white cap
pulled down rakishly over one cold grey eye. 'We can't make it, sir. It's
spoiling for a hurricane, if you ask me.' 'I'm not asking you, Lieutenant Berg,'
said the Commander. 'Throw on the power lights! Rev her up to 8,500! We're
going through!' The pounding of the cylinders increased: ta-pocketa-
pocketa-pocketa-*pocketa-pocketa*. The Commander stared at the ice forming
on the pilot window. He walked over and twisted a row of complicated dials.
'Switch on No. 8 auxiliary!' he shouted. 'Switch on No. 8 auxiliary!' repeated
Lieutenant Berg. 'Full strength in No. 3 turret!' shouted the Commander.
'Full strength in No. 3 turret!' The crew, bending to their various tasks in the
huge, hurtling eight-engined Navy hydroplane, looked at each other and
grinned. 'The Old Man'll get us through,' they said to one another. 'The Old
Man ain't afraid of Hell!' . . .

'Not so fast! You're driving too fast!' said Mrs Mitty. 'What are you driving
so fast for?'

'Hmm?' said Walter Mitty. He looked at his wife, in the seat beside him,
with shocked astonishment. She seemed grossly unfamiliar, like a strange
woman who had yelled at him in a crowd. 'You were up to fifty-five,' she said.
'You know I don't like to go more than forty. You were up to fifty-five.' Walter
Mitty drove on toward Waterbury in silence, the roaring of the SN202
through the worst storm in twenty years of Navy flying fading in the remote,
intimate airways of his mind. 'You're tensed up again,' said Mrs Mitty. 'It's
one of your days. I wish you'd let Dr Renshaw look you over.'

Walter Mitty stopped the car in front of the building where his wife went to
have her hair done. 'Remember to get those overshoes while I'm having my
hair done,' she said. 'I don't need overshoes,' said Mitty. She put her mirror
back into her bag. 'We've been all through that,' she said, getting out of the car.
'You're not a young man any longer.' He raced the engine a little. 'Why don't
you wear your gloves? Have you lost your gloves?' Walter Mitty reached in a
pocket and brought out the gloves. He put them on, but after she had turned
and gone into the building and he had driven on to a red light, he took them off
again. 'Pick it up, brother!' snapped a cop as the light changed, and Mitty
hastily pulled on his gloves and lurched ahead. He drove around the streets
aimlessly for a time, and then he drove past the hospital on his way to the
parking lot.

. . . 'It's the millionaire banker, Wellington McMillan,' said the pretty nurse. 'Yes?' said Walter Mitty, removing his gloves slowly. 'Who has the case?' 'Dr Renshaw and Dr Benbow, but there are two specialists here, Dr Remington from New York and Mr Pritchard-Mitford from London. He flew over.' A door opened down a long, cool corridor and Dr Renshaw came out. He looked distraught and haggard. 'Hello, Mitty,' he said. 'We're having the devil's own time with McMillan, the millionaire banker and close personal friend of Roosevelt. Obstreosis of the ductal tract. Tertiary. Wish you'd take a look at him.' 'Glad to,' said Mitty.

In the operating room there were whispered introductions: 'Dr Remington, Dr Mitty. Mr Pritchard-Mitford, Dr Mitty.' 'I've read your book on strepto-thricosis,' said Pritchard-Mitford, shaking hands. 'A brilliant performance, sir.' 'Thank you,' said Walter Mitty. 'Didn't know you were in the States, Mitty,' grumbled Remington. 'Coals to Newcastle, bringing Mitford and me up here for a tertiary.' 'You are very kind,' said Mitty. A huge, complicated machine, connected to the operating table, with many tubes and wires, began at this moment to go pocketa-pocketa-pocketa. 'The new anaesthetizer is giving way!' shouted an interne. 'There is no one in the East who knows how to fix it!' 'Quiet, man!' said Mitty, in a low, cool voice. He sprang to the machine, which was now going pocketa-pocketa-queep-pocketa-queep. He began fingering delicately a row of glistening dials. 'Give me a fountain pen!' he snapped. Someone handed him a fountain pen. He pulled a faulty piston out of the machine and inserted the pen in its place. 'That will hold for ten minutes,' he said. 'Get on with the operation.' A nurse hurried over and whispered to Renshaw, and Mitty saw the man turn pale. 'Coreopsis has set in,' said Renshaw nervously. 'If you would take over, Mitty?' Mitty looked at him and at the craven figure of Benbow, who drank, and at the grave, uncertain faces of the two great specialists. 'If you wish,' he said. They slipped a white gown on him; he adjusted a mask and drew on thin gloves; nurses handed him shining . . .

'Back it up, Mac! Look out for that Buick!' Walter Mitty jammed on the brakes. 'Wrong lane, Mac,' said the parking-lot attendant, looking at Mitty closely. 'Gee. Yeh,' muttered Mitty. He began cautiously to back out of the lane marked 'Exit Only.' 'Leave her sit there,' said the attendant. 'I'll put her away.' Mitty got out of the car. 'Hey, better leave the key.' 'Oh,' said Mitty, handing the man the ignition key. The attendant vaulted into the car, backed it up with insolent skill, and put it where it belonged.

They're so damn cocky, thought Walter Mitty, walking along Main Street; they think they know everything. Once he had tried to take his chains off, out-side New Milford, and he had got them wound around the axles. A man had had to come out in a wrecking car and unwind them, a young, grinning garage-man. Since then Mrs Mitty always made him drive to a garage to have the chains taken off. The next time, he thought, I'll wear my right arm in a sling; they won't grin at me then. I'll have my right arm in a sling and they'll see I couldn't possibly take the chains off myself. He kicked at the slush on the side-walk. 'Overshoes,' he said to himself, and he began looking for a shoe store.

When he came out into the street again, with the overshoes in a box under his arm, Walter Mitty began to wonder what the other thing was his wife had told him to get. She had told him, twice, before they set out from their house for Waterbury. In a way he hated these weekly trips to town – he was always getting something wrong. Kleenex, he thought, Squibb's, razor blades? No. Toothpaste, toothbrush, bicarbonate, carborundum, initiative and referendum? He gave it up. But she would remember it. 'Where's the what's-its-name?' she would ask. 'Don't tell me you forgot the what's-its-name.' A newsboy went by shouting something about the Waterbury trial.

... 'Perhaps this will refresh your memory.' The District Attorney suddenly thrust a heavy automatic at the quiet figure on the witness stand. 'Have you ever seen this before?' Walter Mitty took the gun and examined it expertly. 'This is my Webley-Vickers 50.80,' he said calmly. An excited buzz ran around the courtroom. The Judge rapped for order. 'You are a crack shot with any sort of firearms, I believe?' said the District Attorney, insinuatingly. 'Objection!' shouted Mitty's attorney. 'We have shown that the defendant could not have fired the shot. We have shown that he wore his right arm in a sling on the night of the fourteenth of July.' Walter Mitty raised his hand briefly and the bickering attorneys were stilled. 'With any known make of gun,' he said evenly, 'I could have killed Gregory Fitzhurst at three hundred feet *with my left hand*.' Pandemonium broke loose in the courtroom. A woman's scream rose above the bedlam and suddenly a lovely, dark-haired girl was in Walter Mitty's arms. The District Attorney struck at her savagely. Without rising from his chair, Mitty let the man have it on the point of the chin. 'You miserable cur!' . . .

'Puppy biscuit,' said Walter Mitty. He stopped walking and the buildings of Waterbury rose up out of the misty courtroom and surrounded him again. A woman who was passing laughed. 'He said "Puppy biscuit",' she said to her companion. 'That man said "Puppy biscuit" to himself.' Walter Mitty hurried on. He went into an A. & P., not the first one he came to but a smaller one farther up the street. 'I want some biscuit for small, young dogs,' he said to the clerk. 'Any special brand, sir?' The greatest pistol shot in the world thought a moment. 'It says "Puppies Bark for It" on the box,' said Walter Mitty.

His wife would be through at the hairdresser's in fifteen minutes, Mitty saw in looking at his watch, unless they had trouble drying it; sometimes they had trouble drying it. She didn't like to get to the hotel first; she would want him to be there waiting for her as usual. He found a big leather chair in the lobby, facing a window, and he put the overshoes and the puppy biscuit on the floor beside it. He picked up an old copy of *Liberty* and sank down into the chair. 'Can Germany Conquer the World Through the Air?' Walter Mitty looked at the pictures of bombing planes and of ruined streets.

... 'The cannonading has got the wind up in young Raleigh, sir,' said the sergeant. Captain Mitty looked up at him through tousled hair. 'Get him to bed,' he said wearily. 'With the others. I'll fly alone.' 'But you can't, sir,' said the sergeant anxiously. 'It takes two men to handle that bomber and the

Archies are pounding hell out of the air. Von Richtman's circus is between here and Saulier.' 'Somebody's got to get that ammunition dump,' said Mitty. 'I'm going over. Spot of brandy?' He poured a drink for the sergeant and one for himself. War thundered and whined around the dugout and battered at the door. There was a rending of wood and splinters flew through the room. 'A bit of a near thing,' said Captain Mitty carelessly. 'The box barrage is closing in,' said the sergeant. 'We only live once, Sergeant,' said Mitty, with his faint, fleeting smile. 'Or do we?' He poured another brandy and tossed it off. 'I never see a man could hold his brandy like you, sir,' said the sergeant. 'Begging your pardon, sir.' Captain Mitty stood up and strapped on his huge Webley-Vickers automatic. 'It's forty kilometres through hell, sir,' said the sergeant. Mitty finished one last brandy. 'After all,' he said softly, 'what isn't?' The pounding of the cannon increased; there was the rat-tat-tatting of machine guns, and from somewhere came the menacing pocketa-pocketa-pocketa of the new flame-throwers. Walter Mitty walked to the door of the dugout humming 'Auprès de Ma Blonde.' He turned and waved to the sergeant. 'Cheerio!' he said....

Something struck his shoulder. 'I've been looking all over this hotel for you,' said Mrs Mitty. 'Why do you have to hide in this old chair? How did you expect me to find you?' 'Things close in,' said Walter Mitty vaguely. 'What?' Mrs Mitty said. 'Did you get the what's-its-name? The puppy biscuit? What's in that box?' 'Overshoes,' said Mitty. 'Couldn't you have put them on in the store?' 'I was thinking,' said Walter Mitty. 'Does it ever occur to you that I am sometimes thinking?' She looked at him. 'I'm going to take your temperature when I get you home,' she said.

They went out through the revolving doors that made a faintly derisive whistling sound when you pushed them. It was two blocks to the parking lot. At the drugstore on the corner she said, 'Wait here for me. I forgot something. I won't be a minute.' She was more than a minute. Walter Mitty lighted a cigarette. It began to rain, rain with sleet in it. He stood up against the wall of the drugstore, smoking.... He put his shoulders back and his heels together. 'To hell with the handkerchief,' said Walter Mitty scornfully. He took one last drag on his cigarette and snapped it away. Then, with that faint, fleeting smile playing about his lips, he faced the firing squad; erect and motionless, proud and disdainful, Walter Mitty the Undefeated, inscrutable to the last.

Interview with a Lemming

THE WEARY scientist, tramping through the mountains of northern Europe in the winter weather, dropped his knapsack and prepared to sit on a rock.

'Careful, brother,' said a voice.

'Sorry,' murmured the scientist, noting with some surprise that a lemming which he had been about to sit on had addressed him. 'It is a source of considerable astonishment to me,' said the scientist, sitting down beside the lemming, 'that you are capable of speech.'

'You human beings are always astonished,' said the lemming, 'when any other animal can do anything you can. Yet there are many things animals can do that you cannot, such as stridulate, or chirr, to name just one. To stridulate, or chirr, one of the minor achievements of the cricket, your species is dependent on the intestines of the sheep and the hair of the horse.'

'We are a dependent animal,' admitted the scientist.

'You are an amazing animal,' said the lemming.

'We have always considered you rather amazing, too,' said the scientist. 'You are perhaps the most mysterious of creatures.'

'If we are going to indulge in adjectives beginning with "m",' said the lemming, sharply, 'let me apply a few to your species – murderous, maladjusted, maleficent, malicious and muffle-headed.'

'You find our behaviour as difficult to understand as we do yours?'

'You, as you would say, said it,' said the lemming. 'You kill, you mangle, you torture, you imprison, you starve each other. You cover the nurturing earth with cement, you cut down elm trees to put up institutions for people driven insane by the cutting down of elm trees, you—'

'You could go on all night like that,' said the scientist, 'listing our sins and our shames.'

'I could go on all night and up to four o'clock tomorrow afternoon,' said the lemming. 'It just happens that I have made a lifelong study of the self-styled higher animal. Except for one thing, I know all there is to know about you, and a singularly dreary, dolorous and distasteful store of information it is, too, to use only adjectives beginning with "d".'

'You say you have made a lifelong study of my species—' began the scientist.

'Indeed I have,' broke in the lemming. 'I know that you are cruel, cunning and carnivorous, sly, sensual and selfish, greedy, gullible and guileful—'

'Pray don't wear yourself out,' said the scientist, quietly. 'It may interest you to know that I have made a lifelong study of lemmings, just as you have

31

made a lifelong study of people. Like you, I have found but one thing about my subject which I do not understand.'

'And what is that?' asked the lemming.

'I don't understand,' said the scientist, 'why you lemmings all rush down to the sea and drown yourselves.'

'How curious,' said the lemming. 'The one thing I don't understand is why you human beings don't.'

The Letters of James Thurber

Adams was a great letter writer of the type that is now almost extinct . . . his circle of friends was larger perhaps and more distinguished than that of any other American of his generation.—*H. S. Commager on 'Letters of Henry Adams.'*

JAMES THURBER was a letter writer of the type that is now completely extinct. His circle of correspondents was perhaps no larger but it was easily more bewildered than that of any other American of his generation. Thurber laid the foundation for his voluminous correspondence during his Formative Period. In those years he wrote to many distinguished persons, none of whom ever replied, among them Admiral Schley, Young Barbarian, Senator Atlee Pomerene, June Caprice, and a man named Unglaub who played first base for the Washington Senators at the turn of the century. Unglaub, in Thurber's estimation, stood head and shoulders above all the rest of his correspondents and, indeed, he said so in his letter to McKinley. Thurber did not write as many letters as Henry Adams or John Jay Chapman or some of the other boys whose correspondence has been published lately, but that is because he never set pen to paper after his forty-third year.

The effect of Thurber's letters on his generation was about the same as the effect of anybody's letters on any generation; that is to say, nil. It is only when a man's letters are published after his death that they have any effect and this effect is usually only on literary critics. Nobody else ever reads a volume of letters and anybody who says he does is a liar. A person may pick up a volume of correspondence now and then and read a letter here and there, but he never gets any connected idea of what the man is trying to say and soon abandons the book for the poems of John Greenleaf Whittier. This is largely because every man whose letters have ever been published was in the habit of writing every third one to a Mrs Cameron or a Mrs Winslow or a Miss Betch, the confidante of a lifetime, with whom he shared any number of gaily obscure little secrets. These letters all read like this: 'Dear Puttums: I love what you say about Mooey! It's so devastatingly true! B—— dropped in yesterday (Icky was out at the time) and gave some sort of report on Neddy but I am afraid I didn't listen (*ut ediendam aut debendo!*). He and Liddy are in Venice, I think I gathered, or Newport. What in the world do you suppose came over Buppa that Great Night? ? ? You, of course, were as splendidly consequent as ever (*in loco sporenti abadabba est*) – but I was deeply disappointed in Sig's reaction. All he can think of, poor fellow, is Margery's "flight." Remind me to tell you some day what Pet said about the Ordeal.' These particular letters are sometimes further obscured by a series of explanatory editorial footnotes, such as 'Probably Harry Boynton or his brother Norton,' 'A neighbour at Bar Harbor,'

'The late Edward J. Belcher,' 'Also sometimes lovingly referred to as Butty, a niece-in-law by his first marriage.' In the end, as I say, one lays the book aside for 'Snow-Bound' in order to get a feeling of reality before going to bed.

Thurber's letters from Europe during his long stay there in 1937 and 1938 (the European Phase) are perhaps the least interesting of all those he, or anybody else, ever wrote. He seems to have had at no time any idea at all, either clear or vague, as to what was going on. A certain Groping, to be sure, is discernible, but it doesn't appear to be toward anything. All this may have been due in great part to the fact that he took his automobile to Europe with him and spent most of his time worrying about running out of gas. The gasoline gauge of his car had got out of order and sometimes registered 'empty' when the tank was half full and 'full' when it contained only two or three gallons. A stronger character would have had the gauge fixed or carried a five-gallon can of *essence* in the back of the car, thus releasing the mind for more mature and significant preoccupations, but not Thurber.

I have been unable to find any one of Thurber's many correspondents who saved any of his letters (Thurber himself kept carbons, although this is not generally known or cared about). 'We threw them out when we moved,' people would tell me, or 'We gave them to the janitor's little boy.' Thurber gradually became aware of this on his return to America (the Final Phase) because of the embarrassed silence that always greeted him when, at his friends' homes, he would say, 'Why don't we get out my letters to you and read them aloud?' After a painful pause the subject was quickly changed, usually by putting up the ping-pong table.

In his last years the once voluminous letter writer ceased writing letters altogether, and such communication as he maintained with the great figures of his time was over the telephone and consisted of getting prominent persons on the phone, making a deplorable sound with his lips, and hanging up. His continual but vain attempts to reach the former Barbara Hutton by phone clouded the last years of his life but at the same time gave him something to do. His last words, to his wife, at the fag end of the Final Phase, were 'Before they put up the ping-pong table, tell them I am not running out of gas.' He was as wrong, and as mixed up, in this particular instance as he was in most others. I am not sure that we should not judge him too harshly.

A Friend to Alexander

'I HAVE taken to dreaming about Aaron Burr every night,' Andrews said. 'What for?' said Mrs Andrews. 'How do I know what for?' Andrews snarled. 'What for, the woman says.'

Mrs Andrews did not flare up; she simply looked at her husband as he lay on the chaise longue in her bedroom in his heavy blue dressing gown, smoking a cigarette. Although he had just got out of bed, he looked haggard and tired. He kept biting his lower lip between puffs.

'Aaron Burr is a funny person to be dreaming about nowadays – I mean with all the countries in the world at war with each other. I wish you would go and see Dr Fox,' said Mrs Andrews, taking her thumb from between the pages of her mystery novel and tossing the book toward the foot of her bed. She sat up straighter against her pillow. 'Maybe haliver oil or B_1 is what you need,' she said. 'B_1 does wonders for people. I don't see why you see *him* in your dreams. *Where* do you see him?'

'Oh, places; in Washington Square or Bowling Green or on Broadway. I'll be talking to a woman in a victoria, a woman holding a white lace parasol, and suddenly there will be Burr, bowing and smiling and smelling like a carnation, telling his stories about France and getting off his insults.'

Mrs Andrews lighted a cigarette, although she rarely smoked until after lunch. 'Who is the woman in the victoria?' she asked.

'What? How do I know? You know about people in dreams, don't you? They are nobody at all, or everybody.'

'You see Aaron Burr plainly enough, though. I mean he isn't nobody or everybody.'

'All right, all right,' said Andrews. 'You have me there. But I don't know who the woman is, and I don't care. Maybe it's Madame Jumel or Mittens Willett or a girl I knew in high school. That's not important.'

'Who is Mittens Willett?' asked Mrs Andrews.

'She was a famous New York actress in her day, fifty years ago or so. She's buried in an old cemetery on Second Avenue.'

'That's very sad,' said Mrs Andrews.

'Why is it?' demanded Andrews, who was now pacing up and down the deep-red carpet.

'I mean she probably died young,' said Mrs Andrews. 'Almost all women did in those days.'

Andrews ignored her and walked over to a window and looked out at a neat, bleak street in the Fifties. 'He's a vile, cynical cad,' said Andrews, suddenly

35

turning away from the window. 'I was standing talking to Alexander Hamilton when Burr stepped up and slapped him in the face. When I looked at Hamilton, who do you suppose he was?'

'I don't know,' said Mrs Andrews. 'Who was he?'

'He was my brother, the one I've told you about, the one who was killed by that drunkard in the cemetery.'

Mrs Andrews had never got that story straight and she didn't want to go into it again now; the facts in the tragic case and her way of getting them mixed up always drove Andrews into a white-faced fury. 'I don't think we ought to dwell on your nightmare,' said Mrs Andrews. 'I think we ought to get out more. We could go to the country for weekends.'

Andrews wasn't listening; he was back at the window, staring out into the street again.

'I wish he'd go back to France and stay there,' Andrews snapped out suddenly the next morning at breakfast.

'Who, dear?' said his wife. 'Oh, you mean Aaron Burr. Did you dream about him again? I don't see why you dream about him all the time. Don't you think you ought to take some Luminal?'

'No,' said Andrews. 'I don't know. Last night he kept shoving Alexander around.'

'Alexander?'

'Hamilton. God knows I'm familiar enough with him to call him by his first name. He hides behind my coat-tails every night, or tries to.'

'I was thinking we might go to the Old Drovers' Inn this weekend,' said Mrs Andrews. 'You like it there.'

'Hamilton has become not only my brother Walter but practically every other guy I have ever liked,' said Andrews. 'That's natural.'

'Of course it is,' she said. They got up from the table. 'I do wish you'd go to Dr Fox.'

'I'm going to the Zoo,' he said, 'and feed popcorn to the rhinoceros. That makes things seem right, for a little while anyway.'

It was two nights later at five o'clock in the morning that Andrews bumbled into his wife's bedroom in pyjamas and bare feet, his hair in his eyes, his eyes wild. 'He got him!' he croaked. 'He got him! The bastard got him. Alexander fired into the air, he fired in the air and smiled at him, just like Walter, and that fiend from hell took deliberate aim – I saw him – I saw him take deliberate aim – he killed him in cold blood, the foul scum!'

Mrs Andrews, not quite awake, was fumbling in the box containing the Nembutal while her husband ranted on. She made him take two of the little capsules, between his sobs.

Andrews didn't want to go to see Dr Fox but he went to humour his wife. Dr Fox leaned back in his swivel chair behind his desk and looked at Andrews. 'Now, just what seems to be the trouble?' he asked.

'Nothing seems to be the trouble,' said Andrews.

The doctor looked at Mrs Andrews. 'He has nightmares,' she said.

'You look a little underweight, perhaps,' said the doctor. 'Are you eating well, getting enough exercise?'

'I'm not underweight,' said Andrews. 'I eat the way I always have and get the same exercise.'

At this, Mrs Andrews sat straighter in her chair and began to talk, while her husband lighted a cigarette. 'You see, I think he's worried about something,' she said, 'because he always has this same dream. It's about his brother Walter, who was killed in a cemetery by a drunken man, only it isn't *really* about him.'

The doctor did the best he could with this information. He cleared his throat, tapped on the glass top of his desk with the fingers of his right hand, and said, 'Very few people are actually *killed* in cemeteries.' Andrews stared at the doctor coldly and said nothing. 'I wonder if you would mind stepping into the next room,' the doctor said to him.

'Well, I hope you're satisfied,' Andrews snapped at his wife as they left the doctor's office a half-hour later. 'You heard what he said. There's nothing the matter with me at all.'

'I'm glad your heart is so fine,' she told him. 'He said it was fine, you know.'

'Sure,' said Andrews. 'It's fine. Everything's fine.' They got into a cab and drove home in silence.

'I was just thinking,' said Mrs Andrews, as the cab stopped in front of their apartment building, 'I was just thinking that now that Alexander Hamilton is dead, you won't see anything more of Aaron Burr.' The cab-driver, who was handing Andrews change for a dollar bill, dropped a quarter on the floor.

Mrs Andrews was wrong. Aaron Burr did not depart from her husband's dreams. Andrews said nothing about it for several mornings, but she could tell. He brooded over his breakfast, did not answer any of her questions, and jumped in his chair if she dropped a knife or spoon. 'Are you still dreaming about that man?' she asked him finally.

'I wish I hadn't told you about it,' he said. 'Forget it, will you?'

'I can't forget it with you going on this way,' she said. 'I think you ought to see a psychiatrist. What does he do now?'

'What does who do now?' Andrews asked.

'Aaron Burr,' she said. 'I don't see why he keeps coming into your dreams now.'

Andrews finished his coffee and stood up. 'He goes around bragging that he did it with his eyes closed,' he snarled. 'He says he didn't even look. He claims he can hit the ace of spades at thirty paces blindfolded. Furthermore, since you asked what he does, he jostles me at parties now.'

Mrs Andrews stood up too and put her hand on her husband's shoulder. 'I think you should stay out of this, Harry,' she said. 'It wasn't any business of yours, anyway, and it happened so long ago.'

'I'm not getting into anything,' said Andrews, his voice rising to a shout. 'It's getting into me. Can't you see that?'

'I see that I've got to get you away from here,' she said. 'Maybe if you slept someplace else for a few nights, you wouldn't dream about him any more. Let's go to the country tomorrow. Let's go to the Lime Rock Lodge.'

Andrews stood for a long while without answering her. 'Why can't we go and visit the Crowleys?' he said finally. 'They live in the country. Bob has a pistol and we could do a little target-shooting.'

'What do you want to shoot a pistol for?' she asked quickly. 'I should think you'd want to get away from that.'

'Yeh,' he said, 'sure,' and there was a far-off look in his eyes. 'Sure.'

When they drove into the driveway of the Crowleys' house, several miles north of New Milford, late the next afternoon, Andrews was whistling 'Bye-Bye, Blackbird.' Mrs Andrews sighed contentedly and then, as her husband stopped the car, she began looking around wildly. 'My bag!' she cried. 'Did I forget to bring my bag?' He laughed his old, normal laugh for the first time in many days as he found the bag and handed it to her, and then, for the first time in many days, he leaned over and kissed her.

The Crowleys came out of the house and engulfed their guests in questions and exclamations. 'How you been?' said Bob Crowley to Andrews heartily, putting an arm around his shoulder.

'Never better,' said Andrews, 'never better. Boy, is it good to be here!'

They were swept into the house to a shakerful of Bob Crowley's icy Martinis. Mrs Andrews stole a happy glance over the edge of her glass at her husband's relaxed face.

When Mrs Andrews awoke the next morning, her husband lay rigidly on his back in the bed next to hers, staring at the ceiling. 'Oh, God,' said Mrs Andrews.

Andrews didn't move his head. 'One Henry Andrews, an architect,' he said suddenly in a mocking tone. 'One Henry Andrews, an architect.'

'What's the matter, Harry?' she asked. 'Why don't you go back to sleep? It's only eight o'clock.'

'That's what he calls me!' shouted Andrews. ' "One Henry Andrews, an architect," he keeps saying in his nasty little sneering voice. "One Henry Andrews, an architect." '

'Please don't yell!' said Mrs Andrews. 'You'll wake the whole house. It's early. People want to sleep.'

Andrews lowered his voice a little. 'I'm beneath him,' he snarled. 'I'm just anybody. I'm a man in a grey suit. "Be on your good behaviour, my good man,' he says to me, "or I shall have one of my lackeys give you a taste of the riding crop." '

Mrs Andrews sat up in bed. 'Why should he say that to you?' she asked. 'He wasn't such a great man, was he? I mean, didn't he try to sell Louisiana to the French, or something, behind Washington's back?'

'He was a scoundrel,' said Andrews, 'but a very brilliant mind.'

Mrs Andrews lay down again. 'I was in hopes you weren't going to dream about him any more,' she said. 'I thought if I brought you up here—'

'It's him or me,' said Andrews grimly. 'I can't stand this forever.'

'Neither can I,' Mrs Andrews said, and there was a hint of tears in her voice.

Andrews and his host spent most of the afternoon, as Mrs Andrews had expected, shooting at targets on the edge of the wood behind the Crowley studio. After the first few rounds, Andrews surprised Crowley by standing with his back to the huge hulk of dead tree trunk on which the targets were nailed, walking thirty paces ahead in a stiff-legged, stern-faced manner, with his revolver held at arm's length above his head, then turning suddenly and firing.

Crowley dropped to the ground, uninjured but scared. 'What the hell's the big idea, Harry?' he yelled.

Andrews didn't say anything, but started to walk back to the tree again. Once more he stood with his back to the target and began stepping off the thirty paces.

'I think they kept their arm hanging straight down,' Bob called to him. 'I don't think they stuck it up in the air.'

Andrews, still counting to himself, lowered his arm, and this time, as he turned at the thirtieth step, he whirled and fired from his hip, three times in rapid succession.

'Hey!' said Crowley.

Two of the shots missed the tree but the last one hit it, about two feet under the target. Crowley looked at his house guest oddly as Andrews began to walk back to the tree again, without a word, his lips tight, his eyes bright, his breath coming fast.

'What the hell?' Crowley said to himself. 'Look, it's my turn,' he called, but Andrews turned, then stalked ahead, unheeding. This time when he wheeled and fired, his eyes were closed.

'Good God Almighty, man!' said Crowley from the grass, where he lay flat on his stomach. 'Hey, give me that gun, will you?' he demanded, getting to his feet.

Andrews let him take it. 'I need a lot more practice, I guess,' he said.

'Not with me standing around,' said Crowley. 'Come on, let's go back to the house and shake up a drink. I've got the jumps.'

'I need a lot more practice,' said Andrews again.

He got his practice next morning just as the sun came up and the light was hard and the air was cold. He had crawled softly out of bed, dressed silently, and crept out of the room. He knew where Crowley kept the target pistol and the cartridges. There would be a target on the tree trunk, just as high as a man's heart. Mrs Andrews heard the shots first and sat sharply upright in bed, crying 'Harry!' almost before she was awake. Then she heard more shots. She got up, put on a dressing gown, and went to the Crowleys' door. She heard them moving about in their room. Alice opened the door and stepped out into the hall when Mrs Andrews knocked. 'Is Harry all right?' asked Mrs Andrews. 'Where is he? What is he doing?'

'He's out shooting behind the studio, Bob says,' Alice told her. 'Bob'll go out and get him. Maybe he had a nightmare, or walked in his sleep.'

'No,' said Mrs Andrews, 'he never walks in his sleep. He's awake.'

'Let's go down and put on some coffee,' said Alice. 'He'll need some.'

Crowley came out of the bedroom and joined the women in the hallway. 'I'll need some too,' he said. 'Good morning, Bess. I'll bring him back. What the hell's the matter with him, anyway?' He was down the stairs and gone before she could answer. She was glad of that.

'Come on,' said Alice, taking her arm. They went down to the kitchen.

Mrs Crowley found the butler in the kitchen, just standing there. 'It's all right, Madison,' she said. 'You go back to bed. Tell Clotheta it's all right. Mr Andrews is just shooting a little. He couldn't sleep.'

'Yes, Ma'am,' mumbled Madison, and went back to tell his wife that they said it was all right.

'It can't be right,' said Clotheta, 'shootin' pistols at this time of night.'

'Hush up,' Madison told her. He was shivering as he climbed back into bed.

'I wish dat man would go 'way from heah,' grumbled Clotheta. 'He's got a bad look to his eyes.'

Andrews brightened Clotheta's life by going away late that afternoon. When he and his wife got in their car and drove off, the Crowleys slumped into chairs and looked at each other and said, 'Well.' Crowley got up finally to mix a drink. 'What do you think is the matter with Harry?' he asked.

'I don't know,' said his wife. 'It's what Clotheta would call the shoots, I suppose.'

'He said a funny thing when I went out and got him this morning,' Crowley told her.

'I could stand a funny thing,' she said.

'I asked him what the hell he was doing there in that freezing air with only his pants and shirt and shoes on. "I'll get him one of these nights," he said.'

'Why don't you sleep in my room tonight?' Mrs Andrews asked her husband as he finished his Scotch-and-water nightcap.

'You'd keep shaking me all night to keep me awake,' he said. 'You're afraid to let me meet him. Why do you always think everybody else is better than I am? I can outshoot him the best day he ever lived. Furthermore, I have a modern pistol. He has to use an old-fashioned single-shot muzzle-loader.' Andrews laughed nastily.

'Is that quite fair?' his wife asked after a moment of thoughtful silence.

He jumped up from his chair. 'What do I care if it's fair or not?' he snarled.

She got up too. 'Don't be mad with me, Harry,' she said. There were tears in her eyes.

'I'm sorry, darling,' he said, taking her in his arms.

'I'm very unhappy,' she sobbed.

'I'm sorry, darling,' he said again. 'Don't you worry about me. I'll be all right. I'll be fine.' She was crying too wildly to say anything more.

When she kissed him good night later on she knew it was really good-bye. Women have a way of telling when you aren't coming back.

'Extraordinary,' said Dr Fox the next morning, letting Andrews' dead left hand fall back upon the bed. 'His heart was as sound as a dollar when I examined him the other day. It has just stopped as if he had been shot.'

Mrs Andrews, through her tears, was looking at her dead husband's right hand. The three fingers next to the index finger were closed in stiffly on the palm, as if gripping the handle of a pistol. The taut thumb was doing its part to hold that invisible handle tightly and unwaveringly. But it was the index finger that Mrs Andrews' eyes stayed on longest. It was only slightly curved inward, as if it were just about to press the trigger of the pistol. 'Harry never even fired a shot,' wailed Mrs Andrews. 'Aaron Burr killed him the way he killed Hamilton. Aaron Burr shot him through the heart. I knew he would. I knew he would.'

Dr Fox put an arm about the hysterical woman and led her from the room. 'She is crazy,' he said to himself. 'Stark, raving crazy.'

The Story of Sailing

PEOPLE who visit you in Bermuda are likely to notice, even before they notice the flowers of the island, the scores of sailing craft which fleck the harbours and the ocean round about. Furthermore, they are likely to ask you about the ships before they ask you about the flowers and this, at least in my own case, is unfortunate, because although I know practically nothing about flowers I know ten times as much about flowers as I know about ships. Or at any rate I did before I began to study up on the subject. Now I feel that I am pretty well qualified to hold my own in any average discussion of rigging.

I began to brush up on the mysteries of sailing a boat after an unfortunate evening when a lady who sat next to me at dinner turned to me and said, 'Do you reef in your gaff-topsails when you are close-hauled or do you let go the mizzen-top-bowlines and cross-jack-braces?' She took me for a sailor and not a landlubber and of course I hadn't the slightest idea what she was talking about.

One reason for this was that none of the principal words (except 'reef') used in the sentence I have quoted is pronounced the way it is spelled: 'gaff-top-sails' is pronounced 'gassles,' 'close-hauled' is pronounced 'cold,' 'mizzen-top-bowlines' is pronounced 'mittens,' and 'cross-jack-braces' is pronounced 'crabapples' or something that sounds a whole lot like that. Thus what the lady really said to me was, 'Do you reef in your gassles when you are cold or do you let go the mittens and crabapples?' Many a visitor who is asked such a question takes the first ship back home, and it is for these embarrassed gentlemen that I am going to explain briefly the history and terminology of sailing.

In the first place, there is no doubt but that the rigging of the modern sailing ship has become complicated beyond all necessity. If you want proof of this you have only to look up the word 'rigging' in the Encyclopædia Britannica. You will find a drawing of a full-rigged modern ship and under it an explanation of its various spars, masts, sails, etc. There are forty-five different major parts, beginning with 'bowsprit' and going on up to 'davit topping-lifts.' Included in between are, among others, these items: the fore-top-mast stay-sail halliards (pron. 'fazzles'), the topgallant mast-yard-and-lift (pron. 'toft'), the mizzen-topgallant-braces (pron. 'maces'), and the fore-top-mast backstays and top-sail tye (pron. 'frassantossle'). The tendency of the average landlubber who studies this diagram for five minutes is to turn to 'Sanscrit' in the encyclopædia and study up on that instead, but only a coward would do that. It is possible to get something out of the article on rigging if you keep at it long enough.

Let us creep up on the formidable modern sailing ship in our stocking feet, beginning with one of the simplest of all known sailing craft, the Norse Herring Boat. Now when the Norse built their sailing boats they had only one idea in mind: to catch herring. They were pretty busy men, always a trifle chilly, and they had neither the time nor the inclination to sit around on the cold decks of their ships trying to figure out all the different kinds of ropes, spars, and sails that might be hung on their masts. Each ship had, as a matter of fact, only one mast. Near the top of it was a crosspiece of wood and on that was hung one simple square sail, no more complicated than the awning of a cigar store. A rope was attached to each end of the crosspiece and the other ends of these ropes were held by the helmsman. By manipulating the ropes he could make the ship go ahead, turn right, or turn left. It was practically impossible to make it turn around, to be sure, and that is the reason the Norsemen went straight on and discovered America, thus proving that it isn't really necessary to turn around.

As the years went on and the younger generations of Norsemen became, like all younger generations, less hardworking and more restless than their forebears, they began to think less about catching herring and more about monkeying with the sails of their ships. One of these restless young Norsemen one day lengthened the mast of his ship, put up another crosspiece about six feet above the first one, and hung another but smaller sail on this new crosspiece, or spar (pronounced, strange as it may seem, 'spar'). Thus was the main topsail born.

After that, innovations in sails followed so fast that the herring boat became a veritable shambles of canvas. A Norseman named Leif the Sailmaker added a second mast to his ship, just in front of the first one, and thus the foremast came into being and with it the fore mainsail and the fore topsail. A Turk named Skvar added a third mast and called it the mizzen. Not to be outdone, a Muscovite named Amir put up a third spar on each of his masts; Skvar put up a fourth; Amir replied with a fifth; Skvar came back with a sixth, and so it went, resulting in the topgallant foresail, the top-topgallant mizzen sail, the top-top-topgallant main topsail, and the tip-top-topgallant-gallant mainsail (pron. 'twee twee twee twa twa').

Practically nobody today sails a full-rigged seven-masted ship, so that it would not be especially helpful to describe in detail all the thousands of different gaffs, sprits, queeps, weems, lugs, miggets, loords (spelled 'leewards'), gessels, grommets, etc., on such a ship. I shall therefore devote what space I have left to a discussion of how to come back alive from a pleasant sail in the ordinary 20- or 30-foot sailing craft such as you are likely to be 'taken for a ride' in down in Bermuda. This type of so-called pleasure ship is not only given to riding on its side, due to coming about without the helmsman's volition (spelled 'jibe' and pronounced 'look out, here we go again!'), but it is made extremely perilous by what is known as the flying jib, or boom.

The boom is worse than the gaff for some people can stand the gaff (hence the common expression 'he can stand the gaff') but nobody can stand the boom when it aims one at him from the floor. With the disappearance of the Norse herring fisherman and the advent of the modern pleasure craft sailor, the boom became longer and heavier and faster. Helmsmen will tell you that they keep swinging the boom across the deck of the ship in order to take advantage of the wind but after weeks of observation it is my opinion that they do it to take advantage of the passengers. The only way to avoid the boom and have any safety at all while sailing is to lie flat on your stomach in the bottom of the ship. This is very uncomfortable on account of the hard boards and because you can't see a thing, but it is the one sure way I know of to go sailing and come back in the boat and not be washed up in the surf. I recommend the posture highly, but not as highly as I recommend the bicycle. My sailing adventures in Bermuda have made me appreciate for the first time the essential wonder of the simple, boomless bicycle.

Here Lies Miss Groby

M ISS GROBY taught me English composition thirty years ago. It wasn't what prose said that interested Miss Groby; it was the way prose said it. The shape of a sentence crucified on a blackboard (parsed, she called it) brought a light to her eye. She hunted for Topic Sentences and Transitional Sentences the way little girls hunt for white violets in springtime. What she loved most of all were Figures of Speech. You remember her. You must have had her, too. Her influence will never die out of the land. A small schoolgirl asked me the other day if I could give her an example of metonymy. (There are several kinds of metonymies, you must recall, but the one that will come to mind most easily, I think, is Container for the Thing Contained). The vision of Miss Groby came clearly before me when the little girl mentioned the old, familiar word. I saw her sitting at her desk, taking the rubber band off the roll-call cards, running it back upon the fingers of her right hand, and surveying us all separately with quick little henlike turns of her head.

Here lies Miss Groby, not dead, I think, but put away on a shelf with the other T squares and rulers whose edges had lost their certainty. The fierce light that Miss Groby brought to English literature was the light of Identification. Perhaps, at the end, she could no longer retain the dates of the birth and death of one of the Lake poets. That would have sent her to the principal of the school with her resignation. Or perhaps she could not remember, finally, exactly how many Cornishmen there were who had sworn that Trelawny should not die, or precisely how many springs were left to Housman's lad in which to go about the woodlands to see the cherry hung with snow.

Verse was one of Miss Groby's delights because there was so much in both its form and content that could be counted. I believe she would have got an enormous thrill out of Wordsworth's famous lines about Lucy if they had been written this way:

> A violet by a mossy stone
> Half hidden from the eye,
> Fair as a star when ninety-eight
> Are shining in the sky.

It is hard for me to believe that Miss Groby ever saw any famous work of literature from far enough away to know what it meant. She was forever climbing up the margins of books and crawling between their lines, hunting for the little gold of phrase, making marks with a pencil. As Palamides hunted the Questing Beast, she hunted the Figure of Speech. She hunted it through the clangorous halls of Shakespeare and through the green forests of Scott.

Night after night, for homework, Miss Groby set us to searching in 'Ivanhoe' and 'Julius Caesar' for metaphors, similes, metonymies, apostrophes, per-
sonifications, and all the rest. It got so that figures of speech jumped out of the
pages at you, obscuring the sense and pattern of the novel or play you were trying to read. 'Friends, Romans, countrymen, lend me your ears.' Take that, for
instance. There is an unusual but perfect example of Container for the Thing
Contained. If you read the funeral oration unwarily – that is to say, for its
meaning – you might easily miss the C.F.T.T.C. Antony is, of course, not
asking for their ears in the sense that he wants them cut off and handed over;
he is asking for the function of those ears, for their power to hear, for, in a word,
the thing they contain.

 At first I began to fear that all the characters in Shakespeare and Scott were
crazy. They confused cause with effect, the sign for the thing signified, the
thing held for the thing holding it. But after a while I began to suspect that it
was I myself who was crazy. I would find myself lying awake at night saying
over and over, 'The thinger for the thing contained.' In a great but probably
misguided attempt to keep my mind on its hinges, I would stare at the ceiling
and try to think of an example of the Thing Contained for the Container. It
struck me as odd that Miss Groby had never thought of that inversion. I finally
hit on one, which I still remember. If a woman were to grab up a bottle of
Grade A and say to her husband, 'Get away from me or I'll hit you with the
milk,' that would be a Thing Contained for the Container. The next day in
class I raised my hand and brought my curious discovery straight out before
Miss Groby and my astonished schoolmates. I was eager and serious about it
and it never occurred to me that the other children would laugh. They
laughed loudly and long. When Miss Groby had quieted them she said to me
rather coldly, 'That was not really amusing, James.' That's the mixed-up kind
of thing that happened to me in my teens.

 In later years I came across another excellent example of this figure of
speech in a joke long since familiar to people who know vaudeville or burlesque
(or radio, for that matter). It goes something like this:

   A: What's your head all bandaged up for?
   B: I got hit with some tomatoes.
   A: How could that bruise you up so bad?
   B: These tomatoes were in a can.

I wonder what Miss Groby would have thought of that one.

I dream of my old English teacher occasionally. It seems that we are always
in Sherwood Forest and that from far away I can hear Robin Hood winding his
silver horn.

 'Drat that man for making such a racket on his cornet!' cries Miss Groby.
'He scared away a perfectly darling Container for the Thing Contained, a
great, big beautiful one. It leaped right back into its context when that man

blew that cornet. It was the most wonderful Container for the Thing Contained I ever saw here in the Forest of Arden.'

'This is Sherwood Forest,' I say to her.

'That doesn't make any difference at all that I can see,' she says to me.

Then I wake up, tossing and moaning.

A Sort of Genius

ON THE morning of Saturday the 16th of September, 1922, a boy named Raymond Schneider and a girl named Pearl Bahmer, walking down a lonely lane on the outskirts of New Brunswick, New Jersey, came upon something that made them rush to the nearest house in Easton Avenue, around the corner, shouting. In that house an excited woman named Grace Edwards listened to them wide-eyed and then telephoned the police. The police came on the run and examined the young people's discovery: the bodies of a man and a woman. They had been shot to death and the woman's throat was cut. Leaning against one of the man's shoes was his calling card, not as if it had fallen there but as if it had been placed there. It bore the name Rev. Edward W. Hall. He had been the rector of the Protestant Episcopal Church of St John the Evangelist in New Brunswick. The woman was identified as Mrs Eleanor R. Mills, wife of the sexton of that church. Raymond Schneider and Pearl Bahmer had stumbled upon what was to go down finally in the annals of our crime as perhaps the country's most remarkable mystery. Nobody was ever found guilty of the murders. Before the case was officially closed, a hundred and fifty persons had had their day in court and on the front pages of the newspapers. The names of two must already have sprung to your mind: Mrs Jane Gibson, called by the avid press 'the pig woman,' and William Carpender Stevens, once known to a hundred million people simply as 'Willie.' The pig woman died eleven years ago, but Willie Stevens is alive. He still lives in the house that he lived in fourteen years ago with Mr and Mrs Hall, at 23 Nichol Avenue, New Brunswick.

It was from that house that the Rev. Mr Hall walked at around 7.30 o'clock on the night of Thursday the 14th of September, 1922, to his peculiar doom. With the activities in that house after Mr Hall's departure the State of New Jersey was to be vitally concerned. No. 23 Nichol Avenue was to share with De Russey's Lane, in which the bodies were found, the morbid interest of a whole nation four years later, when the case was finally brought to trial. What actually happened in De Russey's Lane on the night of September 14th? What actually happened at 23 Nichol Avenue the same night? For the researcher, it is a matter of an involved and voluminous court record, colourful and exciting in places, confused and repetitious in others. Two things, however, stand out as sharply now as they did on the day of their telling: the pig woman's story of the people she saw in De Russey's Lane that night, and Willie Stevens' story of what went on in the house in Nichol Avenue. Willie's story, brought out in cross-examination by a prosecutor whose name you may have forgotten (it was

Alexander Simpson), lacked all the gaudy melodrama of the pig woman's tale, but in it, and in the way he told it on the stand, was the real drama of the Hall-Mills trial. When the State failed miserably in its confident purpose of breaking Willie Stevens down, the verdict was already written on the wall. The rest of the trial was anticlimax. The jury that acquitted Willie, and his sister, Mrs Frances Stevens Hall, and his brother, Henry Stevens, was out only five hours.

A detailed recital of all the fantastic events and circumstances of the Hall-Mills case would fill a large volume. If the story is vague in your mind, it is partly because its edges, even under the harsh glare of investigation, remained curiously obscure and fuzzy. Everyone remembers, of course, that the minister was deeply involved with Mrs Mills, who sang in his choir; their affair had been for some time the gossip of their circle. He was forty-one, she was in her early thirties; Mrs Hall was nearing fifty. On the 14th of September, Mr Hall had dinner at home with his wife, Willie Stevens, and a little niece of Mrs Hall's. After dinner, he said, according to his wife and his brother-in-law, that he was going to call on Mrs Mills. There was something about a payment on a doctor's bill. Mrs Mills had had an operation and the Halls had paid for it (Mrs Hall had inherited considerable wealth from her parents). He left the house at about the same time, it came out later, that Mrs Mills left her house, and the two were found murdered, under a crab apple tree in De Russey's Lane, on the edge of town, some forty hours later. Around the bodies were scattered love letters which the choir singer had written to the minister. No weapons were found, but there were several cartridge shells from an automatic pistol.

The investigation that followed – marked, said one New Jersey lawyer, by 'bungling stupidity' – resulted in the failure of the grand jury to indict anyone. Willie Stevens was questioned for hours, and so was Mrs Hall. The pig woman told her extraordinary story of what she saw and heard in the lane that night, but she failed to impress the grand jurors. Four years went by, and the Hall-Mills case was almost forgotten by people outside of New Brunswick when, in a New Jersey court, one Arthur Riehl brought suit against his wife, the former Louise Geist, for annulment of their marriage. Louise Geist had been, at the time of the murders, a maid in the Hall household. Riehl said in the course of his testimony that his wife had told him 'she knew all about the case but had been given $5,000 to hold her tongue.' This was all that Mr Philip Payne, managing editor of the *Daily Mirror*, nosing around for a big scandal of some sort, needed. His newspaper 'played up' the story until finally, under its goading, Governor Moore of New Jersey appointed Alexander Simpson special prosecutor with orders to reopen the case. Mrs Hall and Willie Stevens were arrested and so was their brother, Henry Stevens, and a cousin, Henry de la Bruyere Carpender.

At a preliminary hearing in Somerville the pig woman, with eager stridency, told her story again. About 9 o'clock on the night of September 14th, she heard a wagon going along Hamilton Road near the farm on which she raised her pigs. Thieves had been stealing her corn and she thought maybe they were at it

again. So she saddled her mule, Jenny (soon to become the most famous quad-
ruped in the country), and set off in grotesque pursuit. In the glare of an automobile's headlights in De Russey's Lane, she saw a woman with white hair
who was wearing a tan coat, and a man with a heavy moustache, who looked
like a coloured man. These figures she identified as Mrs Hall and Willie
Stevens. Tying her mule to a cedar tree, she started toward the scene on foot
and heard voices raised in quarrel: 'Somebody said something about letters.'
She now saw three persons (later on she increased this to four), and a flashlight
held by one of them illumined the face of a man she identified first as Henry
Carpender, later as Henry Stevens, and it 'glittered on something' in the man's
hand. Suddenly there was a shot, and as she turned and ran for her mule, there
were three more shots; a woman's voice screamed, 'Oh, my! Oh, my! Oh, my!'
and the voice of another woman moaned, 'Oh, Henry!' The pig woman rode
wildly home on her mule, without investigating further. But she had lost one
of her moccasins in her flight, and some three hours later, at 1 o'clock, she rode
her mule back again to see if she could find it. This time, by the light of the
moon, she saw Mrs Hall, she said, kneeling in the lane, weeping. There was no
one else there. The pig woman did not see any bodies.

Mrs Jane Gibson became, because of her remarkable story, the chief witness
for the State, as Willie Stevens was to become the chief witness for the defence.
If he and his sister were not in De Russey's Lane, as the pig woman had shrilly
insisted, it remained for them to tell the detailed story of their whereabouts and
their actions that night after Mr Hall left the house. The grand jury this time
indicted all four persons implicated by the pig woman, and the trial began on
November 3rd, 1926.

The first persons Alexander Simpson called to the stand were 'surprise witnesses.' They were a Mr and Mrs John S. Dixon, who lived in North Plainfield,
New Jersey, about twelve miles from New Brunswick. It soon became apparent
that they were to form part of a net that Simpson was preparing to draw around
Willie Stevens. They testified that at about 8.30 on the night of the murders
Willie had appeared at their house, wearing a loose-fitting suit, a derby, a wing
collar with bow tie, and, across his vest, a heavy gold chain to which was
attached a gold watch. He had said that his sister had let him out there from her
automobile and that he was trying to find the Parker Home for the Aged, which
was at Bound Brook. He stuttered and he told them that he was an epileptic.
They directed him to a trolley car and he went stumbling away. When Mrs
Dixon identified Willie as her visitor, she walked over to him and took his
right hand and shook it vigorously, as if to wring recognition out of him. Willie
stared at her, said nothing. When she returned to the stand, he grinned widely.
That was one of many bizarre incidents which marked the progress of the
famous murder trial. It deepened the mystery that hung about the strange
figure of Willie Stevens. People could hardly wait for him to take the stand.

William Carpender Stevens had sat in court for sixteen days before he was
called to the witness chair, on the 23rd of November, 1926. On that day the
trial of Albert B. Fall and Edward L. Doheny, defendants in the notorious

Teapot Dome scandal, opened in Washington, but the nation had eyes only for a small, crowded courtroom in Somerville, New Jersey. Willie Stevens, after all these weeks, after all these years, was to speak out in public for the first time. As the *New York Times* said, 'He had been pictured as "Crazy Willie," as a town character, as an oddity, as a butt for all manner of jokes. He had been compared inferentially to an animal, and the hint of an alien racial strain in his parentage had been thrown at him.' Moreover, it had been prophesied that Willie would 'blow up' on the stand, that he would be trapped into contradictions by the 'wily' and 'crafty' Alexander Simpson, that he would be tricked finally into blurting out his guilt. No wonder there was no sound in the courtroom except the heavy tread of Willie Stevens' feet as he walked briskly to the witness stand.

Willie Stevens was an ungainly, rather lumpish man, about five feet ten inches tall. Although he looked flabby, this was only because of his loose-fitting clothes and the way he wore them; despite his fifty-four years, he was a man of great physical strength. He had a large head and a face that would be hard to forget. His head was covered with a thatch of thick, bushy hair, and his heavy black eyebrows seemed always to be arched, giving him an expression of perpetual surprise. This expression was strikingly accentuated by large, prominent eyes which, seen through the thick lenses of the spectacles he always wore, seemed to bulge unnaturally. He had a heavy, drooping, walrus moustache, and his complexion was dark. His glare was sudden and fierce; his smile, which came just as quickly, lighted up his whole face and gave him the wide, beaming look of an enormously pleased child. Born in Aiken, South Carolina, Willie Stevens had been brought to New Brunswick when he was two years old. When his wealthy parents died, a comfortable trust fund was left to Willie. The other children, Frances and Henry, had inherited their money directly. Once, when Mrs Hall was asked if it was not true that Willie was 'regarded as essential to be taken care of in certain things,' she replied, 'In certain aspects.' The quality of Willie's mentality, the extent of his eccentricity, were matters the prosecution strove to establish on several occasions. Dr Laurence Runyon, called by the defence to testify that Willie was not an epileptic and had never stuttered, was cross-examined by Simpson. Said the doctor, 'He may not be absolutely normal mentally, but he is able to take care of himself perfectly well. He is brighter than the average person, although he has never advanced as far in school learning as some others. He reads books that are above the average and makes a good many people look like fools.' 'A sort of genius, in a way, I suppose?' said Simpson. To which the doctor quietly replied, 'Yes, that is just what I mean.'

There were all sorts of stories about Willie. One of them was that he had once started a fire in his back yard and then, putting on a fireman's helmet, had doused it gleefully with a pail of water. It was known that for years he had spent most of every day at the firehouse of Engine Company No. 3 in Dennis Street, New Brunswick. He played cards with the firemen, ran errands for them, argued and joked with them, and was a general favourite. Sometimes he went out and bought a steak, or a chicken, and it was prepared and eaten in the firehouse by the firemen and Willie. In the days when the engine company had been a volunteer organization, Willie was an honorary member and always carried, in the firemen's parades, a flag he had bought and presented to the firehouse, an elaborate banner costing sixty or seventy dollars. He had also bought the black-and-white bunting with which the front of the firehouse was draped whenever a member of the company died.

After his arrest, he had whiled away the time in his cell reading books on metallurgy. There was a story that when his sister-in-law, Mrs Henry Stevens, once twitted him on his heavy reading, he said, 'Oh, that is merely the bread and butter of my literary repast.' The night before the trial opened, Willie's chief concern was about a new blue suit that had been ordered for him and that did not fit him to his satisfaction. He had also lost a collar button, and that worried him; Mrs Henry Stevens hurried to the jail before the court convened and brought him another one, and he was happy. At the preliminary hearing weeks before, Simpson had declared with brutal directness that Willie Stevens did indeed look like a coloured man, as the pig woman had said. At this Willie had half risen from his chair and bared his teeth, as if about to leap on the prosecutor. But he had quickly subsided. Willie Stevens all through the trial had sat quietly, staring. He had been enormously interested when the pig woman, attended by a doctor and a nurse, was brought in on a stretcher to give her testimony. This was the man who now, on trial for his life, climbed into the witness chair in the courtroom at Somerville.

There was an immense stir. Justice Charles W. Parker rapped with his gavel. Mrs Hall's face was strained and white; this was an ordeal she and her family had been dreading for weeks. Willie's left hand gripped his chair tightly, his right hand held a yellow pencil with which he had fiddled all during the trial. He faced the roomful of eyes tensely. His own lawyer, Senator Clarence E. Case, took the witness first. Willie started badly by understating his age ten years. He said he was forty-four. 'Isn't it fifty-four?' asked Case. Willie gave the room his great, beaming smile. 'Yes,' he chortled, boyishly, as if amused by his slip. The spectators smiled. It didn't take Willie long to dispose of the Dixons, the couple who had sworn he stumbled into their house the night of the murder. He answered half a dozen questions on this point with strong emphasis, speaking slowly and clearly: he had never worn a derby, he had never had epilepsy, he had never stuttered, he had never had a gold watch and chain. Mr Case held up Willie's old silver watch and chain for the jury to see. When he handed them back, Willie, with fine nonchalance, compared his watch with the clock on the courtroom wall, gave his sister a large, reassuring smile, and turned to his questioner with respectful attention. He described, with technical accuracy, an old revolver of his (the murders had been done with an automatic pistol, not a revolver, but a weapon of the same calibre as Willie's). He said he used to fire off the gun on the Fourth of July; remembering these old holidays, his eyes lighted up with childish glee. From this mood he veered suddenly into indignation and anger. 'When was the last time you saw the revolver?' was what set him off. 'The last time I saw it was in this courthouse!' Willie almost shouted. 'I think it was in October, 1922, when I was taken and put through a very severe grilling by – I cannot mention every person's name, but I remember Mr Toolan, Mr Lamb, and Detective David, and they did everything but strike me. They cursed me frightfully.' The officers had got him into an automobile 'by a subterfuge,' he charged. 'Mr David said he simply wanted me to go out in the country, to ask me a very few questions, that I would not be very long.' It transpired later that on this trip Willie himself had had a question to ask Detective David: would the detective, if they passed De Russey's Lane, be kind enough to point it out to him? Willie had never seen the place, he told the detective, in his life. He said that Mr David showed him where it was.

When Willie got to the night of September 14th, 1922, in his testimony his anger and indignation were gone; he was placid, attentive, and courteous. He explained quietly that he had come home for supper that night, had gone to his room afterward, and 'remained in the house, leaving it at 2.30 in the morning with my sister.' Before he went to bed, he said, he had closed his door to confine to his own room the odour of tobacco smoke from his pipe. 'Who objected to that?' asked Mr Case. Willie gave his sudden, beaming grin. 'Everybody,' he said, and won the first of several general laughs from the courtroom. Then he told the story of what happened at 2.30 in the morning. It is necessary, for a well-rounded picture of Willie Stevens, to give it here at some length. 'I was awakened by my sister knocking at my door,' said Willie, 'and I immediately rose and went to the door and she said, "I want you to come down to the church as Edward has not come home; I am very much worried" – or words to that effect. I immediately got dressed and accompanied her down to the church. I went through the front door, followed a small path that led directly to the back of the house past the cellar door. We went directly down Redmond Street to Jones Avenue, from Jones Avenue we went to George Street; turning into George Street we went directly down to Commercial Avenue. There our movements were blocked by an immense big freight automobile. We had to wait there maybe half a minute until it went by, going toward New York.

'I am not at all sure whether we crossed right there at Commercial Avenue or went a little further down George Street and went diagonally across to the church. Then we stopped there and looked at the church to see whether there were any lights. There were no lights burning. Then Mrs Hall said, "We might as well go down and see if it could not be possible that he was at the Mills' house." We went down there, down George Street until we came to Carman Street, turned down Carman Street, and got in front of the Mills' house and stood there two or three minutes to see if there were any lights in the Mills' apartment. There were none.' Willie then described, street by street, the return home, and ended with 'I opened the front door with my latchkey. If you wish me, I will show it to you. My sister said, "You might as well go to bed. You can do no more good." With that I went upstairs to bed.' This was the story that Alexander Simpson had to shake. But before Willie was turned over to him, the witness told how he heard that his brother-in-law had been killed. 'I remember I was in the parlour,' said Willie, 'reading a copy of the *New York Times*. I heard someone coming up the steps and I glanced up and I heard my aunt, Mrs Charles J. Carpender, say, "Well, you might as well know it – Edward has been shot." ' Willie's voice was thick with emotion. He was asked what happened then. 'Well,' he said, 'I simply let the paper go – that way' (he let his left hand fall slowly and limply to his side) 'and I put my head down, and I cried.' Mr Case asked him if he was present at, or had anything to do with, the murder of Mr Hall and Mrs Mills. 'Absolutely nothing at all!' boomed Willie, coming out of his posture of sorrow, belligerently erect. The attorney for the defence turned, with a confident little bow, to Alexander Simpson. The special prosecutor sauntered over and stood in front of the witness. Willie took in his breath sharply.

Alexander Simpson, a lawyer, a state senator, slight, perky, capable of harsh tongue-lashings, given to sarcasm and innuendo, had intimated that he would 'tie Willie Stevens into knots.' Word had gone around that he intended to 'flay' the eccentric fellow. Hence his manner now came as a surprise. He spoke in a gentle, almost inaudible voice, and his attitude was one of solicitous friendliness. Willie, quite unexpectedly, drew first blood. Simpson asked him if he had ever earned his livelihood. 'For about four or five years,' said Willie, 'I was employed by Mr Siebold, a contractor.' Not having anticipated an affirmative reply, Simpson paused. Willie leaned forward and said, politely, 'Do you wish his address?' He did this in good faith, but the spectators took it for what the *Times* called a 'sally,' because Simpson had been in the habit of letting loose a swarm of investigators on anyone whose name was brought into the case. 'No, thank you,' muttered Simpson, above a roar of laughter. The prosecutor now set about picking at Willie's story of the night of September 14th: he tried to find out why the witness and his sister had not knocked on the Mills' door to see if Mr Hall were there. Unfortunately for the steady drumming of questions, Willie soon broke the prosecutor up with another laugh. Simpson had occasion to mention a New Brunswick boarding house called The Bayard, and he pronounced 'Bay' as it is spelled. With easy politeness, Willie corrected him. '*Bi*yard,' said Willie. 'Biyard?' repeated Simpson. Willie smiled, as at an apt pupil. Simpson bowed slightly. The spectators laughed again.

Presently the witness made a slip, and Simpson pounced on it like a stooping falcon. Asked if he had not, at the scene of the murder, stood 'in the light of an automobile while a woman on a mule went by,' Willie replied, 'I never remember that occurrence.' Let us take up the court record from there. 'Q. – You would remember if it occurred, wouldn't you? A. – I certainly would, but I don't remember of ever being in an automobile and the light from the automobile shone on a woman on a mule. Q. – Do you say you were not there, or you don't remember? A. – I say positively I was not there. Q. – Why did you say you don't *remember*? A. – Does not that cover the same thing? Q. – No, it don't, because you might be there and not remember it. A. – Well, I will withdraw that, if I may, and say I was not there positively.' Willie assumed an air of judicial authority as he 'withdrew' his previous answer, and he spoke his positive denial with sharp decision. Mr Simpson abruptly tried a new tack. 'You have had a great deal of experience in life, Mr Stevens,' he said, 'and have read a great deal, they say, and know a lot about human affairs. Don't you think it sounds rather fishy when you say you got up in the middle of the night to go and look for Dr Hall and went to the house and never even knocked on the door – with your experience of human affairs and people that you met and all that sort of thing – don't that seem rather fishy to you?' There was a loud bickering of attorneys before Willie could say anything to this. Finally Judge Parker turned to the witness and said, 'Can you answer that, Mr Stevens?' 'The only way I can answer it, Your Honour,' said Willie, scornfully, 'is that I don't see that it is at all "fishy." ' The prosecutor jumped to something else: 'Dr Hall's church was not your church, was it?' he asked. 'He was not a *Doctor*, sir,' said Willie, once more the instructor. 'He was the Reverend *Mister* Hall.' Simpson paused, nettled. 'I am glad you corrected me on that,' he said. The courtroom laughed again.

The prosecutor now demanded that Willie repeat his story of what happened at 2.30 A.M. He hoped to establish, he intimated, that the witness had learned it 'by rote.' Willie calmly went over the whole thing again, in complete detail, but no one of his sentences was the same as it had been. The prosecutor asked him to tell it a third time. The defence objected vehemently. Simpson vehemently objected to the defence's objection. The Court: 'We will let him tell it once more.' At this point Willie said, 'May I say a word?' 'Certainly,' said Simpson. 'Say all you want.' Weighing his words carefully, speaking with slow emphasis, Willie said, 'All I have to say is I was never taught, as you insinuate, by any person whatsoever. That is my best recollection from the time I started out with my sister to this present minute.' Simpson did not insist further on a third recital. He wanted to know now how Willie could establish the truth of his statement that he was in his room from 8 or 9 o'clock until his sister knocked on the door at 2.30 A.M. 'Why,' said Willie, 'if a person sees me go upstairs and does not see me come downstairs, isn't that a conclusion that I was in my room?' The court record shows that Mr Simpson replied, 'Absolutely.' 'Well,' said Willie expansively, 'that is all there was to it.' Nobody but the pig woman had testified to seeing Willie after he went up to his room that night. Barbara Tough, a servant who had been off during the day, testified that she got back to the Hall home about 10 o'clock and noticed that Willie's door was closed (Willie had testified that it wouldn't stay closed unless he locked it). Louise Geist, of the annulment suit, had testified that she had not seen Willie that night after dinner. It was Willie's story against the pig woman's. That day in court he overshadowed her. When he stepped down from the witness chair, his shoulders were back and he was smiling broadly. Headlines in the *Times* the next day said, 'Willie Stevens Remains Calm Under Cross-Examination. Witness a Great Surprise.' There was a touch of admiration, almost of partisanship, in most of the reporters' stories. The final verdict

c*

could be read between the lines. The trial dragged on for another ten days, but on the 3rd of December, Willie Stevens was a free man.

He was glad to get home. He stood on the porch of 23 Nichol Avenue, beaming at the house. Reporters had followed him there. He turned to them and said, solemnly, 'It is one hundred and four days since I've been here. And I want to get in.' They let him go. But two days later, on a Sunday, they came back and Mrs Hall received them in the drawing room. They could hear Willie in an adjoining room, talking spiritedly. He was, it came out, discussing metallurgy with the Rev. J. Mervin Pettit, who had succeeded Mr Hall as rector of the Church of St John the Evangelist.

Willie Stevens, going on seventy, no longer visits the firehouse of No. 3 Engine Company. His old friends have caught only glimpses of him in the past few years, for he has been in feeble health, and spends most of his time in his room, going for a short ride now and then in his chauffeur-driven car. The passer by, glancing casually into the car, would not recognize the famous figure of the middle 1920's. Willie has lost a great deal of weight, and the familiar beaming light no longer comes easily to his eyes.

After Willie had been acquitted and sent home, he tried to pick up the old routine of life where he had left it, but people turned to stare after him in the street, and boys were forever at his heels, shouting, 'Look out, Willie, Simpson is after you!' The younger children were fond of him and did not tease him, and once in a while Willie could be seen playing with them, as boisterously and whimsically as ever. The firemen say that if he encountered a ragged child he would find out where it lived, and then give one of his friends the money to buy new clothes for it. But Willie's adventures in the streets of the town became fewer and farther apart. Sometimes months would elapse between his visits to the firehouse. When he did show up in his old haunts, he complained of headaches, and while he was still in his fifties, he spent a month in bed with a heart ailment. After that, he stayed close to home, and the firemen rarely saw him. If you should drop by the firehouse, and your interest in Willie seems friendly, they will tell you some fond stories about him.

One winter Willie took a Cook's tour of Hawaii. When he came back, he told the firemen he had joined an organization which, for five dollars, gave its subscribers a closer view of the volcanoes than the ordinary tourist could get. Willie was crazy about the volcanoes. His trip, however, was spoiled, it came out, because someone recognized and pointed him out as the famous Willie Stevens of the Hall-Mills case. He had the Cook's agent cancel a month's reservation at a hotel and rearrange his schedule so that he could leave on the next ship. He is infuriated by any reference to the murders or to the trial. Some years ago a newspaper printed a paragraph about a man out West who was 'a perfect double for Willie Stevens.' Someone in the firehouse showed it to Willie and he tore the paper to shreds in a rage.

Willie still spends a great deal of time reading 'heavy books' – on engineering, on entomology, on botany. Those who have seen his famous room at 23 Nichol Avenue – he has a friend in to visit him once in a while – say that it is filled with books. He has no use for detective stories or the Western and adventure magazines his friends the firemen read. When he is not reading scientific tomes, he dips into the classics or what he calls the 'worth-while poets.' He used to astound the firemen with his wide range of knowledge. There was the day a salesman of shaving materials dropped in at the engine-house. Finding that Willie had visited St Augustine, Florida, he mentioned an old Spanish chapel there. Willie described it and gave its history, replete with dates, and greatly impressed the caller. Another time someone mentioned a certain kind of insect which he said was found in this country. 'You mean they used to be,' said Willie. 'That type of insect has been extinct in this country for forty years.' It turned out that it had been, too. On still another occasion Willie fell to discussing flowers with some visitor at the firehouse and reeled off a Latin designation – *crassinae carduaceae*, or something of the sort. Then he turned, grinning, to the listening firemen. 'Zinnias to you,' he said.

Willie Stevens' income from the trust fund established for him is said to be around forty dollars a week. His expenditures are few, now that he is no longer able to go on long trips. The firemen like especially to tell about the time that Willie went to Wyoming, and attended a rodeo. He told the ticket-seller he wanted to sit in a box and the man gave him a single ticket. Willie explained that he wanted the whole box to himself, and he planked down a ten-dollar bill for it. Then he went in and sat in the box all alone. 'I had a hell of a time!' he told the firemen gleefully when he came back home.

De Russey's Lane, which Detective David once pointed out to Willie Stevens, is now, you may have heard, entirely changed. Several years ago it was renamed Franklin Boulevard, and where the Rev. Mr Edward W. Hall and Mrs Eleanor Mills lay murdered there is now a row of neat brick and stucco houses. The famous crab apple tree under which the bodies were found disappeared the first weekend after the murders. It was hacked to pieces, roots and all, by souvenir-hunters.

Memorial

S HE CAME all the way from Illinois by train in a big wooden crate many years ago, a frightened black poodle, not yet a year old. She felt terrible in body and worse in mind. These contraptions that men put on wheels, in contravention of that law of nature which holds that the feet must come in contact with the ground in travelling, dismayed her. She was never able to ride 1,000 yards in an automobile without getting sick at her stomach, but she was always apologetic about this frailty, never, as she might well have been, reproachful.

She tried patiently at all times to understand Man's way of life: the rolling of his wheels, the raising of his voice, the ringing of his bells; his way of searching out with lights the dark protecting corners of the night; his habit of building his beds inside walls, high above the nurturing earth. She refused, with all courtesy, to accept his silly notion that it is better to bear puppies in a place made of machined wood and clean blue cloth than in the dark and warm dirt beneath the oak flooring of the barn.

The poodle was hand in glove with natural phenomena. She raised two litters of puppies, taking them in her stride, the way she took the lightning and the snow. One of these litters, which arrived ahead of schedule, was discovered under the barn floor by a little girl of two. The child gaily displayed on her right forearm the almost invisible and entirely painless marks of teeth which had gently induced her to put down the live black toys she had found and wanted to play with.

The poodle had no vices that I can think of, unless you could count her incurable appetite for the tender tips of the young asparagus in the garden and for the black raspberries when they ripened on the bushes in the orchard. Sometimes, as punishment for her depredations, she walked into bees' nests or got her long shaggy ears tangled in fence wire. She never snarled about the penalties of existence or whimpered about the trials and grotesqueries of life with Man.

She accepted gracefully the indignities of the clipping machine which, in her maiden days, periodically made a clown of her for the dog shows, in accordance with the stupid and unimaginative notion that this most sensitive and dignified of animals is at heart a buffoon. The poodle, which can look as husky as a Briard when left shaggy, is an outdoors dog and can hold its own in the field with the best of the retrievers, including the Labrador.

The poodle won a great many ribbons in her bench days, but she would have traded all her medals for a dish of asparagus. She knew it was show time when the red rubber bib was tied around her neck. That meant a ride in a car to bedlam.

Like the great Gammeyer of Tarkington's *Gentle Julia*, the poodle I knew seemed sometimes about to bridge the mysterious and conceivably narrow gap that separates instinct from reason. She could take part in your gaiety and your sorrow; she trembled to your uncertainties and lifted her head at your assurances. There were times when she seemed to come close to a pitying comprehension of the whole troubled scene and what lies behind it. If poodles, who walk so easily upon their hind legs, ever do learn the little tricks of speech and reason, I should not be surprised if they made a better job of it than Man, who would seem to be surely but not slowly slipping back to all fours.

The poodle kept her sight, her hearing, and her figure up to her quiet and dignified end. She knew that the Hand was upon her and she accepted it with a grave and unapprehensive resignation. This, her dark intelligent eyes seemed to be trying to tell me, is simply the closing of full circle, this is the flower that grows out of Beginning; this – not to make it too hard for you, friend – is as natural as eating the raspberries and raising the puppies and riding into the rain.

A Ride with Olympy

OLYMPY SEMENTZOFF called me '*Monsieur*' because I was the master of the Villa Tamisier and he was the gardener, the Russian husband of the French caretaker, Maria. I called him '*Monsieur*,' too, because I could never learn to call any man Olympy and because there was a wistful air of *ancien régime* about him. He drank Bénédictine with me and smoked my cigarettes; he also, as you will see, drove my car. We conversed in French, a language alien to both of us, but more alien to me than to him. He said '*gauche*' for both 'right' and 'left' when he was upset, but when I was upset I was capable of flights that put the French people on their guard, wide-eyed and wary. Once, for instance, when I cut my wrist on a piece of glass I ran into the lobby of a hotel shouting in French, 'I am sick with a knife!' Olympy would have known what to say (except that it would have been his left wrist in any case) but he wouldn't have shouted: his words ran softly together and sounded something like the burbling of water over stones. Often I did not know what he was talking about; rarely did he know what I was talking about. There was a misty, faraway quality about this relationship, in French, of Russia and Ohio. The fact that the accident Olympy and I were involved in fell short of catastrophe was, in view of everything, something of a miracle.

Olympy and Maria 'came with' the villa my wife and I rented on Cap d'Antibes. Maria was a deep-bosomed, large-waisted woman, as persistently pleasant as Riviera weather in a good season; no mistral ever blew in the even climate of her temperament. She must have been more than forty-five but she was as strong as a root; once when I had trouble getting a tough cork out of a wine bottle she took hold and whisked it out as if it had been a maidenhair fern. On Sundays her son came over from the barracks in Antibes and we all had a glass of white Bordeaux together, sometimes the Sementzoffs' wine, sometimes our own. Her son was eighteen and a member of the Sixth Regiment of Chasseurs Alpins, a tall, sombre boy, handsome in his uniform and cape. He was an *enfant du premier lit*, as the French say. Maria made her first bed with a sergeant of the army who was *cordonnier* for his regiment during the war and seemed somehow to have laid by quite a little money. After the war the sergeant-shoemaker resigned from the army, put his money in investments of some profoundly mysterious nature in Indo-China, and lost it all. '*Il est mort*,' Maria told us, '*de chagrin*.' Grief over his ill-fortune brought on a decline; the *chagrin*, Maria said, finally reached his brain, and he died at the age of thirty-eight. Maria had to sell their house to pay the taxes, and go to work.

60

Olympy Sementzoff, Maria's second husband, was shy, not very tall, and wore a beard; in his working clothes you didn't notice much more than that. When he was dressed for Sunday – he wore a fine double-breasted jacket – you observed that his mouth was sensitive, his eyes attractively sad, and that he wore his shyness with a certain air. He worked in a boat factory over near Cannes – Maria said that he was a *spécialiste de bateaux*; odd jobs about the villa grounds he did on his off days. It was scarcely light when he got up in the morning, for he had to be at work at seven; it was almost dark when he got home. He was paid an incredibly small amount for what he did at the factory and a handful of sous each month for what he did about the grounds. When I gave him a hundred francs for some work he had done for me in the house – he could repair anything from a drain to a watch – he said, '*Oh, monsieur, c'est trop!*' '*Mais non, monsieur,*' said I. '*Ce n'est pas beaucoup.*' He took it finally, after an exchange of bows and compliments.

The elderly wife of the Frenchman from whom we rented the villa told us, in a dark whisper, that Olympy was a White Russian and that there was perhaps a *petit mystère* about him, but we figured this as her own fanciful bourgeois alarm. Maria did not make a mystery out of her husband. There was the Revolution, most of Olympy's brothers and sisters were killed – one knew how that was – and he escaped. He was, of course, an exile and must not go back. If she knew just who he was in Russia and what he had done, she didn't make it very clear. He was in Russia and he escaped; she had married him thirteen years before; *et puis, voilà!* It would have been nice to believe that there was the blood of the Czars in Olympy, but if there was anything to the ancient legend that all the stray members of the Imperial House took easily and naturally to driving a taxi, that let Olympy out. He was not a born chauffeur, as I found out the day I came back from our automobile ride on foot and – unhappily for Maria – alone.

Olympy Sementzoff rode to and from his work in one of those bastard agglomerations of wheels, motor and superstructure that one saw only in France. It looked at first glance like the cockpit of a cracked-up plane. Then you saw that there were two wheels in front and a single wheel in back. Except for the engine – which Maria said was a 'Morgan *moteur*' – and the wheels and tyres, it was handmade. Olympy's boss at the boat factory had made most of it, but Olympy himself had put on the *ailes*, or fenders, which were made of some kind of wood. The strange canopy that served as a top was Maria's proud handiwork; it seemed to have been made of canvas and kitchen aprons. The thing had a right-hand drive. When the *conducteur* was in his seat he was very low to the ground: you had to bend down to talk to him. There was a small space beside the driver in which another person could sit, or crouch. The whole affair was not much larger than an overturned cabinet victrola. It got bouncingly under way with all the racket of a dog fight and in full swing was capable of perhaps thirty miles an hour. The contraption had cost Olympy three thousand francs, or about a hundred dollars. He had driven it for three years and was hand in glove with its mysterious mechanism. The gadgets on the dash and on the floorboard, which he pulled or pushed to make the thing go, seemed to include fire tongs, spoons, and doorknobs. Maria miraculously managed to squeeze into the seat beside the driver in an emergency, but I could understand why she didn't want to drive to the Nice Carnival in the 'Morgan.' It was because she didn't that I suggested Olympy should take her over one day in my Ford sedan. Maria had given us to understand that her *mari* could drive any car – he could be a chauffeur if he wanted to, a *bon* chauffeur. All I would have to do, *voyez-vous*, was to take Olympy for a turn around the Cap so that he could get the hang of the big car. Thus it was that one day after lunch we set off.

Half a mile out of Antibes on the shore road, I stopped the car and changed places with Olympy, letting the engine run. Leaning forward, he took a tense grip on a steering wheel much larger than he was used to and too far away from him. I could see that he was nervous. He put his foot on the clutch, tentatively, and said, '*Embrayage?*' He had me there. My knowledge of French automotive terms is inadequate and volatile. I was forced to say I didn't know. I couldn't remember the word for clutch in any of the three languages, French, Italian and German, in which it was given in my 'Motorist's Guide' (which was back at the villa). Somehow '*embrayage*' didn't sound right for clutch (it is, though). I knew it wouldn't do any good for an American writer to explain in French to a Russian boat specialist the purpose that particular pedal served; furthermore, I didn't really know. I compromised by putting my left foot on the brake. '*Frein*,' I said. '*Ah*,' said Olympy, unhappily. This method of indicating what something might be by demonstrating what it wasn't had a disturbing effect. I shifted my foot to the accelerator – or rather pointed my toe at it – and suddenly the word for that, even the French for gasoline, left me. I was growing a little nervous myself. '*Benzina*,' I said, in Italian, finally. '*Ah?*' said Olympy. Whereas we had been one remove from reality to begin with, we were now two, or perhaps three, removes. A polyglot approach to the fine precision of a gas engine is roundabout and dangerous. We both lost a little confidence in each other. I suppose we should have given up right then, but we didn't.

Olympy decided the extra pedal was the *embrayage*, shifted into low from neutral, and the next thing I knew we were making a series of short forward bounds like a rabbit leaping out of a wheat field to see where he is. This form of locomotion takes a lot out of man and car. The engine complained in loud, rhythmic whines. And then Olympy somehow got his left foot on the starter and there was a familiar undertone of protest; this set his right foot to palpitating on the accelerator and the rabbit-jumps increased in scope. Abandoning my search for the word for starter, I grabbed his left knee and shouted '*Ça commence!*' Just what was commencing Olympy naturally couldn't figure – probably some habitual and ominous idiosyncrasy of the machinery. He gave me a quick, pale look. I shut off the ignition, and we discussed the starter situation, breathing a little heavily. He understood what it was, finally, and presently we were lurching ahead again, Olympy holding her in low gear, like a wrestler in a clinch, afraid to risk shifting into second. He tried it at last and with a jamming jolt and a roar we went into reverse: the car writhed like a tortured leopard and the engine quit.

I was puzzled and scared, and so was Olympy. Only a foolish pride in masculine fortitude kept us going. I showed him the little jog to the right you have to make to shift into second and he started the engine and we were off again, jolting and lurching. He made the shift, finally, with a noise like lightning striking a foundry – and veered swoopingly to the right. We barely missed a series of staunch granite blocks, set in concrete, that mark ditches and soft shoulders. We whisked past a pole. The leaves of a vine hanging on a wall slapped at me through the window. My voice left me. I was fascinated and paralysed by the swift passes disaster was making at my head. At length I was able to grope blindly toward the ignition switch, but got my wrist on the klaxon button. When I jerked my arm away, Olympy began obediently sounding the horn. We were riding on the edge of a ditch. I managed somehow to shut off the ignition and we rolled to a stop. Olympy, unused to a left-hand drive, had forgotten there was a large portion of the car to his right, with me in it. I told him, '*A gauche, à gauche, toujours à gauche!*' '*Ah,*' said Olympy, but there was no comprehension in him. I could see he didn't know we had been up against the vines of villa walls: intent on the dark problem of gearshifting, he had been oblivious of where the car and I had been. There was a glint in his eye now. He was determined to get the thing into high on his next attempt; we had come about half a mile in the lower gears.

The road curved downhill as it passed Eden Roc and it was here that an elderly English couple, unaware of the fact that hell was loose on the highway, were walking. Olympy was in second again, leaning forward like a racing bicycle rider. I shouted at him to look out, he said '*Oui*' – and we grazed the old man and his wife. I glanced back in horror: they were staring at us, mouths and eyes wide, unable to move or make a sound. Olympy raced on to a new peril: a descending hairpin curve, which he negotiated in some far-fetched manner, with me hanging onto the emergency brake. The road straightened out, I let go the brake, and Olympy slammed into high with the desperate gesture of a man trying to clap his hat over a poised butterfly. We began to whiz: Olympy hadn't counted on a fast pickup. He whirled around a car in front of us with a foot to spare. '*Lentement!*' I shouted, and then '*Gauche!*' as I began to get again the whimper of poles and walls in my ears. '*Ça va mieux, maintenant,*' said Olympy, quietly. A wild thought ran through my head that maybe this was the way they used to drive in Russia in the old days.

Ahead of us now was one of the most treacherous curves on the Cap. The road narrowed and bent, like a croquet wicket, around a high stone wall that shut off your view of what was coming. What was coming was usually on the wrong side of the road, so it wouldn't do to shout '*Gauche!*' now. We made the turn all right. There was a car coming, but it was well over on its own side. Olympy apparently didn't think so. He whirled the wheel to the right, didn't take up the play fast enough in whirling it back, and there was a tremendous banging crash, like a bronze monument falling. I had a glimpse of Olympy's right hand waving around like the hand of a man hunting for something under a table. I didn't know what his feet were doing. We were still moving, heavily, with a ripping noise and a loud roar. *'Poussez le phare!'* I shouted, which means 'push the headlight!' *'Ah-h-h-h,'* said Olympy. I shut off the ignition and pulled on the hand brake, but we had already stopped. We got out and looked at the pole we had sideswiped and at the car. The right front fender was crumpled and torn and the right back one banged up, but nothing else had been hurt. Olympy's face was so stricken when he looked at me that I felt I had to cheer him up. *'Il fait beau,'* I announced, which is to say that the weather is fine. It was all I could think of.

I started for a garage that Olympy knew about. At the first street we came to he said *'Gauche'* and I turned left. *'Ah, non,'* said Olympy. *'Gauche,'* and he pointed the other way. 'You mean *droit?'* I asked just that way. *'Ah!'* said Olympy. *'C'est bien ça!'* It was as if he had thought of something he hadn't been able to remember for days. That explained a great deal.

I left Olympy and the car at the garage; he said he would walk back. One of the garage men drove me into Juan-les-Pins and I walked home from there – and into a look of wild dismay in Maria's eyes. I hadn't thought about that: she had seen us drive away together and here I was, alone. *'Où est votre mari?'* I asked her, hurriedly. It was something of a failure as a reassuring beginning. I had taken the question out of her own mouth, so I answered it. 'He has gone for a walk,' I told her. Then I tried to say that her husband was *bon*, but I pronounced it *beau*, so that what I actually said was that her husband was handsome. She must have figured that he was not only dead but laid out. There was a *mauvais quart d'heure* for both of us before the drooping figure of Olympy finally appeared. He explained sadly to Maria that the mechanism of the Ford is strange and curious compared to the mechanism of the Morgan. I agreed with him. Of course, he protested, he would pay for the repairs to the car, but Maria and I both put down that suggestion. Maria's idea of my work was that I was paid by the City of New York and enjoyed a tremendous allowance. Olympy got forty francs a day at the boat factory.

That night, at dinner, Maria told us that her *mari* was pacing up and down in their little bedroom at the rear of the house. He was in a state. I didn't want an attack of *chagrin* to come on him as it had on the *cordonnier* and perhaps reach his brain. When Maria was ready to go we gave her a handful of cigarettes for Olympy and a glass of Bénédictine. The next day, at dawn, I heard the familiar *tintamarre* and *hurlement* and *brouhaha* of Olympy's wonderful contraption getting under way once more. He was off to the boat factory and his forty francs a day, his dollar and thirty cents. It would have cost him two weeks' salary to pay for the fenders, but he would have managed it somehow. When I went down to breakfast, Maria came in from the kitchen with a large volume, well fingered and full of loose pages, which she handed to me. It was called *Le Musée d'Art* and subtitled *Galerie des Chefs-d'œuvre et Précis de l'Histoire de l'Art au XIXᵉ Siécle, en France et à l'Etranger (1000 gravures, 58 planches hors texte)*. A present to *Monsieur* from Olympy Sementzoff, with his compliments. The incident of the automobile was thus properly rounded off with an exchange of presents: cigarettes, Bénédictine, and *Le Musée d'Art*. It seemed to me the way such things should always end, but perhaps Olympy and I were ahead of our day – or behind it.

La Grande Ville de Plaisir

THERE is an old saying that if Paris had a street like La Canebière it would be a little Marseilles, to which I shall add that if Marseilles had a Promenade des Anglais it would be a little Nice. Marseilles is famous for the dark dangers of its back streets and for mysterious doings along its waterfront. Just the other day boxes containing six thousand gold watches, in transit from Geneva to Buenos Aires, were eased of their treasure and magically filled with chunks of cement on a quay in Marseilles. You may have read about that: the police news of Marseilles has a habit of getting on the international press wires. The activities of lawbreakers in Nice, on the other hand, may often be read about only in the local papers, of which my favourite is the enormously interesting *L'Eclaireur de Nice et du Sud-Est*. The *voleurs* of Nice take, as a rule, one watch at a time, or one wallet, but they frequently manage it in a picturesque fashion.

If you should see a fat and jovial priest drop a well-filled billfold behind him on the Promenade, return it to him, bow politely, wink, and proceed on your way. Tarry not to make an acquaintance that will show rapid signs of ripening into a pleasant and perhaps profitable companionship. The dropped wallet is the opening move in an ancient swindle that works like a charm in this friendly climate. When I was in Nice twelve years ago the wolves in priests' clothing (sometimes it was in the clothing of retired philanthropists or bankers) reaped, as the saying goes, a rich harvest. I remember a professor of economics in a Pennsylvania college who waited for three hours in a café for his old pal the priest to show up. This particular variant of the venerable racket had begun with a most interesting talk about faith in one's fellow-man and had ended by the professor agreeing to prove his own faith in his fellow-man by allowing the priest to walk around the block with his (the professor's) wallet. Usually the old game is worked with considerably more subtlety; often several enjoyable weeks drift by before the holy father (or the philanthropist or the banker) feels the fruit is ripe enough for the plucking. Always in the end a gentleman of great faith is left sitting in a café, or a hotel room, looking anxiously at his wristwatch (unless, of course, he has lent that to his good friend, too). In the winter of 1925 the Riviera edition of the Chicago *Tribune*, for which I was a reporter, ran every day on its front page a warning about the swindlers; it didn't seem to do much good.

The general run of waywardness in Nice may be on a lesser scale than that of Marseilles, but it is infinitely more fascinating. *Inconnus* are found mysteriously injured, *malheureux* get into all kinds of curious difficulties, *indélicats* are found wandering around with nothing on. If you have to keep your ear to the ground and your eye on the *Eclaireur* to learn about them, it is partly because Nice is a carnival city whose daily news is drowned in a trumpeting of ballyhoo and a showering of confetti. The *Syndicat d'Initiative* and the Rotary Club – surely the strongest outside the United States – and the other organizations that go in for rosy pictures of this *grande ville de plaisir* dwell so loudly on the climate and the carnival that the casual visitor would not imagine anything out of the way ever happened here. And yet, like another Poictesme, it is a place in which almost anything is more than likely to happen. The night I arrived in the city recently a *malheureux* ran across the Place Masséna bleeding copiously from a cut throat and gurgling, '*Je vais mourir!*' (He didn't die, however.) The next night a man scurried past me hotly pursued by a woman who kept screaming 'Police!' (Nobody paid any attention.)

It is always with a sense of high expectation that I set out into the city. If the day's excitement doesn't break actually about my head, I can always read about it in the *Eclaireur*. At 2.30 yesterday afternoon (I see by the paper before me), in the Rue Barla, an Algerian named Tayeb Mihoubi was stabbed by a Moroccan named Mohamed ben Mohamed; one Mme Grocorini, having irked a gentleman named Valerio Franchi, was slashed by the gentleman's knife and when a M. Ricci rashly intervened, he was slashed, too. Knives rise and fall on this lovely littoral as easily and for as little provocation as a woman's tears. There are thousands of Italians and Corsicans in Nice, and a great scattering of Algerians, Moroccans, and sombre dark men from a dozen other countries. The city has been a place of sojourn and foray ever since it was founded by the Phocaeans twenty centuries ago; it has been overrun by Ligurians, Celts, Romans, Saracens, Englishmen, and Americans. It has a tradition of restlessness.

One of the most remarkable manifestations of the restlessness of Nice and the surrounding country is the *bagarre*. *Bagarre* means 'violent disorder, uproar, crush, squabble, scuffle, fray.' Today's *Eclaireur* tells of the final disposition, in the courts, of a famous *bagarre*, more exactly known as '*La Fusillade de la Place Arson*,' which took place as long ago as August, 1936 (the wheels of justice turn slowly in the south). As is usually the case with *bagarres*, nobody knows exactly how or why this one started, but it had something to do with politics. In the end scores of men were involved and more than two hundred shots were fired. Nobody was killed or even seriously injured, which the *Eclaireur* admits it is at a loss to understand, and so am I. Most of the shooting took place at close quarters; there must have been a kind of carnival touch about so much spectacular and aimless gunfire. Anyway, the case has been finally disposed of: eight men were fined twenty-five francs each, or less than a dollar, for illegal possession of firearms. That was all. The *Eclaireur* intimates that it was not considered discreet to prosecute the defendants on any more serious or relevant charges. Such a procedure, one gathers, could easily start a *bagarre* all over again – perhaps right there in the courtroom.

Of recent *bagarres*, the one that has interested me most took place in a village a few miles from Nice, but since it was of the very scheme and rhythm of many a similar happening within the city's limits, I must report it. It will give you as clear an idea as may be had of what a *bagarre* is like. The *Eclaireur* launches into the puzzling story in this manner: 'In spite of promises given, in spite of appeals for calm, the closing of the Institute of Actinology was not accomplished without incident.' I do not know what an institute of actinology is or why it should be difficult to close one without incident; probably anywhere else in the world it would be child's play to close an institute of actinology. But not in Nice or vicinity. It was the Messrs Mandouce, Guenon, and Billet, and a Mme Veran, who tried to close this one. M. Guenon was immediately set upon by a young man named Roba, who was accompanied by the Messrs Lanteri, Bernardi, and Grindou. M. Roba beat M. Guenon savagely about the head either with a rock or a *poing américain* (brass knuckles). A M. Monti drifted into the scuffle from somewhere, rescued M. Guenon, and took him to a doctor, who bandaged his wounds. Afterward, M. Guenon went to a café run by a M. Laugier and was having a glass of something to steady his nerves when one Vincent Martino entered, saw the injured man's bandages, and asked him what had happened. Before he could get a reply, M. Martino was punched in the head by a M. Baracco. From here on the story loses its sharp clarity. M. Martino whipped out a gun, but hastily hid it in a cardboard box when a policeman entered. M. Guenon and M. Baracco drop quietly out of the tortured narrative at this point, but M. Martino was led off to the police station. That didn't cause things to quiet down. 'A crowd of three hundred people gathered about the café,' says the *Eclaireur*, 'shouting and gesticulating. Women mingled in the crowd, also shouting and gesticulating.' Presently some cops shouldered their way through the mob, not to restore order, it turns out, but to hunt for M. Martino's gun, which the first *agent* had neglected to seize. They found the gun and went away. The crowd stayed and grew increasingly menacing as the night wore on, so that M. Laugier finally had to close the café. We learn that the police investigations went on late into the night, but just what angles of the involved case they were investigating is not made clear; I have an idea, though, they were concentrating on M. Martino's gun. The *Eclaireur* ends the story with this musical sentence: '*Dans la rue, le calme est long à revenir.*' That, then, is a typical *bagarre*, violent, cloudy, complicated. It is no use trying to fit the incidents together into a logical pattern. The *Eclaireur* and the police gave that up long ago. And so did I.

There is an embarrassing richness of clippings before me, cut from the *Eclaireurs* of only one week. Several standing headlines recur frequently, one of them the simple phrase '*Les Pochards.*' A *pochard* is a drunk. The headline has something of the slangy, sardonic force of 'Among the Soused' or 'With the Cockeyed.' The stories deal briefly with the activities of gentlemen who, while in their cups, have caused a slight 'scandal' here, a mild 'outrage' there. Another headline, '*Les Conducteurs Imprudents et Maladroits,*' tops almost every day a considerable list of automobile accidents. I note that just yesterday a big Hispano-Suiza sports roadster, driven by a baron, knocked down a lamp-post on the Promenade des Anglais and that shortly afterwards another *imprudent* knocked down a palm tree. The Promenade is more dangerous than the Place de la Concorde. I remember that when I was here before, the *Eclaireur* ran a picture of a Promenade traffic cop who was in the hospital for no less than the seventh time as the result of having been knocked down by a motorist on that broad thoroughfare.

My clippings deal with a dozen other varied and spectacular episodes, but I shall go into detail only about the curious case of M. Antoine Semeria, aged forty-seven, a *mécanicien-dentiste*, because it is typical of a special class of bizarre goings on in this Paradise on the Bay of the Angels. M. Semeria was dragged up before M. Giocanti, *commissaire* of police, because he had refused to pay his fare on an autobus. He explained to the *commissaire* that it was his invariable custom not to pay for riding on autobuses. Ride on them he would, pay he would not, and that was that – the *commissaire* would see. M. Giocanti listened patiently for a while and then directed that M. Semeria be put away in a hospital for observation. M. Semeria was placed in the hospital, escaped immediately, boarded the first bus that came along, once more refused to pay, and was hauled up before the *commissaire* again before you could say Giocanti.

I have touched on only one or two special phases of the rich life of this great, colourful city of almost 250,000 inhabitants (not counting the visitors, who nearly double the permanent population) that sprawls between the mountains and the sea. Up on the hill back of the town is the old Roman quarter called Cimiez, where Queen Victoria stayed, a region almost as sedate and quiet as it was in her time, but considerably more crowded. From the heights above the city you can look down on a panorama as diverse as life itself: the streets of the shopkeepers and the bourgeoisie in the more modern part of town; the narrow *rues* of the Vieille-Ville down by the sea, where the Italians live; the *faubourg* of the Port of Nice, which visitors rarely get to; and the region around the Place Masséna (*'centre de l'animation, cœur de la ville'*), which visitors seldom get away from. The main thoroughfare of the tourists' quarter is, of course, the Promenade des Anglais. It was in hotels along this boulevard that Isadora Duncan, Rudolph Valentino, Harry Sinclair, and Papa Laemmle lived when I was here before. In those four you have a coloured-postcard picture of this *centre de vie joyeuse* in the gay days before the depression. It was an exciting winter, the winter of 1925. Nowadays I more or less wander around, an outsider on a visit, but that season I was in the midst of the excitement.

I think it was the Hôtel Ruhl et Anglais that I called up the night, twelve years ago, when a wire came to us on the *Tribune* saying that Serge Yessenin, Isadora Duncan's former husband, had killed himself in Moscow. I was directed to get the great lady on the phone and find out what she had to say (it sometimes seemed to me that this nasty business of interviewing bereaved women was what editors figured me to be cut out for in my days as a newspaperman). The hotel reported that Miss Duncan was out and was not expected back before 1 o'clock in the morning. At a little after one (ours was a morning newspaper) I got her on the phone. It came out that she had not yet heard about the death of the man with whom she had once led such a tumultuous life. I am sure I must have managed it all very badly; I was scared. I remember that she said nothing but 'No, no, no, no,' which she repeated a dozen times, and that finally she let the receiver fall. I called back the hotel, and speaking English to a puzzled French night clerk, shouted at him to do something about Miss Duncan. I have no idea what he did. I never saw Isadora Duncan. The next day, however, she granted interviews to other reporters and, according to the *Eclaireur*, told them she felt sure that the poem which Yessenin is reported to have written in his own blood before he died was a poem to her. It was, I believe, on the Promenade des Anglais of this violent city that Isadora Duncan met her tragic and implausible end when a scarf she was wearing trailed out of the car she was riding in, caught in a wheel, and choked her to death. I remember my phone call to Isadora Duncan all too clearly. I remember, too, how indestructibly healthy Valentino, who had only a few months to live, looked. And how Harry Sinclair, consenting warily to an interview, never once met my gaze but stared at me out of the corner of his right eye.

Nobody, however, so purely typified for me the faintly sinister fascination of this ancient city of the Phocaeans as did a tall young Hindu who showed up silently and ominously in the little office of the *Tribune* one night. We had a week before advertised for a proofreader who knew English and more than fifty persons had answered the ad, among them the young Hindu. They were an amazing group: a Belgian woman of seventy-five, a former captain in the British Army, a Russian prince, a Scotch teacher, a French painter, all sorts and conditions of drifters and dreamers – the flotsam of fifty nations that you can raise, with one signal or another, from Cimiez up on the hill to the steep streets of the old town by the sea. The editor had finally hired the former British Army man. But our Hindu, who appeared so softly out of the night, swore vehemently that it was he who had been hired. His dark stare was menacing, his perfect English had a dangerous edge. He was as straight-backed as a knife. 'I have come for the job I was hired for,' he said. 'I am ready to start work.' The editor, looking a little grey, said he had hired another man. 'Oh, no, you haven't,' said the Hindu quietly, and then shouted, 'You hired me!' There was an unbearably long silence while he glared at each of us in turn. Then, suddenly turning on the editor again, he cried, 'I know who you are and all about you! You are Lame-Leg Charlie, the dope fiend! Remember this – you haven't seen the last of me!' And the door somehow opened behind him and he was gone. The editor's name was not Charlie, he was not lame, and he didn't take dope. Our visitor's dark threat and his darker revelations, which were never cleared up, left us all a little shaken. It turned out that we *had* seen the last of our Hindu, but there was never a night that I didn't expect him to show up again to wreak whatever peculiar vengeance it is that frustrated Hindu proofreaders go in for. I put this story in because Nice is like that.

Nice is like this, too: One day in 1926 the mistral, that violent and unpredictable wind from the Alps, came to town, like a cavalcade of desperadoes drunk and firing from both hips. It knocked over chimneys, ripped off signs, tore shutters loose from windows. I was walking with a lady in the Avenue Félix-Faure when the terror descended. The lady walked, I am happy to say, very fast – so fast that we were able to step clear of fifty tons of bricks that suddenly roared and thundered to the pavement behind us. A high parapet surmounting a row of six one-story shops and forming a false second-story front had been toppled into the street by the wind hurricaning behind it. I can still see with too great clarity the hand of a man who was killed in the wreckage, sticking up out of his tomb of bricks. A few moments before, I had been abreast of him. The lady, as I have said, was a fast walker.

All this, then, past and present, is Nice, the capital of gaiety, the mother city of this bright shore of winter playgrounds. If I have made her seem perhaps a trifle too violent, I must make some amends. Nice has her quiet moments, her tranquil *quartiers*, she has even her proud memories of a holy visitation. It is nice to know as you walk past the trim façade of the Hôtel Beau-Rivage on the Quai des Etats-Unis that on a November day fifty years ago a certain obscure Frenchman named Martin decided to stay there one night with his two daughters, Céline and Thérèse. It is nice to know that from one of the wide windows Thérèse Martin looked out on the palm trees and the deep blue of the Bay of the Angels. It is an enchanting view. Who knows what high resolve it may not have inspired in the young girl who was to become perhaps the most beloved of all the saints in the calendar to the people of her country – Sainte Thérèse de l'Enfant Jésus, France's 'Little Flower.' Or you can walk into the peaceful old graveyard of the English Church of the Holy Trinity and ponder on the modest tombstone of a reverend English gentleman, Henry Francis Lyte, of Lower Brixham in Devon, whose prayer that he might 'leave behind some blessing for his fellows, some fair trust to guide, to cheer, to elevate mankind' was answered in, of all places, Nice, where just before he died, in November, 1847, he was moved to write the surely immortal hymn that begins 'Abide with me, fast falls the eventide.'

Eventide in November falls very fast indeed in Nice. The darkness caught me one afternoon, two months ago, in the little graveyard, but not before I had seen the gleam of a small white card tacked to the church door. I went over to see if some fair trust might not be lettered on it. The living actuality of Nice abruptly overtook me, there in the gloaming, dispelling my mood of reverie. The card sadly announced that because of numerous thefts, the place of worship had to be kept locked; visitors were requested to ask the sexton for the key.

There's No Place Like Home

IDLING through a London bookstore in the summer of 1937, I came upon a little book called 'Collins' Pocket Interpreters: France.' Written especially to instruct the English how to speak French in the train, the hotel, the quandary, the dilemma, etc., it is, of course, equally useful – I might also say equally depressing – to Americans. I have come across a number of these helps-for-travellers, but none that has the heavy impact, the dark, cumulative power of Collins'. A writer in a London magazine mentions a phrase book got out in the era of Imperial Russia which contained this one magnificent line: 'Oh, dear, our postillion has been struck by lightning!' but that fantastic piece of disaster, while charming and provocative – though, I daresay, quite rare even in the days of the Czars – is to Mr Collins' modern, workaday disasters as Fragonard is to George Bellows, or Sarah Orne Jewett to William Faulkner. Let us turn the pages of this appalling little volume.

Each page has a list of English expressions one under the other, which gives them the form of verse. The French translations are run alongside. Thus, on the first page, under 'The Port of Arrival,' we begin (quietly enough) with 'Porter, here is my baggage!' – '*Porteur, voici mes bagages!*' From then on disaster follows fast and follows faster until in the end, as you shall see, all hell breaks loose. The volume contains three times as many expressions to use when one is in trouble as when everything is going all right. This, my own experience has shown, is about the right ratio, but God spare me from some of the difficulties for which the traveller is prepared in Mr Collins' melancholy narrative poem. I am going to leave out the French translations because, for one thing, people who get involved in the messes and tangles we are coming to invariably forget their French and scream in English anyway. Furthermore, the French would interrupt the fine, free flow of the English and spoil what amounts to a dramatic tragedy of an overwhelming and original kind. The phrases, as I have said, run one under the other, but herein I shall have to run them one after the other (you can copy them down the other way, if you want to).

Trouble really starts in the canto called 'In the Customs Shed.' Here we have: 'I cannot open my case.' 'I have lost my keys.' 'Help me to close this case.' 'I did not know that I had to pay.' 'I don't want to pay so much.' 'I cannot find my porter.' 'Have you seen porter 153?' That last query is a little master stroke of writing, I think, for in those few words we have a graphic picture of a tourist lost in a jumble of thousands of bags and scores of customs men, looking frantically for one of at least a hundred and fifty-three porters.

We feel that the tourist will not find porter 153, and the note of frustration has been struck.

Our tourist (accompanied by his wife, I like to think) finally gets on the train for Paris – having lost his keys and not having found his porter – and it comes time presently to go to the dining car, although he probably has no appetite, for the customs men, of course, have had to break open that one suitcase. Now, I think, it is the wife who begins to crumble: 'Someone has taken my seat.' 'Excuse me, sir, that seat is mine.' 'I cannot find my ticket!' 'I have left my ticket in the compartment.' 'I will go and look for it.' 'I have left my gloves (my purse) in the dining car.' Here the note of frenzied disintegration, so familiar to all travellers abroad, is sounded. Next comes 'The Sleeper,' which begins, ominously, with 'What is the matter?' and ends with 'May I open the window?' 'Can you open this window, please?' We realize, of course, that *nobody* is going to be able to open the window and that the tourist and his wife will suffocate. In this condition they arrive in Paris, and the scene there, on the crowded station platform, is done with superb economy of line: 'I have left something in the train.' 'A parcel, an overcoat.' 'A macintosh, a stick.' 'An umbrella, a camera.' 'A fur, a suitcase.' The travellers have now begun to go completely to pieces, in the grand manner.

Next comes an effective little interlude about an airplane trip, which is one of my favourite passages in this swift and sorrowful tragedy: 'I want to reserve a place in the plane leaving tomorrow morning.' 'When do we start?' 'Can we get anything to eat on board?' 'When do we arrive?' 'I feel sick.' 'Have you any paper bags for air-sickness?' 'The noise is terrible.' 'Have you any cotton wool?' 'When are we going to land?' This brief masterpiece caused me to cancel an air trip from London to Paris and go the easy way, across the Channel.

We now come to a section called 'At the Hotel,' in which things go from worse to awful: 'Did you not get my letter?' 'I wrote to you three weeks ago.' 'I asked for a first-floor room.' 'If you can't give me something better, I shall go away.' 'The chambermaid never comes when I ring.' 'I cannot sleep at night, there is so much noise.' 'I have just had a wire. I must leave at once.' Panic has begun to set in, and it is not appeased any by the advent of 'The Chambermaid': 'Are you the chambermaid?' 'There are no towels here.' 'The sheets on this bed are damp.' 'This room is not clean.' 'I have seen a mouse in the room.' 'You will have to set a mouse trap here.' The bells of hell at this point begin to ring in earnest: 'These shoes are not mine.' 'I put my shoes here, where are they now?' 'The light is not good.' 'The bulb is broken.' 'The radiator is too warm.' 'The radiator doesn't work.' 'It is cold in this room.' 'This is not clean, bring me another.' 'I don't like this.' 'I can't eat this. Take it away!'

I somehow now see the tourist's wife stalking angrily out of the hotel, to get away from it all (without any shoes on), and, properly enough, the booklet seems to follow her course – first under 'Guides and Interpreters': 'You are asking too much.' 'I will not give you any more.' 'I shall call a policeman.' 'He can settle this affair.' Then under 'Inquiring the Way': 'I am lost.' 'I was looking for—' 'Someone robbed me.' 'That man robbed me.' 'That man is following me everywhere.' She rushes to 'The Hairdresser,' where, for a change, everything goes quite smoothly until: 'The water is too hot, you are scalding me!' Then she goes shopping, but there is no surcease: 'You have not given me the right change.' 'I bought this two days ago.' 'It doesn't work.' 'It is broken.' 'It is torn.' 'It doesn't fit me.' Then to a restaurant for a snack and a reviving cup of tea: 'This is not fresh.' 'This piece is too fat.' 'This doesn't smell very nice.' 'There is a mistake in the bill.' 'While I was dining someone has taken my purse.' 'I have left my glasses (my watch) (a ring) in the lavatory.' Madness has now come upon her and she rushes wildly out into the street. Her husband, I think, has at the same time plunged blindly out of the hotel to find her. We come then, quite naturally, to 'Accident', which is calculated to keep the faint of heart – nay, the heart of oak – safely at home by his own fireside: 'There has been an accident!' 'Go and fetch a policeman quickly.' 'Is there a doctor near here?' 'Send for the ambulance.' 'He is seriously injured.' 'She has been run over.' 'He has been knocked down.' 'Someone has fallen in the water.' 'The ankle, the arm.' 'The back, a bone.' 'The face, the finger.' 'The foot, the head.' 'The knee, the leg.' 'The neck, the nose.' 'The wrist, the shoulder.' 'He has broken his arm.' 'He has broken his leg.' 'He has a sprained ankle.' 'He has a sprained wrist.' 'He is losing blood.' 'He has fainted.' 'He has lost consciousness.' 'He has burnt his face.' 'It is swollen.' 'It is bleeding.' 'Bring some cold water.' 'Help me to carry him.' (Apparently, you just let *her* lie there, while you attend to him – but, of course, she was merely run over, whereas he has taken a terrific tossing around.)

We next see the husband and wife back in their room at the dreary hotel, both in bed, and both obviously hysterical. This scene is entitled 'Illness': 'I am feeling very ill, send for the doctor.' 'I have pains in—' 'I have pains all over.' 'The back, the chest.' 'The ear, the head.' 'The eyes, the heart.' 'The joints, the kidneys.' 'The lungs, the stomach.' 'The throat, the tongue.' 'Put out your tongue.' 'The heart is affected.' 'I feel a pain here.' 'He is not sleeping well.' 'He cannot eat.' 'My stomach is out of order.' 'She is feverish.' 'I have caught a cold.' 'I have caught a chill.' 'He has a temperature.' 'I have a cough.' 'Will you give me a prescription?' 'What must I do?' 'Must I stay in bed?' 'I feel better.' 'When will you come and see me again?' 'Biliousness, rheumatism.' 'Insomnia, sunstroke.' 'Fainting, a fit.' 'Hoarseness, sore throat.' 'The medicine, the remedy.' 'A poultice, a draught.' 'A tablespoonful, a teaspoonful.' 'A sticking plaster, senna.' 'Iodine.' That last suicidal bleat for iodine is, to me, a masterful touch.

Our couple finally get on their feet again, for travellers are tough – they've got to be – but we see under the next heading, 'Common Words and Phrases,' that they are left forever punch-drunk and shattered: 'Can I help you?' 'Excuse me.' 'Carry on!' 'Look here!' 'Look down there!' 'Look up there!' 'Why, how?' 'When, where?' 'Because.' 'That's it!' 'It is too much, it is too dear.' 'It is very cheap.' 'Who, what, which?' 'Look out!' Those are Valkyries, one feels, riding around, and above, and under our unhappy husband and wife. The book sweeps on to a mad operatic ending of the tragedy, with all the

strings and brasses and wood winds going full blast: 'Where are we going?'
'Where are you going?' 'Come quickly and see!' 'I shall call a policeman.'
'Bring a policeman!' 'I shall stay here.' 'Will you help me?' 'Help! Fire!'
'Who are you?' 'I don't know you.' 'I don't want to speak to you.' 'Leave me
alone.' 'That will do.' 'You are mistaken.' 'It was not I.' 'I didn't do it.' 'I will
give you nothing.' 'Go away now!' 'It has nothing to do with me.' 'Where
should one apply?' 'What must I do?' 'What have I done?' 'I have done
nothing.' 'I have already paid you.' 'I have paid you enough.' 'Let me pass!'
'Where is the British consulate?' The oboes take that last, despairing wail, and
the curtain comes down.

Let Your Mind Alone!

FOR HELEN

Destructive Forces in Life

T HE mental efficiency books go into elaborate detail about how to attain Masterful Adjustment, as one of them calls it, but it seems to me that the problems they set up, and knock down, are in the main unimaginative and pedestrian: the little fusses at the breakfast-table, the routine troubles at the office, the familiar anxieties over money and health – the welter of workaday annoyances which all of us meet with and usually conquer without extravagant wear and tear. Let us examine, as a typical instance, a brief case history presented by the learned Mr David Seabury, author of *What Makes Us Seem So Queer, Unmasking Our Minds, Keep Your Wits, Growing Into Life*, and *How to Worry Successfully*. I select it at random. 'Frank Fulsome,' writes Mr Seabury, 'flung down the book with disgust and growled an insult at his wife. That little lady put her hands to her face and fled from the room. She was sure Frank must hate her to speak so cruelly. Had she known it, he was not really speaking to her at all. The occasion merely gave vent to a pent-up desire to "punch his fool boss in the jaw".' This is, I believe, a characteristic Seabury situation. Many of the women in his treatises remind you of nobody so much as Ben Bolt's Alice, who 'wept with delight when you gave her a smile, and trembled with fear at your frown'. The little ladies most of us know would, instead of putting their hands to their faces and fleeing from the room, come right back at Frank Fulsome. Frank would perhaps be lucky if he didn't get a punch in the jaw himself. In any case, the situation would be cleared up in approximately three minutes. This 'had she known' business is not as common among wives today as Mr Seabury seems to think it is. The Latent Content (as the psychologists call it) of a husband's mind is usually as clear to the wife as the Manifest Content, frequently much clearer.

I could cite a dozen major handicaps to Masterful Adjustment which the thought technicians never touch upon, a dozen situations not so easy of analysis and solution as most of theirs. I will, however, content myself with one. Let us consider the case of a man of my acquaintance who had accomplished Discipline of Mind, overcome the Will to Fail, mastered the Technique of Living – had, in a word, practically attained Masterful Adjustment – when he was called on the phone one afternoon about five o'clock by a man named Bert Scursey. The other man, whom I shall call Harry Conner, did not answer the phone, however; his wife answered it. As Scursey told me the story later, he had no intention when he dialled the Conners' apartment at the Hotel Graydon of doing more than talk with Harry. But, for some strange reason, when Louise Conner answered, Bert Scursey found himself pretending to be, and imitating the voice of, a coloured woman. This Scursey is by way of being an excellent mimic, and a coloured woman is one of the best things he does.

'Hello,' said Mrs Conner. In a plaintive voice, Scursey said, 'Is dis heah Miz Commah?' 'Yes, this is Mrs Conner,' said Louise. 'Who is speaking?' 'Dis heah's Edith Rummum,' said Scursey. 'Ah used wuck fo you frens was nex doah you place a Sou Norwuck.' Naturally, Mrs Conner did not follow this, and demanded rather sharply to know who was calling and what she wanted. Scursey, his voice soft with feigned tears, finally got it over to his friend's wife that he was one Edith Rummum, a coloured maid who had once worked for some friends of the Conners' in South Norwalk, where they had lived some years before. 'What is it you want, Edith?' asked Mrs Conner, who was completely taken in by the impostor (she could not catch the name of the South Norwalk friends, but let that go). Scursey – or Edith, rather – explained in a

A Mentally Disciplined Husband with Mentally Undisciplined Wife

pitiable, hesitant way that she was without work or money and that she didn't know what she was going to do; Rummum, she said, was in the jailhouse because of a cutting scrape on a roller-coaster. Now, Louise Conner happened to be a most kind-hearted person, as Scursey well knew, so she said that she could perhaps find some laundry work for Edith to do. 'Yessum,' said Edith. 'Ah laundas.' At this point, Harry Conner's voice, raised in the room behind his wife, came clearly to Scursey, saying, 'Now, for God's sake, Louise, don't go giving our clothes out to somebody you never saw or heard of in your life.' This interjection of Conner's was in firm keeping with a theory of logical behaviour which he had got out of the Mind and Personality books. There was no Will to Weakness here, no Desire to Have His Shirts Ruined, no False Sympathy for the Coloured Woman Who Has Not Organised Her Life.

But Mrs Conner who often did not listen to Mr Conner, in spite of his superior mental discipline, prevailed.* 'Where are you now, Edith?' she asked. This disconcerted Scursey for a moment, but he finally said, 'Ah's jes rounda

* This sometimes happens even when the husband is mentally disciplined and the wife is not.

corna, Miz Commah.' 'Well, you come over to the Hotel Graydon,' said Mrs Conner. 'We're in Apartment 7-A on the seventh floor.' 'Yessm,' said Edith. Mrs Conner hung up and so did Scursey. He was now, he realized, in something of a predicament. Since he did not possess a streamlined mind, as Dr Mursell has called it, and had definitely a Will to Confuse, he did not perceive that his little joke had gone far enough. He wanted to go on with it, which is a characteristic of woolgatherers, pranksters, wags, wish-fulfillers, and escapists generally. He enjoyed fantasy as much as reality, probably even more, which is a sure symptom of Regression, Digression, and Analogical Redintegration. What he finally did, therefore, was to call back the Conners and get Mrs Conner on the phone again. 'Jeez, Miss Commah,' he said, with a hint of panic in his voice, 'Ah cain' fine yo apottoman!' 'Where are you, Edith?' she asked. 'Lawd, Ah doan know,' said Edith. 'Ah's on *some* floah in de Hotel Graydon.' 'Well, listen, Edith, you took the elevator, didn't you?' 'Das whut Ah took,' said Edith uncertainly. 'Well, you go back to the elevator and tell the boy you want to get off at the seventh floor. I'll meet you at the elevator.' 'Yessm,' said Edith, with even more uncertainty. At this point, Conner's loud voice, speaking to his wife, was again heard by Scursey. 'Where in the hell is she calling from?' demanded Conner, who had developed Logical Reasoning. 'She must have wandered into somebody else's apartment if she is calling you from this building, for God's sake!' Whereupon, having no desire to explain where Edith was calling from, Scursey hung up.

After an instant of thought, or rather Disintegrated Phantasmagoria, Scursey rang the Conners again. He wanted to prevent Louise from going out to the elevator and checking up with the operator. This time, as Scursey had hoped, Harry Conner answered, having told his wife that he would handle this situation. 'Hello!' shouted Conner, irritably. 'Who is this?' Scursey now abandoned the role of Edith and assumed a sharp, fussy, masculine tone. 'Mr Conner,' he said, crisply, 'this is the office. I am afraid we shall have to ask you to remove this coloured person from the building. She is blundering into other people's apartments, using their phones. We cannot have that sort of thing, you know, at the Graydon.' The man's words and his tone infuriated Conner. 'There are a lot of sort of things I'd like to see you not have at the Graydon!' he shouted. 'Well, please come down to the lobby and do something about the situation,' said the man, nastily. 'You're damned right I'll come down!' howled Conner. He banged down the receiver.

Bert Scursey sat in a chair and gloated over the involved state of affairs which he had created. He decided to go over to the Graydon, which was just up the street from his own apartment, and see what was happening. It promised to have all the confusion which his disorderly mind so deplorably enjoyed. And it did have. He found Conner in a tremendous rage in the lobby, accusing an astonished assistant manager of having insulted him. Several persons in the lobby watched the curious scene. 'But, Mr Conner,' said the assistant manager, a Mr Bent, 'I have no idea what you are talking about.' 'If you listen, you'll find out!' bawled Harry Conner. 'In the first place, the coloured woman's coming to the hotel was no idea of mine. I've never seen her in my life and I don't want to see her! I want to go to my *grave* without seeing her!' He had forgotten what the Mind and Personality books had taught him; never raise your voice in anger, always stick to the point. Naturally, Mr Bent could only believe that his guest had gone out of his mind. He decided to humour him. 'Where is this – ah – coloured woman, Mr Conner?' he asked, warily. He was somewhat pale and was fiddling with a bit of paper. A dabbler in psychology books himself, he knew that coloured women are often Sex Degradation symbols, and he wondered if Conner had not fallen out of love with his wife without realizing it. (This theory, I believe, Mr Bent has clung to ever since, although the Conners are one of the happiest couples in the country.) 'I don't know where she is!' cried Conner. 'She's up on some other floor phoning my wife! *You* seemed to know all about it! I had nothing to do with it! I opposed it from the start! But I want no insults from you no matter *who* opposed it!' 'Certainly not, certainly not,' said Mr Bent, backing slightly away. He began to wonder what he was going to do with this maniac.

At this juncture Scursey, who had been enjoying the scene at a safe distance, approached Conner and took him by the arm. 'What's the matter, old boy?' he asked. 'H'lo, Bert,' said Conner, sullenly. And then, his eyes narrowing, he began to examine the look on Scursey's face. Scursey is not good at deadpanning; he is only good on the phone. There was a guilty grin on his face. 'You—' said Conner, bitterly, remembering Scursey's pranks of mimicry, and he turned on his heel, walked to the elevator, and, when Scursey tried to get in too, shoved him back into the lobby. That was the end of the friendship between the Conners and Bert Scursey. It was more than that. It was the end of Harry Conner's stay at the Graydon. It was, in fact, the end of his stay in New York City. He and Louise live in Oregon now, where Conner accepted a less important position than he had held in New York because the episode of Edith had turned him against Scursey, Mr Bent, the Graydon, and the whole metropolitan area.

Anybody can handle the Frank Fulsomes of the world, but is there anything to be done about the Bert Scurseys? Can we so streamline our minds that the antics of the Scurseys roll off them like water off a duck's back? I don't think so. I believe the authors of the inspirational books don't think so, either, but are afraid to attack the subject. I imagine they have been hoping nobody would bring it up. Hardly anybody goes through life without encountering his Bert Scursey and having his life – and his mind – accordingly modified. I have known a dozen Bert Scurseys. I have often wondered what happened to some of their victims. There was, for example, the man who rang up a waggish friend of mine by mistake, having got a wrong number. 'Is this the Shu-Rite Shoestore?' the caller asked, querulously. 'Shu-Rite Shoestore, good morning!' said my friend, brightly. 'Well,' said the other, 'I just called up to say that the shoes I bought there a week ago are shoddy. They're made, by God, of cardboard. I'm going to bring them in and show you. I want satisfaction!' 'And you shall have it!' said my friend. 'Our shoes are, as you say, shoddy.

There have been many complaints, many complaints. Our shoes, I am afraid, simply go to pieces on the foot. We shall, of course, refund your money.' I know another man who was always being roused out of bed by people calling a certain railway which had a similar phone number. 'When can I get a train to Buffalo?' a sour-voiced woman demanded one morning about seven o'clock. 'Not till 2 A.M. tomorrow, madam,' said this man. 'But that's ridiculous!' cried the woman. 'I know,' said the man, 'and we realize that. Hence we include, in the regular fare, a taxi which will call for you in plenty of time to make the train. Where do you live?' The lady, slightly mollified, told him an address in the Sixties. 'We'll have a cab there at one-thirty, madam,' he said. 'The driver will handle your baggage.' 'Now I can count on that?' she said. 'Certainly, madam,' he told her. 'One-thirty, sharp.'

Just what changes were brought about in that woman's character by that call, I don't know. But the thing might have altered the colour and direction of her life, the pattern of her mind, the whole fabric of her nature. Thus we see that a person might build up a streamlined mind, a mind awakened to a new life, a new discipline, only to have the whole works shot to pieces by so minor and unpredictable a thing as a wrong telephone number. On the other hand, the undisciplined mind would never have the fortitude to consider a trip to Buffalo at two in the morning, nor would it have the determination to seek redress from a shoe-store which had sold it a faulty pair of shoes. Hence the undisciplined mind runs far less chance of having its purposes thwarted, its plans distorted, its whole scheme and system wrenched out of line. The undisciplined mind, in short, is far better adapted to the confused world in which we live today than the streamlined mind. This is, I am afraid, no place for the streamlined mind.

Sex *ex* Machina

WITH the disappearance of the gas mantle and the advent of the short circuit, man's tranquillity began to be threatened by everything he put his hand on. Many people believe that it was a sad day indeed when Benjamin Franklin tied that key to a kite string and flew the kite in a thunderstorm; other people believe that if it hadn't been Franklin, it would have been someone else. As, of course, it was in the case of the harnessing of steam and the invention of the gas engine. At any rate, it has come about that so-called civilized man finds himself today surrounded by the myriad mechanical devices of a technological world. Writers of books on how to control your nerves, how to conquer fear, how to cultivate calm, how to be happy in spite of everything, are of several minds as regards the relation of man and the machine. Some of them are prone to believe that the mind and body, if properly disciplined, can get the upper hand of this mechanized existence. Others merely ignore the situation and go on to the profitable writing of more facile chapters of inspiration. Still others attribute the whole menace of the machine to sex, and so confuse the average reader that he cannot always be certain whether he has been knocked down by an automobile or is merely in love.

Dr Bisch, the *Be-Glad-You're-Neurotic* man, has a remarkable chapter which deals, in part, with man, sex, and the machine. He examines the case of three hypothetical men who start across a street on a red light and get in the way of an oncoming automobile. A dodges successfully; B stands still, 'accepting the situation with calm and resignation,' thus becoming one of my favourite heroes in modern *belles-lettres*; and C hesitates, wavers, jumps backward and forward, and finally runs head-on into the car. To lead you through Dr Bisch's complete analysis of what was wrong with B and C would occupy your whole day. He mentions what the McDougallians would say ('Instinct!'), what the Freudians would retort ('Complexes!'), and what the behaviourists would shout ('Conditioned reflexes!'). He also brings in what the physiologists would say – deficient thyroid, hypoadrenal functioning, and so on. The average sedentary man of our time who is at all suggestible must emerge from this chapter believing that his chances of surviving a combination of instinct, complexes, reflexes, glands, sex, and present-day traffic conditions are about equal to those of a one-legged blind man trying to get out of a labyrinth.

Let us single out what Dr Bisch thinks the Freudians would say about poor Mr C, who ran right into the car. He writes, ' "Sex hunger," the Freudians would declare. "Always keyed up and irritable because of it. Undoubtedly suffers from insomnia and when he does sleep his dream life must be productive, distorted, and possibly frightening. Automobile unquestionably has sex significance for him – to C the car is both enticing and menacing at one and the same time. . . . A thorough analysis is indicated. . . . It might take months. But then, the man needs an analysis as much as food. He is heading for a complete nervous collapse." ' It is my studied opinion, not to put too fine a point on it, that Mr C is heading for a good mangling, and that if he gets away with only a nervous collapse, it will be a miracle.

I have not always, I am sorry to say, been able to go the whole way with the Freudians, or even a very considerable distance. Even though, as Dr Bisch says, 'One must admit that the Freudians have had the best of it thus far. At least they have received the most publicity.' It is in matters like their analysis of men and machines, of Mr C and the automobile, that the Freudians and I part company. Of course, the analysis above is simply Dr Bisch's idea of what the Freudians would say, but I think he has got it down pretty well. Dr Bisch himself leans towards the Freudian analysis of Mr C, for he says in this same chapter, 'An automobile bearing down upon you may be a sex symbol at that, you know, especially if you dream it.' It is my contention, of course, that even if you dream it, it is probably not a sex symbol, but merely an automobile bearing down upon you. And if it bears down upon you in real life, I am sure it is an automobile. I have seen the same behaviour that characterized Mr C displayed by a squirrel (Mr S) that lives in the grounds of my house in the country. He is a fairly tame squirrel, happily mated and not sex-hungry, if I am any judge, but nevertheless he frequently runs out towards my automobile when I start down the driveway, and then hesitates, wavers, jumps forward and backward, and occasionally would run right into the car except that he is awfully fast on his feet and that I always hurriedly put on the brake of the 1935 V-8 Sex Symbol that I drive.

I have seen this same behaviour in the case of rabbits (notoriously uninfluenced by any sex symbols save those of other rabbits), dogs, pigeons, a doe, a young hawk (which flew at my car), a blue heron that I encountered on a country road in Vermont, and once, near Paul Smiths in the Adirondacks, a fox. They all acted exactly like Mr C. The hawk, unhappily, was killed. All the others escaped with nothing worse, I suppose, than a complete nervous collapse. Although I cannot claim to have been conversant with the private life and the secret compulsions, the psychoneuroses and the glandular activities of all these animals, it is nevertheless my confident and unswervable belief that there was nothing at all the matter with any one of them. Like Mr C, they suddenly saw a car swiftly bearing down upon them, got excited, and lost their heads. I do not believe, you see, there was anything the matter with Mr C, either. But I do believe that, after a thorough analysis lasting months, with a lot of harping on the incident of the automobile, something might very well come to be the matter with him. He might even actually get to suffering from the delusion that he believes automobiles are sex symbols.

It seems to me worthy of note that Dr Bisch, in reciting the reactions of three persons in the face of an oncoming car, selected three men. What would have happened had they been Mrs A, Mrs B, and Mrs C? You know as well as I do: all three of them would have hesitated, wavered, jumped forward and backward, and finally run head-on into the car if some man hadn't grabbed them. (I used to know a motorist who, every time he approached a woman standing on a kerb preparing to cross the street, shouted, 'Hold it, stupid!') It is not too much to say that, with a car bearing down upon them, ninety-five women out of a hundred would act like Mr C – or Mr S, the squirrel, or Mr F, the fox. But it is certainly too much to say that ninety-five out of every hundred women look upon an automobile as a sex symbol. For one thing, Dr Bisch points out that the automobile serves as a sex symbol because of the 'mechanical principle

Happily-mated Rabbit Terrified by Motor-car

involved'. But only one woman in a thousand really knows anything about the mechanical principle involved in an automobile. And yet, as I have said, ninety-five out of a hundred would hesitate, waver, and jump, just as Mr C did. I think we have the Freudians here. If we haven't proved our case with rabbits and a blue heron, we have certainly proved it with women.

To my notion, the effect of the automobile and of other mechanical contrivances on the state of our nerves, minds and spirits is a problem which the popular psychologists whom I have dealt with know very little about. The sexual explanation of the relationship of man and the machine is not good enough. To arrive at the real explanation, we have to begin very far back, as far back as Franklin and the kite, or at least as far back as a certain man and woman who appear in a book of stories written more than sixty years ago by Max Adler. One story in this book tells about a housewife who bought a combination ironing-board and card-table, which some New England genius had thought up in his spare time. The husband, coming home to find the devilish contraption in the parlour, was appalled. 'What is that thing?' he demanded. His wife explained that it was a card-table, but that if you pressed a button underneath, it would become an ironing-board. Whereupon she pushed the button and the table leaped a foot into the air, extended itself, and became an ironing-board. The story goes on to tell how the thing finally became so finely sensitized that it would change back and forth if you merely touched it – you didn't have to push the button. The husband stuck it in the attic (after it had leaped up and struck him a couple of times while he was playing euchre), and on windy nights it could be heard flopping and banging around, changing from a card-table to an ironing-board and back. The story serves as one example of our dread heritage of annoyance, shock, and terror arising out of the nature of mechanical contrivances *per se*. The mechanical principle involved in this damnable invention had, I believe, no relationship to sex whatsoever. There are certain analysts who see sex in anything, even a leaping ironing-board, but I think we can ignore these scientists.

No man (to go on) who has wrestled with a self-adjusting card-table can ever be quite the man he once was. If he arrives at the state where he hesitates, wavers, and jumps at every mechanical device he encounters, it is not, I submit, because he recognizes the enticements of sex in the device, but only because he recognizes the menace of the machine as such. There might very well be, in every descendant of the man we have been discussing, an inherited desire to jump at, and conquer, mechanical devices before they have a chance to turn into something twice as big and twice as menacing. It is not reasonable to expect that his children and their children will have entirely escaped the stigma of such traumata. I myself will never be the man I once was, nor will my descendants probably ever amount to much, because of a certain experience I had with an automobile.

I had gone out to the barn of my country place, a barn which was used both as a garage and a kennel, to quiet some large black poodles. It was 1 A.M. of a pitch-dark night in winter and the poodles had apparently been terrified by some kind of a prowler, a tramp, a turtle, or perhaps a fiend of some sort. Both my poodles and I myself believed, at the time, in fiends, and still do. Fiends who materialize out of nothing and nowhere, like winged pigweed or Russian thistle. I had quite a time quieting the dogs, because their panic spread to me and mine spread back to them again, in a kind of vicious circle. Finally, a hush as ominous as their uproar fell upon them, but they kept looking over their shoulders, in a kind of apprehensive way. 'There's nothing to be afraid of,' I told them as firmly as I could, and just at that moment the klaxon of my car, which was just behind me, began to shriek. Everybody has heard a klaxon on a car suddenly begin to sound; I understand it is a short circuit that causes it. But very few people have heard one scream behind them while they were quieting six or eight alarmed poodles in the middle of the night in an old barn. I jump now whenever I hear a klaxon, even the klaxon on my own car when I push the button intentionally. The experience has left its mark. Everybody, from the day of the jumping card-table to the day of the screaming klaxon, has had similar shocks. You can see the result, entirely unsuperinduced by sex, in the strained faces and muttering lips of people who pass you on the streets of great, highly mechanized cities. There goes a man who picked up one of those trick matchboxes that whir in your hands; there goes a woman who tried to change a fuse without turning off the current; and yonder toddles an ancient who cranked an old Reo with the spark advanced. Every person carries in his consciousness the old scar, or the fresh wound, of some harrowing misadventure with a contraption of some sort. I know people who would not deposit a nickel and a dime in a cigarette-vending machine and push the lever even if a diamond necklace came out. I know dozens who would not climb into an aeroplane even if it didn't move off the ground. In none of these people have I discerned what I would call a neurosis, an 'exaggerated' fear; I have discerned only a natural caution in a world made up of gadgets that whir and whine and whiz and shriek and sometimes explode.

I should like to end with the case history of a friend of mine in Ohio named Harvey Lake. When he was only nineteen, the steering bar of an old electric runabout broke off in his hand, causing the machine to carry him through a fence and into the grounds of the Columbus School for Girls. He developed a fear of automobiles, trains, and every other kind of vehicle that was not pulled by a horse. Now, the psychologists would call this a complex and represent the fear as abnormal, but I see it as a purely reasonable apprehension. If Harvey Lake had, because he was catapulted into the grounds of the Columbus School for Girls, developed a fear of girls, I would call that a complex; but I don't call his normal fear of machines a complex. Harvey Lake never in his life got into a plane (he died in a fall from a porch), but I do not regard that as neurotic, either, but only sensible.

I have, to be sure, encountered men with complexes. There was, for example, Marvin Belt. He had a complex about aeroplanes that was quite interesting. He was not afraid of machinery, or of high places, or of crashes. He was simply afraid that the pilot of any plane he got into might lose his mind. 'I imagine myself high over Montana,' he once said to me, 'in a huge, perfectly safe tri-motored plane. Several of the passengers are dozing, others are reading, but I am keeping my eyes glued on the door of the cockpit. Suddenly the pilot steps out of it, a wild light in his eyes, and in a falsetto like that of a little girl he says to me, "Conductor, will you please let me off at One-Hundred-and-Twenty-fifth Street?"' 'But,' I said to Belt, 'even if the pilot does go crazy, there is still the co-pilot.' 'No, there isn't,' said Belt. 'The pilot has hit the co-pilot over the head with something and killed him.' Yes, the psychoanalysts can have Marvin Belt. But they can't have Harvey Lake, or Mr C, or Mr S, or Mr F, or, while I have my strength, me.

The Breaking up of the Winships

THE trouble that broke up the Gordon Winships seemed to me, at first, as minor a problem as frost on a window-pane. Another day, a touch of sun, and it would be gone. I was inclined to laugh it off, and, indeed, as a friend of both Gordon and Marcia, I spent a great deal of time with each of them, separately, trying to get them to laugh it off, too – with him at his club, where he sat drinking Scotch and smoking too much, and with her in their apartment, that seemed so large and lonely without Gordon and his restless moving around and his quick laughter. But it was no good; they were both adamant. Their separation has lasted now more than six months. I doubt very much that they will ever go back together again.

It all started one night at Leonardo's, after dinner, over their Bénédictine. It started innocently enough, amiably even, with laughter from both of them, laughter that froze finally as the clock ran on and their words came out sharp and flat and stinging. They had been to see 'Camille'. Gordon hadn't liked it very much. Marcia had been crazy about it because she is crazy about Greta Garbo. She belongs to that considerable army of Garbo admirers whose enchantment borders almost on fanaticism and sometimes even touches the edges of frenzy. I think that, before everything happened, Gordon admired Garbo, too, but the depth of his wife's conviction that here was the greatest figure ever seen in our generation on sea or land, on screen or stage, exasperated him that night. Gordon hates (or used to) exaggeration, and he respects (or once did) detachment. It was his feeling that detachment is a necessary thread in the fabric of a woman's charm. He didn't like to see his wife get herself 'into a sweat' over anything and, that night at Leonardo's, he unfortunately used that expression and made that accusation.

Marcia responded, as I get it, by saying, a little loudly (they had gone on to Scotch and soda), that a man who had no abandon of feeling and no passion for anything was not altogether a man, and that his so-called love of detachment simply covered up a lack of critical appreciation and understanding of the arts in general. Her sentences were becoming long and wavy, and her words formal. Gordon suddenly began to pooh-pooh her; he kept saying 'Pooh!' (an annoying mannerism of his, I have always thought). He wouldn't answer her arguments or even listen to them. That, of course, infuriated her. 'Oh, pooh to you, too!' she finally more or less shouted. He snapped at her, 'Quiet, for God's sake! You're yelling like a prizefight manager!' Enraged at that, she had recourse to her eyes as weapons and looked steadily at him for a while with the expression of one who is viewing a small and horrible animal,

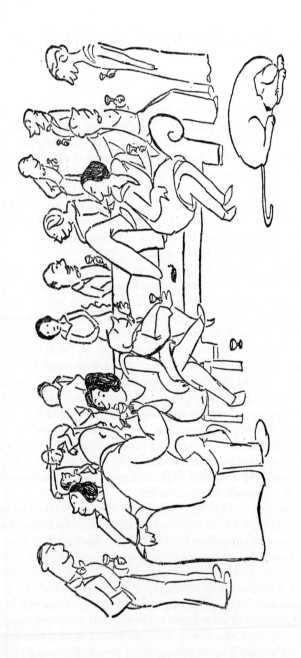

such as a horned toad. They then sat in moody and brooding silence for a long time, without moving a muscle, at the end of which, getting a hold on herself, Marcia asked him, quietly enough, just exactly what actor on the screen or on the stage, living or dead, he considered greater than Garbo. Gordon thought a moment and then said, as quietly as she had put the question, 'Donald Duck.' I don't believe that he meant it at the time, or even thought that he meant it. However that may have been, she looked at him scornfully and said that that speech just about perfectly represented the shallowness of his intellect and the small range of his imagination. Gordon asked her not to make a spectacle of herself – she had raised her voice slightly – and went on to say that her failure to see the genius of Donald Duck proved conclusively to him that she was a woman without humour. That, he said, he had always suspected; now, he said, he knew it. She had a great desire to hit him, but instead she sat back and looked at him with her special Mona Lisa smile, a smile rather more of contempt than, as in the original, of mystery. Gordon hated that smile, so he said that Donald Duck happened to be exactly ten times as great as Garbo would ever be and that anybody with a brain in his head would admit it instantly. Thus the Winships went on and on, their resentment swelling, their sense of values blurring, until it ended up with her taking a taxi home alone (leaving her vanity bag and one glove behind her in the restaurant) and with him making the rounds of the late places and rolling up to his club around dawn. There, as he got out, he asked his taxi-driver which he liked better, Greta Garbo or Donald Duck, and the driver said he liked Greta Garbo best. Gordon said to him, bitterly, 'Pooh to you, too, my good friend!' and went to bed.

The next day, as is usual with married couples, they were both contrite, but behind their contrition lay sleeping the ugly words each had used and the cold glances and the bitter gestures. She phoned him, because she was worried. She didn't want to be, but she was. When he hadn't come home, she was convinced he had gone to his club, but visions of him lying in a gutter or under a table, somehow horribly mangled, haunted her, and so at eight o'clock she called him up. Her heart lightened when he said, 'Hullo,' gruffly: he was alive, thank God! His heart may have lightened a little, too, but not very much, because he felt terrible. He felt terrible and he felt that it was her fault that he felt terrible. She said that she was sorry and that they had both been very silly, and he growled something about he was glad she realized *she'd* been silly, anyway. That attitude put a slight edge on the rest of her words. She asked him shortly if he was coming home. He said sure he was coming home; it was his home, wasn't it? She told him to go back to bed and not be such an old bear, and hung up.

The next incident occurred at the Clarkes' party a few days later. The Winships had arrived in fairly good spirits to find themselves in a buzzing group of cocktail-drinkers that more or less revolved around the tall and languid figure of the guest of honour, an eminent lady novelist. Gordon late in the evening won her attention and drew her apart for one drink together and, feeling a little high and happy at that time, as is the way with husbands, mentioned

lightly enough (he wanted to get it out of his subconscious) the argument that
he and his wife had had about the relative merits of Garbo and Duck. The tall
lady, lowering her cigarette-holder, said, in the spirit of his own gaiety, that he
could count her in on his side. Unfortunately, Marcia Winship, standing some
ten feet away, talking to a man with a beard, caught not the spirit but only a
few of the words of the conversation, and jumped to the conclusion that her
husband was deliberately reopening the old wound, for the purpose of humili-
ating her in public. I think that in another moment Gordon might have brought
her over, and put his arm around her, and admitted his 'defeat' – he was feeling
pretty fine. But when he caught her eye, she gazed through him, freezingly,
and his heart went down. And then his anger rose.

   Their fight, naturally enough, blazed out again in the taxi they took to go
home from the party. Marcia wildly attacked the woman novelist (Marcia had
had quite a few cocktails), defended Garbo, excoriated Gordon, and laid into
Donald Duck. Gordon tried for a while to explain exactly what had happened,
and then he met her resentment with a resentment that mounted even higher,
the resentment of the misunderstood husband. In the midst of it all she slapped
him. He looked at her for a second under lowered eyelids and then said, coldly,
if a bit fuzzily, 'This is the end, but I want you to go to your grave knowing
that Donald Duck is *twenty times* the artist Garbo will ever be, the longest day
you, or she, ever live, if you *do* – and I can't understand, with so little to live
for, why you should!' Then he asked the driver to stop the car, and he got out,
in wavering dignity. 'Caricature! Cartoon!' she screamed after him. 'You and
Donald Duck both, you –' The driver drove on.

   The last time I saw Gordon – he moved his things to the club the next day,
forgetting the trousers to his evening clothes and his razor – he had convinced
himself that the point at issue between him and Marcia was one of extreme
importance involving both his honour and his integrity. He said that now it
could never be wiped out and forgotten. He said that he sincerely believed
Donald Duck was as great a creation as any animal in all the works of Lewis
Carroll, probably even greater, perhaps much greater. He was drinking and
there was a wild light in his eye. I reminded him of his old love of detachment,
and he said to the hell with detachment. I laughed at him, but he wouldn't
laugh. 'If,' he said, grimly, 'Marcia persists in her silly belief that that Swede
is great and that Donald Duck is merely a caricature, I cannot conscientiously
live with her again. I believe that he is great, that the man who created him is a
genius, probably our only genius. I believe, further, that Greta Garbo is just
another actress. As God is my judge, I believe that! What does she expect me
to do, go whining back to her and pretend that I think Garbo is wonderful and
that Donald Duck is simply a cartoon? Never!' He gulped down some Scotch
straight. 'Never!' I could not ridicule him out of his obsession. I left him and
went over to see Marcia.

   I found Marcia pale, but calm, and as firm in her stand as Gordon was in his.
She insisted that he had deliberately tried to humiliate her before that gawky
so-called novelist, whose clothes were the dowdiest she had ever seen and

whose affectations obviously covered up a complete lack of individuality and intelligence. I tried to convince her that she was wrong about Gordon's attitude at the Clarkes' party, but she said she knew him like a book. Let him get a divorce and marry that creature if he wanted to. They can sit around all day, she said, and all night, too, for all I care, and talk about their precious Donald Duck, the damn comic strip! I told Marcia that she shouldn't allow herself to get so worked up about a trivial and nonsensical matter. She said it was not silly and nonsensical to her. It might have been once, yes, but it wasn't now. It had made her see Gordon clearly for what he was, a cheap, egotistical, resentful cad who would descend to ridiculing his wife in front of a scrawny, horrible stranger who could not write and never would be able to write. Furthermore, her belief in Garbo's greatness was a thing she could not deny and would not deny, simply for the sake of living under the same roof with Gordon Winship. The whole thing was part and parcel of her integrity as a woman and as an – as an, well, as a woman. She could go to work again; he would find out.

There was nothing more that I could say or do. I went home. That night, however, I found that I had not really dismissed the whole ridiculous affair, as I hoped I had, for I dreamed about it. I had tried to ignore the thing, but it had tunnelled deeply into my subconscious. I dreamed that I was out hunting with the Winships and that, as we crossed a snowy field, Marcia spotted a rabbit and, taking quick aim, fired and brought it down. We all ran across the snow toward the rabbit, but I reached it first. It was quite dead, but that was not what struck horror into me as I picked it up. What struck horror into me was that it was a white rabbit and was wearing a vest and carrying a watch. I woke up with a start. I don't know whether that dream means that I am on Gordon's side or on Marcia's. I don't want to analyse it. I am trying to forget the whole miserable business.

My Memories of D. H. Lawrence

I F you wander around in bookstores you will have come upon several books about D. H. Lawrence: Mr John Middleton Murry's autobiography, Frieda Lawrence's memoirs, Keith Winter's *roman à clef* called *Impassioned Pygmies*, etc. These are all comparatively recent; a complete bibliography going back to the time of Lawrence's death would run into hundreds of items, maybe thousands. The writing man is pretty much out of it if he hasn't written something about how hard it was to understand, to talk to, and to get along generally with D. H. Lawrence; and I do not propose to be out of it. I had my difficult moments on account of the Master, and I intend to tell about them – if Mr Murry will quit talking for a moment and let me talk.

I first met D. H. Lawrence on a train platform in Italy twelve years ago. He was pacing up and down. There was no mistaking the reddish, scraggly beard, the dark, beetling eyebrows, the intense, restless eyes. He had the manner of a man who was waiting for something; in this case, I think it was the train. I had always wanted to meet the great artist and here was my golden opportunity. I finally screwed my courage up to the accosting point and I walked over and accosted him. 'D. H. Lawrence?' I said. He frowned, stopped, pulled a watch out of his vest pocket, and held it up to me so that I could see the dial. 'No speak Eyetalian,' he said. 'Look for yourself.' Then he walked away. It had been about 10.12 or 10.13 A.M. by his watch (I had 10.09 myself, but I may have been slow). Since we both got on the train that pulled into the station a few minutes later, I contrived to get into the same compartment with him and to sit down next to him. I found him quite easy to talk to. He seemed surprised that I spoke English – on the platform he had taken me for an Italian who wanted to know what time it was. It turned out after a few minutes of rather puzzling conversation that his name was George R. Hopkins and that he had never heard of D. H. Lawrence. Hopkins was a resident of Fitchburg, Massachusetts, where he had a paper factory. He wished to God he was back in the United States. He was a strong Coolidge man, thought every French person was depraved, and hadn't been able to find a decent cup of coffee in all Europe. He had a married daughter, and two sons in Penn State, and had been having trouble with a molar in his lower jaw ever since he arrived at Le Havre, some three weeks before. He wouldn't let anybody monkey with it, he said, except a certain Dr Karns in Fitchburg. Karns was an Elk and a bird-dog fancier in addition to being the best dentist in the United States.

This encounter did not discourage me. I determined to meet D. H. Lawrence before I came back to America, and eventually I sat down and wrote him a note, asking him for the opportunity of meeting him (I had found out where he was living at the time – in Florence, I believe, though I may be wrong). I explained that I was a great admirer of his – I addressed him simply as Dear Master – and that I had some ideas about sex which I thought might interest him. Lawrence never received the letter, it transpired later, because I had unfortunately put it in the wrong envelope. He got instead a rather sharp note which I had written the same evening to a psychoanalyst in New York who had offered to analyse me at half his usual price. This analyst had come across some sketches I had made and had apparently jumped to the conclusion that it

Dr Karns

would be interesting to try to get at what was behind them. I had addressed this man in my note simply as 'sir' and I had told him that if he wanted to analyse somebody he had better begin with himself, since it was my opinion there was something the matter with him. As for me, I said, there was nothing the matter with me. This, of course, was the letter that Lawrence got, owing to the shifting of envelopes, and I was later to understand why I never heard from Lawrence and also why I kept hearing from the analyst all the time. I hung around Europe for several months waiting for a letter from Lawrence, and finally came home, in a low state of mind.

I eventually met, or rather talked with, D. H. Lawrence about six months after I got back to New York. He telephoned me one evening at my apartment. 'Hello,' I said into the transmitter. 'Hello,' a voice said. 'Is this Mr Thurber?' 'Yes,' I said. 'Well, this is D. H. Lawrence,' said the voice. I was taken back; for a moment I couldn't say a word, I was so surprised and excited. 'Well,

well,' I said, finally, 'I didn't know you were on this side.' 'This is the right side to be on, isn't it?' he asked, in a rather strained voice (I felt that he was excited, too). 'Yes, it is,' I said. 'Well,' said Lawrence, 'they turned me over on my right side because my left side hurt me so.' Thereupon he began to sing 'Frankie and Johnny'. He turned out to be a waggish friend of mine who had heard my stories about trying to get in touch with D. H. Lawrence, and was having me on.

I never did get to meet D. H. Lawrence, but this I rarely admit. Whenever I am at a cocktail-party of literary people and the subject of Lawrence comes up, I tell my own little anecdote about the Master: how he admired Coolidge, how he had trouble with his teeth, how he liked to sing 'Frankie and Johnny'. These anecdotes are gaining considerable currency and I have no doubt that they will begin to creep into biographies of the man in a short time. Meanwhile I have become what you could almost call allergic to famous writers. I suppose this is the natural outgrowth of my curious and somewhat disturbing relationship with D. H. Lawrence. I cannot truthfully say that any part of that relationship was satisfactory, and therefore I am trying to forget D. H. Lawrence, which makes me about the only writer in the world who is. It is a distinction of a sort.

Nine Needles

ONE of the more spectacular minor happenings of the past few years which I am sorry that I missed took place in the Columbus, Ohio, home of some friends of a friend of mine. It seems that a Mr Albatross, while looking for something in his medicine cabinet one morning, discovered a bottle of a kind of patent medicine which his wife had been taking for a stomach ailment. Now, Mr Albatross is one of those apprehensive men who are afraid of patent medicines and of almost everything else. Some weeks before, he had encountered a paragraph in a Consumers' Research bulletin which announced that this particular medicine was bad for you. He had thereupon ordered his wife to throw out what was left of her supply of the stuff and never buy any more. She had promised, and here now was another bottle of the perilous liquid. Mr Albatross, a man given to quick rages, shouted the conclusion of the story at my friend: 'I threw the bottle out of the bathroom window and the medicine chest after it!' It seems to me that must have been a spectacle worth going a long way to see.

I am sure that many a husband has wanted to wrench the family medicine cabinet off the wall and throw it out of the window, if only because the average medicine cabinet is so filled with mysterious bottles and unidentifiable objects of all kinds that it is a source of constant bewilderment and exasperation to the American male. Surely the British medicine cabinet and the French medicine cabinet and all the other medicine cabinets must be simpler and better ordered than ours. It may be that the American habit of saving everything and never throwing anything away, even empty bottles, causes the domestic medicine cabinet to become as cluttered in its small way as the American attic becomes cluttered in its major way. I have encountered few medicine cabinets in this country which were not pack-jammed with something between a hundred and fifty and two hundred different items, from dental floss to boracic acid, from razor blades to sodium perborate, from adhesive tape to coconut oil. Even the neatest wife will put off clearing out the medicine cabinet on the ground that she has something else to do that is more important at the moment, or more diverting. It was in the apartment of such a wife and her husband that I became enormously involved with a medicine cabinet one morning not long ago.

I had spent the week-end with this couple – they live on East Tenth Street near Fifth Avenue – such a week-end as left me reluctant to rise up on Monday morning with bright and shining face and go to work. They got up and went to work, but I didn't. I didn't get up until about two-thirty in the afternoon. I had my face all lathered for shaving and the washbowl was full of hot water when suddenly I cut myself with the razor. I cut my ear. Very few men cut their ears with razors, but I do, possibly because I was taught the old Spencerian free-wrist movement by my writing teacher in the grammar grades. The ear bleeds rather profusely when cut with a razor and is difficult to get at.

'And the Medicine Chest After It!'

More angry than hurt, I jerked open the door of the medicine cabinet to see if I could find a styptic pencil and out fell, from the top shelf, a little black paper packet containing nine needles. It seems that this wife kept a little paper packet containing nine needles on the top shelf of the medicine cabinet. The packet fell into the soapy water of the wash-bowl, where the paper rapidly disintegrated, leaving nine needles at large in the bowl. I was, naturally enough, not in the best condition, either physical or mental, to recover nine needles from a wash-bowl. No gentleman who has lather on his face and whose ear is bleeding is in the best condition for anything, even something involving the handling of nine large blunt objects.

It did not seem wise to me to pull the plug out of the wash-bowl and let the needles go down the drain. I had visions of clogging up the plumbing system of the house, and also a vague fear of causing short circuits somehow or other (I know very little about electricity and I don't want to have it explained to me). Finally, I groped very gently around the bowl and eventually had four of the needles in the palm of one hand and three in the palm of the other – two I couldn't find. If I had thought quickly and clearly, I wouldn't have done that. A lathered man whose ear is bleeding and who has four wet needles in one hand and three in the other may be said to have reached the lowest known point of human efficiency. There is nothing he can do but stand there. I tried transferring the needles in my left hand to the palm of my right hand, but I couldn't get them off my left hand. Wet needles cling to you. In the end, I wiped the needles off on to a bath-towel which was hanging on a rod above the bath-tub. It was the only towel that I could find. I had to dry my hands afterwards on the bath-mat. Then I tried to find the needles in the towel. Hunting for seven needles in a bath-towel is the most tedious occupation I have ever engaged in. I could find only five of them. With the two that had been left in the bowl, that meant there were four needles in all missing – two in the wash-bowl and two others lurking in the towel or lying in the bath-tub under the towel. Frightful thoughts came to me of what might happen to anyone who used that towel or washed his face in the bowl or got into the tub, if I didn't find the missing needles. Well, I didn't find them. I sat down on the edge of the tub to think, and I decided finally that the only thing to do was wrap up the towel in a newspaper and take it away with me. I also decided to leave a note for my friends explaining as clearly as I could that I was afraid there were two needles in the bath-tub and two needles in the wash-bowl, and that they better be careful.

I looked everywhere in the apartment, but I could not find a pencil, or a pen, or a typewriter. I could find pieces of paper, but nothing with which to write on them. I don't know what gave me the idea – a movie I had seen, perhaps, or a story I had read – but I suddenly thought of writing a message with a lipstick. The wife might have an extra lipstick lying around and, if so, I concluded it would be in the medicine cabinet. I went back to the medicine cabinet and began poking around in it for a lipstick. I saw what I thought looked like the metal tip of one, and I got two fingers around it and began to pull gently – it was under a lot of things. Every object in the medicine cabinet began to slide. Bottles broke in the wash-bowl and on the floor; red, brown, and white liquids spurted; nail files, scissors, razor blades, and miscellaneous objects sang and clattered and tinkled. I was covered with perfume, peroxide, and cold cream.

It took me half an hour to get the débris all together in the middle of the bathroom floor. I made no attempt to put anything back in the medicine cabinet. I knew it would take a steadier hand than mine and a less shattered spirit. Before I went away (only partly shaved) and abandoned the shambles, I left a note saying that I was afraid there were needles in the bath-tub and the wash-bowl and that I had taken their towel and that I would call up and tell them everything – I wrote it in iodine with the end of a toothbrush. I have not yet called up, I am sorry to say. I have neither found the courage nor thought up the words to explain what happened. I suppose my friends believe that I deliberately smashed up their bathroom and stole their towel. I don't know for sure, because they have not yet called me up, either.

A Couple of Hamburgers

IT had been raining for a long time, a slow, cold rain falling out of iron-coloured clouds. They had been driving since morning and they still had a hundred and thirty miles to go. It was about three o'clock in the afternoon. 'I'm getting hungry,' she said. He took his eyes off the wet, winding road for a fraction of a second and said, 'We'll stop at a dog-wagon.' She shifted her position irritably. 'I wish you wouldn't call them *dog*-wagons,' she said. He pressed the klaxon button and went around a slow car. 'That's what they are,' he said. 'Dog-wagons.' She waited a few seconds. '*Decent* people call them *diners*,' she told him, and added, 'Even if you call them diners, I don't like them.' He speeded up a hill. 'They have better stuff than most restaurants,' he said. 'Anyway, I want to get home before dark and it takes too long in a restaurant. We can stay our stomachs with a couple of hamburgers.' She lighted a cigarette and he asked her to light one for him. She lighted one deliberately and handed it to him. 'I wish you wouldn't say "stay our stomachs",' she said. 'You know I hate that. It's like "sticking to your ribs". You say that all the time.' He grinned. 'Good old American expressions, both of them,' he said. 'Like sow belly. Old pioneer term, sow belly.' She sniffed. 'My ancestors were pioneers, too. You don't have to be vulgar just because you were a pioneer.' 'Your ancestors never got as far west as mine did,' he said. 'The real pioneers travelled on their sow belly and got somewhere.' He laughed loudly at that. She looked out at the wet trees and signs and telephone poles going by. They drove on for several miles without a word; he kept chortling every now and then.

'What's that funny sound?' she asked, suddenly. It invariably made him angry when she heard a funny sound. 'What funny sound?' he demanded. 'You're always hearing funny sounds.' She laughed briefly. 'That's what you said when the bearing burned out,' she reminded him. 'You'd never have noticed it if it hadn't been for me.' 'I noticed it, all right,' he said. 'Yes,' she said. 'When it was too late.' She enjoyed bringing up the subject of the burned-out bearing whenever he got to chortling. 'It was too late when *you* noticed it, as far as that goes,' he said. Then, after a pause, 'Well, what does it sound like *this* time? All engines make a noise running, you know.' 'I know all about that,' she answered. 'It sounds like – it sounds like a lot of safety-pins being jiggled around in a tumbler.' He snorted. 'That's your imagination. Nothing gets the matter with a car that sounds like a lot of safety-pins. I happen to know that.' She tossed away her cigarette. 'Oh, sure,' she said. 'You always happen to know everything.' They drove on in silence.

'I want to stop somewhere and get something to *eat!*' she said loudly. 'All right, all right!' he said. 'I've been watching for a dog-wagon, haven't I? There hasn't been any. I can't make you a dog-wagon.' The wind blew rain in on her and she put up the window on her side all the way. 'I won't stop at just any old diner,' she said. 'I won't stop unless it's a cute one.' He looked around at her. 'Unless it's a *what* one?' he shouted. 'You know what I mean,' she said. 'I mean a decent, clean one where they don't slosh things at you. I hate to have a lot of milky coffee sloshed at me.' 'All right,' he said. 'We'll find a cute one, then. You pick it out. I wouldn't know. I might find one that was cunning but not cute.' That struck him as funny and he began to chortle again. 'Oh, shut up,' she said.

Five miles farther along they came to a place called 'Sam's Diner'. 'Here's one,' he said, slowing down. She looked it over. 'I don't want to stop there,' she said. 'I don't like the ones that have nicknames.' He brought the car to a stop at one side of the road. 'Just what's the matter with the ones that have nicknames?' he asked with edgy, mock interest. 'They're always Greek ones,' she told him. 'They're always Greek ones,' he repeated after her. He set his teeth firmly together and started up again. After a time, 'Good old Sam, the Greek,' he said, in a singsong. 'Good old Connecticut Sam Beardsley, the Greek.' 'You didn't see his name,' she snapped. 'Winthrop, then,' he said. 'Old Samuel Cabot Winthrop, the Greek dog-wagon man.' He was getting hungry.

On the outskirts of the next town she said, as he slowed down, 'It looks like a factory kind of town.' He knew that she meant she wouldn't stop there. He drove on through the place. She lighted a cigarette as they pulled out into the open again. He slowed down and lighted a cigarette for himself. 'Factory kind of town than *I* am!' he snarled. It was ten miles before they came to another town. 'Torrington,' he growled. 'Happen to know there's a dog-wagon here because I stopped in it once with Bob Combs. Damn cute place, too, if you ask me.' 'I'm not asking you anything,' she said, coldly. 'You think you're *so* funny. I think I know the one you mean,' she said, after a moment. 'It's right in the town and it sits at an angle from the road. They're never so good, for some reason.' He glared at her and almost ran up against the kerb. 'What the hell do you mean "sits at an angle from the road"?' he cried. He was very hungry now. 'Well, it isn't silly,' she said calmly. 'I've noticed the ones that sit at an angle. They're cheaper, because they fitted them into funny little pieces of ground. The big ones parallel to the road are the best.' He drove right through Torrington, his lips compressed. 'Angle from the *road*, for God's sake!' he snarled, finally. She was looking out of her window.

On the outskirts of the next town there was a diner called 'The Elite Diner'. 'This looks –' she began. 'I see it, I see it!' he said. 'It doesn't happen to look any cuter to me than any goddam –' she cut him off. 'Don't be such a sorehead, for Lord's sake,' she said. He pulled up and stopped beside the diner, and turned on her. 'Listen,' he said, grittingly, 'I'm going to put down a couple of hamburgers in this place even if there isn't one single inch of chintz or cretonne in the whole –' 'Oh, be still,' she said. 'You're just hungry and mean like a child. Eat your old hamburgers, what do I care?' Inside the place they sat down on stools and the counterman walked over to them, wiping up the counter top with a cloth as he did so. 'What'll it be, folks?' he said. 'Bad day, ain't it? Except for ducks.' 'I'll have a couple of –' began the husband, but his wife cut in. 'I just want a packet of cigarettes,' she said. He turned around slowly on his stool and stared at her as she put a dime and a nickel in the cigarette machine and ejected a packet of Lucky Strikes. He turned to the counterman again. 'I want a couple of hamburgers,' he said. 'With mustard and lots of onion. *Lots* of onion!' She hated onions. 'I'll wait for you in the car,' she said. He didn't answer and she went out.

He finished his hamburgers and his coffee slowly. It was terrible coffee. Then he went out to the car and got in and drove off, slowly humming 'Who's Afraid of the Big Bad Wolf?' After a mile or so, 'Well,' he said, 'what was the matter with "The Elite Diner", milady?' 'Didn't you see that cloth the man was wiping the counter with?' she demanded. 'Ugh!' She shuddered. 'I didn't happen to want to eat any of the counter,' he said. He laughed at that comeback. 'You didn't even notice it,' she said. 'You never notice anything. It was filthy.' 'I noticed they had some damn fine coffee in there,' he said. 'It was swell.' He knew she loved good coffee. He began to hum his tune again; then he whistled it; then he began to sing it. She did not show her annoyance, but she knew that he knew she was annoyed. 'Will you be kind enough to tell me what time it is?' she asked. 'Big *bad* wolf, big *bad* wolf – five minutes o' five – tum-dee-*doo*-dee-dum-m.' She settled back in her seat and took a cigarette from her case and tapped it on the case. 'I'll wait till we get home,' she said. 'If you'll be kind enough to speed up a little.' He drove on at the same speed. After a time he gave up the 'Big Bad Wolf' and there was deep silence for two miles. Then suddenly he began to sing, very loudly, *H-A-double-R-I-G-A-N spells Harrr-i-gan –* ' She gritted her teeth. She hated that worse than any of his songs except 'Barney Google'. He would go on to 'Barney Google' pretty soon, she knew. Suddenly she leaned slightly forward. The straight line of her lips began to curve up ever so slightly. She heard the safety-pins in the tumbler again. Only now they were louder, more insistent, ominous. He was singing too loud to hear them. 'Is a *name* that *shame* has never been con-*nec*-ted with – *Harrr-i-gan, that's me!*' She relaxed against the back of the seat, content to wait.

Bateman Comes Home

(Written After Reading Several Recent Novels about the Deep South and Confusing them a Little – as the Novelists Themselves Do – with Tobacco Road *and* God's Little Acre)

OLD NATE BIRGE sat on the rusted wreck of an ancient sewing-machine in front of Hell Fire, which was what his shack was known as among the neighbours and to the police. He was chewing on a splinter of wood and watching the moon come up lazily out of the old cemetery in which nine of his daughters were lying, only two of whom were dead. He began to mutter to himself. 'Bateman be comin' back any time now wid a thousan' dollas fo' his ol' pappy,' said Birge. 'Bateman ain' goin' let his ol' pappy starve nohow.' A high, cracked voice spoke inside the house, in a toneless singsong. 'Bateman see you in hell afore he do anything 'bout it,' said the voice. 'Who dat?' cried Birge, standing up. 'Who dat sayin' callumy 'bout Bateman? Good gahd amighty!' He sat down quickly again. His feet hurt him, since he had gangrene in one of them and Bless-Yo-Soul, the cow, had stepped on the other one that morning in Hell Hole, the pasture behind Hell Fire. A woman came to the door with a skillet in her hand. Elviry Birge was thin and emaciated and dressed in a tattered old velvet evening gown. 'You oughtn' speak thataway 'bout Bateman at thisatime,' said Birge. 'Bateman's a good boy. He go 'way in 1904 to make his pappy a thousan' dollas.' 'Thuh hell wuth thut,' said Elviry, even more tonelessly than usual. 'Bateman ain' goin' brang we-all no thousan' dollas. Bateman got heself a place fo' dat thousan' dollas.' She shambled back into the house. 'Elviry's gone crazy,' muttered Birge to himself.

A large woman with a heavy face walked into the littered yard, followed by a young man dressed in a tight blue suit. The woman carried two suitcases; the young man was smoking a cigarette and running a pocket comb through his hair. 'Who dat?' demanded Birge, peering into the dark. 'It's me, yore Sister Sairy,' said the large woman. 'An' tuckered as a truck horse.' The young man threw his cigarette on the ground and spat at its burning end. 'Mom shot a policeman in Chicago,' he said, sulkily, 'an' we hadda beat it.' 'Whut you shoot a policeman fo', Sairy?' demanded Birge, who had not seen his sister for twenty years. 'Gahdam it, you cain' go 'round doin' that!' 'That'll be one o' Ramsay's jokes,' said Sairy. 'Ramsay's a hand for jokes, he is. Seems like that's all he *is* a hand for.' 'Ah, shut yore trap before I slap it shut,' said Ramsay. He had never been in the deep South before and he didn't like it. 'When do we eat?' he asked. 'Ev'body goin' 'round shootin' policemen,' muttered Birge, hobbling about the yard. 'Seem lak ev'body shootin' policemen 'cept Bateman. Bateman, he's a good boy.' Elviry came to the door again, still carrying the skillet; as they had had no food since Coolidge's first term, she used it merely as a weapon. 'Whut's ut?' she asked, frowning into the dark. The moon, grown tired, had sunk back into the cemetery again. 'Come ahn out, cackle-puss, an' find out,' said Ramsay. 'Look heah, boy!' cried Birge. 'I want me more rev'rence outa you, gahdam it!' 'Hello, Elviry,' said Sairy, sitting on one of her suitcases. 'We come to visit you. Ain't you glad?' Elviry didn't move from the doorway.

'We-all thought you-all was in *She*cago,' said Elviry, in her toneless voice. 'We-all was in all Chicago,' said Ramsay, 'but we-all is here all, now all.' He spat. 'Dam ef he ain' right, too,' said Birge, chuckling. 'Lawdy gahd! You bring me a thousan' dollas, boy?' he asked, suddenly. 'I ain't brought nobody no thousand dollars,' growled Ramsay. 'Whine you make yerself a thousand dollars, you old buzzard?' 'Don' lem call me buzzard, Elviry!' shouted Birge. 'Cain' you hit him wid somethin'? Hit him wid dat skillet!' Elviry made for Ramsay with her skillet, but he wrested it away from her and struck her over the head with it. The impact made a low, dull sound, like *sponk*. Elviry fell unconscious, and Ramsay sat down on her, listlessly. 'Hell va place ya got here,' he said.

At this juncture a young blonde girl, thin and emaciated but beautiful in the light of the moon (which had come up again), ran into the yard. 'Wheah you bin, gal?' demanded Birge. 'Faith is crazy,' he said to the others, 'an' they ain' nobody knows why, 'cause I give her a good Christian upbringin' ef avah a man did. Look heah, gal, yo' Aunt Sairy heah fo' a visit, gahdam it, an' nobody home to welcome her. All my daughters 'cept Prudence bin gone fo' two weeks now. Prudence, she bin gone fo' two yeahs.' Faith sat down on the stoop. 'Clay an' me bin settin' fire to the auditorium,' she said. Birge began whittling at a stick. 'Clay's her third husban',' he said. ' 'Pears lak she should pay some 'tention to her fifth husban', or leastwise her fo'th, but she don'. I don' understan' wimmin. Seem lak ev'body settin' fire to somethin' ev'time I turn my back. Wonder any buildin's standin' in the whole gahdam United States. You see anythin' o' Bateman, gal?' 'I ain' seen anythin' o' anybody,' said Faith. 'Now that is a bald-face lie by a daughter I brought up in the feah o' hell fire,' said Birge. 'Look heah, gal, you cain' set fire to no buildin' 'thout you see somebody. Gahd's love give that truth to this world. Speak to yo' Aunt Sairy, gal. She jest kill heself a *po*liceman in *She*cago.' 'Did you kill a policeman, Aunt Sairy?' Faith asked her. Sairy didn't answer her, but she spoke to Ramsay. 'You sit on this suitcase an' let me sit on Elviry a while,' she said. 'Do as yo' motha tells you, boy,' said Birge. 'Ah, shut up!' said Ramsay, smoking.

Ben Turnip, a half-witted neighbour boy with double pneumonia, came into the yard, wearing only overalls. 'Ah seed you-all was a-settin',' he said, bursting into high, toneless laughter. 'Heah's Bateman! Heah's Bateman!' cried Birge, hobbling with many a painful gahdam over to the newcomer. 'You bring me a thousan' dollas, Bateman?' Elviry came to, pushed Ramsay off her, and got up. 'That ain' Bateman, you ol' buzzard,' she said, scornfully.

'That's only Ben Turnip an' him turned in the haid, too, lak his motha afore him.' 'Go 'long, woman,' said Birge. 'I reckon I know moan son. You bring yo' ol' pappy a thousan' dollas, Bateman?' 'Ah seed you-all was a-settin',' said Ben Turnip. Suddenly he became very excited, his voice rising to a high singsong. 'He-settin', I-settin', you-settin', we-settin',' he screamed. 'Deed-a-bye, deed-a-bye, deed-a-bye, die!' 'Bateman done gone crazy,' mumbled Birge. He went back and sat down on the sewing-machine. 'Seem lak ev'body gone crazy. Now, that's a pity,' he said, sadly. 'Nuts,' said Ramsay.

'S'pose you-all did see me a-settin',' said Ben Turnip, belligerently. 'Whut uv ut? Cain' Ah set?' 'Sho, sho, set yosef, Bateman,' said Birge. 'I'll whang ovah his haid wid Elviry's skillet fust pusson say anything 'bout you settin'. Set yosef.' Ben sat down on the ground and began digging with a stick. 'I done brong you a thousan' dollas,' said Ben. Birge leaped from his seat. 'Glory gahd to Hallerlugie!' he shouted. 'You heah de man, Elviry? Bateman done –'

If you keep on long enough it turns into a novel.

Remembrance of Things Past

I READ the other day about some chickens that got drunk on mash; out in Iowa, I believe it was. I was reminded of the last chickens that I got drunk. They belonged to a French woman who owned a farm in Normandy, near Granville, where I stayed from early spring until late autumn, ten years ago. The drunken chickens make as good a point of beginning as any for my recollections of Madame Goriaut, who owned the farm. I feel that I owe her some small memoir.

I recall the little farmhouse clearly. I saw it first in a slanting rain, as I walked past sheep meadows in which poppies were blooming. A garrulous, tall old man with a blowing white beard walked with me to the farm. He dealt in clocks and watches and real estate, and it was in his dim, ticking shop in the village of Cassis that I had heard of Madame Goriaut's and the room on the second floor which she rented out when she could. I think he went along to be sure that he would get his commission for directing me there.

The room was long and high and musty, with a big, soft bed, and windows that looked out on the courtyard of the place. It was like a courtyard, anyway, in form and in feeling. It should have held old wagon wheels and busy men in leather aprons, but the activity I remember was that of several black-and-white kittens stalking each other in a circular bed of red geraniums, which, of course, is not like a courtyard, but nevertheless I remember the space in front of the house as being like a courtyard. A courtyard, let us say, with black-and-white kittens stalking each other in a circular bed of red geraniums.

The kittens were wild and unapproachable. Perhaps the fear of man had been struck into their hearts by Madame Goriaut. She was a formidable woman, almost, in a way, *épouvantable* (*épouvantable* was her favourite word – everything was *épouvantable:* the miserable straw crop, the storms off the Channel, the state of the nation, America's delay in getting into the War). Madame was large and shapeless and possessed of an unforgettable toothiness. Her smile, under her considerable moustache, was quick and savage and frightening, like a flash of lightning lighting up a ruined woods. Whether she was tremendously amused (as by the fidgetings of a hanging rabbit – they hang rabbits for the table in Normandy) or tremendously angry (as over the breaking of a crock by her sulky little daughter) you could not determine by her expression. She raised her upper lip and showed her teeth and bellowed, in anger as well as in gaiety. You could identify her moods only by her roaring words, which reverberated around the house like the reports of shotguns. There was no mid-point in her spirit: she was either greatly pleased, usually about nothing much, or greatly displeased, by very little more.

Like many French people in the provinces, Madame Goriaut believed that all Americans were rich. She would ask me if I had not paid a thousand francs for my shoes. My spectacle rims were of solid gold, to be sure. I carried – was it not so? – a thousand dollars in my pockets for tobacco and odds and ends. I would turn my pockets inside out to show her this was not true. At these times she frightened me. It was not too fantastic to conceive of Madame Goriaut creeping into one's room at night with a kitchen knife and a basket, come to pluck one's thousand dollars and one's life as she might pluck spinach. I was always slightly alarmed by her. She had but little English – 'I love you,' 'kiss me,' 'thousand dollars,' 'no,' and 'yes'. I don't know where she learned these words, but she enjoyed repeating them, in that order, and with heavy delight, like a child who has learned a poem. Sometimes she gave me the shudders saying, *apropos* of nothing at all, 'I love you, kiss me, thousand dollars, no, yes.'

Madame Goriaut was a widow. Her husband had been a great professor, she told me. He had died a few years before, leaving her the farm, no money, and two five-act plays in blank verse. She showed the plays to me the first day I was there. They were written in ink in a fine hand, I picked them up and put them down with an imitation of awed pleasure. I wondered what her husband could have been like, the great professor. I found out a little now and then. Once I asked her if she had a photograph of him and she said no, because he had believed that in the transference of one's image to a film or plate there departed a certain measure of one's substance. Did I believe this was true? I said I did indeed. I was afraid to refute any of the convictions of the great professor when madame put them to me with her leer and her fierce, sudden laugh. Of these convictions the only other I remember is that M. Goriaut believed he would come back after death as a *hirondelle*, or swallow. There were a lot of swallows around the farmhouse and the barns, and Madame Goriaut asked me if I thought that one of them was her husband. I asked her, in turn, if any of the swallows had ever made her a sign. She bellowed with laughter. I couldn't tell much about that laugh. I couldn't tell what she had thought of her husband alive, or what she believed of him dead.

I got the chickens drunk one Sunday morning by throwing to them pieces of bread soaked in Calvados, strong, new Calvados. Madame had invaded my room one Saturday night after dinner to ask me again why America had got into the War so late. She was bitter on that subject. While she talked she noticed that I had a bottle of Bénédictine on my desk. She said that Bénédictine was not the thing; I must have Calvados, the grand *eau de vie* of the region; she would give me a bottle of it. She went downstairs and brought it up to me, a large bottle. '*Voilà!*' she roared, planking it down on the table. I thanked her. Later she charged me seven francs for it on my weekly bill. I couldn't drink the stuff, it was so green and violent, so I fed it to the chickens. They got very drunk and fell down and got up and fell down again. Madame did not know what was the matter, and she raged around the village about a new disease that had come to kill the chickens and to impoverish her. The chickens were all right by Monday morning – that is, physically. Mentally, I suppose, it was their worst day.

Once I went with Madame Goriaut and her daughter, who was about seven but was peaked and whiny and looked twelve, to a village fair in Cassis. The little girl led the family donkey by his halter. It turned out when we got there that they were going to offer the donkey for sale; it seems that they offered him for sale every year at the fair. Madame hung a little sign around his neck saying that he was for sale; she had carried the sign to the fair wrapped in a newspaper. Nobody bought the donkey, but one man stepped up and asked how old he was. The little girl replied, 'Twelve years!' Madame Goriaut flew into one of her rages and cuffed the child to the ground with the back of her hand. 'But he has only eight years, monsieur!' she bellowed at the man, who was moving away. She followed him, bellowing, but he evaded her and she returned, still bellowing. She told me later that the donkey was twenty-four years old. Her daughter, she said, would make some man a miserable wife one day.

After the fair we went to a three-table *terrasse* on a narrow pavement in front of a tawdry café in the village and she ordered Calvados. There was, I noticed, a small insect in my glass when it was set in front of me. I called to the waiter, but he had gone back into the café and didn't hear me. Madame asked what was the matter, and I showed her the insect in the bottom of the glass. She shrugged, said '*Ah, là!*' and exchanged glasses with me. She drank the insect placidly. When I paid for the drinks, I brought out a new five-franc note. The little girl's eyes widened and she grabbed for it. '*Quel joli billet de cinq francs!*' she squealed. Her mother slapped her down again, shouting that the *joli billet* belonged to monsieur, who was a wealthy gentleman unused to *épouvantables* children. The little girl cried sullenly. '*Par exemple!*' cried madame, with her toothy leer. 'But you may make her a small present when you leave us.' We had another drink against the black day when I should leave them.

The day I left a man came for me and my bags in a two-wheeled cart. It was getting on toward November and Normandy was growing chill. A cold rain was falling. I piled my bags in the back of the cart and was about to shake hands with madame when the little girl squealed that I had not given her the present I had promised her. I took a five-franc note from my bill-fold and handed it to her. She grabbed it and ran, screaming in delight, a delight that turned to terror as madame, bellowing her loudest, set off in pursuit. They disappeared around a corner of the house, and I could hear them screaming and bellowing in the orchard behind the house. I climbed into the cart and told the man to drive on. He said it was always like that with the young ones nowadays, they wanted everything for themselves. I was gone long before madame came back, as I suppose she did, to say good-bye. I couldn't have faced her. I sometimes wonder about the little girl. She must be seventeen by now, and is probably already making some man a miserable wife.

Something About Polk

HURRYING towards Shiloh through the pages of Mr W. E. Woodward's *Meet General Grant*, a book published nine years ago, which I only recently came upon – in the library of a summer hotel – I ran into a provocative marginal note, indignantly written with pencil, on page 73. In the middle of that page occurs this sentence by Mr Woodward: 'James K. Polk, an insignificant Tennessee politician, who was almost unknown to the American people, was nominated by the Democrats. . . .' The pencilled note in the margin opposite this said sharply, 'Governor of Tennessee. Twice Speaker of the House of Representatives. The Jackson leader in the fight against the U.S. Bank. Almost unknown?'

I left General Grant and Mr Woodward to shift for themselves, and gave myself up to quiet contemplation of this astonishing note. Here was the bold imprint of a person who, eighty or more years after Polk's death, could actually give three facts about the man. I was moved to wonder and a kind of admiration for this last of the Polk men, rising up so unexpectedly out of that margin, shaking a white, tense fist, defending his hero. For of all our array of Presidents, there was none less memorable than James K. Polk. If ten patriots, picked at random, were asked to list the names of all the Presidents, it is likely that most of them would leave out the name of the eleventh. Even if they remembered his name, surely none of them could put down a fact about him. He was a man of no arresting achievement. The achievements that our mysterious marginal apologist puts down are certainly not the kind of achievements that make a man well known. Who knows the name of the present Governor of Tennessee? How many people know the name of the Speaker of the House? (Did I hear somebody say Joe Cannon?)

There are a number of other Presidents whom the average patriot, in making a list, might leave out, but in his day each of these others was notable for something unusual, no matter how minor. Pierce was thrown from his horse in the Mexican War, wearing the uniform of a brigadier-general; he was the youngest man to be elected to the Presidency up to that time. Andrew Johnson's wife taught him to write; he was said to have been cockeyed one day when, as Vice-President, he addressed the Senate; he was the only President who was ever impeached. Buchanan was the only bachelor President. Tyler served eggnogs and mint juleps in the White House. The first Harrison died in office. And so it goes, the enlivening story of all the Presidents except Polk. It is unquestionably true that he was almost unknown to the American people when he was elected. They never got to know him well; after his term was over, he retired to his home and died there three months later.

The trouble with Polk was that he never did anything to catch the people's eye; he never gave them anything to remember him by; nothing happened to him. He never cut down a cherry-tree, he didn't tell funny stories, he was not impeached, he was not shot, he didn't drink heavily, he didn't gamble, he wasn't involved in scandal. He was a war President, to be sure, but his activities in the White House during the Mexican War were overshadowed by the activities in the field of an old buzzard named Zachary Taylor, whose soldiers called him 'Old Rough and Ready'. Polk never had a nickname; it is likely that he was James to his friends, not Jim. His closest friend – his Farley, his Harry Daugherty – was a man you have never heard of. His name was Gideon J. Pillow.

James K. Polk seemed destined to be overshadowed by other men. He was once even overshadowed by a mythical man, and many who have forgotten the name of Polk will remember the name of the mythical man. In 1844 the Whigs circulated the story that Polk had once taken a gang of negroes to the South to be sold, each one branded 'J.K.P.'. When asked where they got this infamous story, the Whigs said they had read it in an authoritative travel book written by one Baron Von Roorback. There was no such man, but the word 'roorback', meaning a last-minute political trick, has gone into the American language. And the real man the mythical man wrote about has been forgotten. I encountered the Roorback story in Carl Sandburg's *Abraham Lincoln: The Prairie Years*, in which I also found an anecdote about Mrs Polk, but none about Mr Polk. Thus he was even overshadowed by his wife. It seems that at a reception following Polk's inaugural, someone said to Mrs Polk, 'Madam, you have a very genteel assemblage tonight,' to which Mrs Polk replied, 'Sir, I have never seen it otherwise.' It wasn't very much, to be sure, but it was something; it has lived a hundred years. The President himself that night does not appear to have opened his trap.

One begins to feel sorry for poor Mr Polk and the oblivion that has fallen upon him. Here is a President of the United States unremembered for any deed, unremembered even for any anecdote. I am for the formation of a Society for the Invention of Amusing Anecdotes about James K. Polk. I am willing to suggest a few myself to get the thing started. In fifty or a hundred years these anecdotes will begin to appear in histories and biographies. The forgotten President deserves a break; after all, he was a splendid gentleman. Let us see what we can do for James K. Polk, whom Abraham Lincoln once called a 'bewildered, confounded, miserably perplexed man.'

We might begin with that crack of Lincoln's. Old Gideon Pillow, let us say, came to Polk one day and told him that Abe Lincoln had said he was 'bewildered, confounded, and miserably perplexed.' 'You tell Lincoln,' said Polk, 'that I've never been so bewildered I couldn't tell the back of a shovel from a piece of writing paper.' A little cruel, to be sure, but then Lincoln had asked for it; at least we are showing that our man had spirit. He also had a nice whimsey. A Democrat office-seeker once stormed into his office (we will say) and confronted the President. 'First they tell me to see Gideon Pillow and then they tell me to see you,' said the man. 'I don't know *where* to go.' 'Ah,' said the President, 'shunted from Pillow to Polk.' Not one of the great puns, perhaps, but it shows our man was human and quick on the uptake. Personally, I think everybody is going to like this new anecdote, about Polk and General Zachary Taylor (that's what we need, anecdotes of the Lincoln-Grant variety). It seems that an indignant Whig came to Polk one day and told him that General Taylor was drinking too much. 'He has to,' said Polk. 'If he didn't see twice as many of those cowardly Mexicans as there really are, he wouldn't have the heart to fight them.' The Whig visitor was outraged. 'Do you mean to say you recommend drinking?' he demanded. 'Not for myself, if that's what you mean,' said Polk. 'You see, what *I* have to look at is Whigs.'

These are all that I can think of myself, and I am afraid that none of them is going to hurl our hero into immortality, but at least they are a start in the right direction. Let somebody else try it. There's no great rush.

The French Far West

IN ONE of the many interesting essays that make up his book called 'Abinger Harvest,' Mr E. M. Forster, discussing what he sees when he is reluctantly dragged to the movies in London, has set down a sentence that fascinates me. It is: 'American women shoot the hippopotamus with eyebrows made of platinum.' I have given that remarkable sentence a great deal of study, but I still do not know whether Mr Forster means that American women have platinum eyebrows or that the hippopotamus has platinum eyebrows or that American women shoot platinum eyebrows into the hippopotamus. At any rate, it faintly stirred in my mind a dim train of elusive memories which were brightened up suddenly and brought into sharp focus for me when, one night, I went to see *The Plainsman,* a hard-riding, fast-shooting movie dealing with warfare in the Far West back in the bloody seventies. I knew then what Mr Forster's curious and tantalizing sentence reminded me of. It was like nothing in the world so much as certain sentences which appeared in a group of French paperback dime (or, rather, twenty-five-centime) novels that I collected a dozen years ago in France. *The Plainsman* brought up these old pulp thrillers in all clarity for me because, like that movie, they dealt mainly with the stupendous activities of Buffalo Bill and Wild Bill Hickok; but in them were a unique fantasy, a special inventiveness, and an imaginative abandon beside which the movie treatment of the two heroes pales, as the saying goes, into nothing. In the moving from one apartment to another some years ago, I somehow lost my priceless collection of *contes héroïques du Far-Ouest,* but happily I find that a great many of the deathless adventures of the French Buffalo Bill and Wild Bill Hickok remain in my memory. I hope that I shall recall them, for anodyne, when with eyes too dim to read I pluck finally at the counterpane.

In the first place, it should perhaps be said that in the eighteen-nineties the American dime-novel hero who appears to have been most popular with the French youth – and adult – given to such literature was Nick Carter. You will find somewhere in one of John L. Stoddard's published lectures – there used to be a set in almost every Ohio bookcase – an anecdote about how an American tourist, set upon by *apaches* in a dark *rue* in Paris in the nineties, caused them to scatter in terror merely by shouting, '*Je suis Nick Carter!*' But at the turn of the century, or shortly thereafter, Buffalo Bill became the favourite. Whether he still is or not, I don't know – perhaps Al Capone or John Dillinger has taken his place. Twelve years ago, however, he was going great guns – or perhaps I should say great dynamite, for one of the things I most clearly remember about the Buffalo Bill of the French authors was that he always carried with him sticks of dynamite which, when he was in a particularly tough spot – that is, surrounded by more than two thousand Indians – he hurled into their midst, destroying them by the hundred. Many of the most inspired paperbacks that I picked up in my quest were used ones I found in those little stalls along the Seine. It was there, for instance, that I came across one of my favourites, *Les Aventures du Wild Bill dans le Far-Ouest*.

Wild Bill Hickok was, in this wonderful and beautiful tale, an even more prodigious manipulator of the six-gun than he seems to have been in real life, which, as you must know, is saying a great deal. He frequently mowed down a hundred or two hundred Indians in a few minutes with his redoubtable pistol. The French author of this masterpiece for some mysterious but delightful reason referred to Hickok sometimes as Wild Bill and sometimes as Wild Bird. '*Bonjour, Wild Bill!*' his friend Buffalo Bill often said to him when they met, only to shout a moment later, '*Regardez, Wild Bird! Les Peaux-Rouges!*' The two heroes spent a great deal of their time, as in *The Plainsman*, helping each other out of dreadful situations. Once, for example, while hunting Seminoles in Florida, Buffalo Bill fell into a tiger trap that had been set for him by the Indians – he stepped onto what turned out to be sticks covered with grass, and plunged to the bottom of a deep pit. At this point our author wrote, "'*Mercy me!*' *s'écria Buffalo Bill*.' The great scout was rescued, of course, by none other than Wild Bill, or Bird, who, emerging from the forest to see his old comrade in distress, could only exclaim, '*My word!*'

It was, I believe, in another volume that one of the most interesting characters in all French fiction of the Far West appeared, a certain Major Preston, alias Preeton, alias Preslon (the paperbacks rarely spelled anyone's name twice in succession the same way). This hero, we were told when he was introduced, 'had distinguished himself in the Civil War by capturing Pittsburgh,' a feat which makes Lee's invasion of Pennsylvania seem mere child's play. Major Preeton (I always preferred that alias) had come out West to fight the Indians with cannon, since he believed it absurd that nobody had thought to blow them off the face of the earth with cannon before. How he made out with his artillery against the forest skulkers I have forgotten, but I have an indelible memory of a certain close escape that Buffalo Bill had in this same book. It seems that, through an oversight, he had set out on a scouting trip without his dynamite – he also carried, by the way, cheroots and a flashlight – and hence, when he stumbled upon a huge band of redskins, he had to ride as fast as he could for the nearest fort. He made it just in time. 'Buffalo Bill,' ran the story, 'clattered across the drawbridge and into the fort just ahead of the Indians, who, unable to stop in time, plunged into the moat and were drowned.' It may have been in this same tale that Buffalo Bill was once so hard pressed that he had to send for Wild Bird to help him out. Usually, when one was in trouble, the other showed up by a kind of instinct, but this time Wild Bird was nowhere to be found. It was a long time, in fact, before his whereabouts were discovered. You will never guess where he was. He was 'taking the baths at Atlantic City under orders of his physician.' But he came riding across the country in one day to

Buffalo Bill's side, and all was well. Major Preeton, **it** sticks in my mind, got bored with the service in the Western hotels and went 'back to Philadelphia' (Philadelphia appears to have been the capital city of the United States at this time). The Indians in all these tales – and this is probably what gave Major Preeton his great idea – were seldom seen as individuals or in pairs or small groups, but prowled about in well-ordered columns of squads. I recall, however, one drawing (the paperbacks were copiously illustrated) which showed two *Peaux-Rouges* leaping upon and capturing a scout who had wandered too far from his drawbridge one night. The picture represented one of the Indians as smilingly taunting his captive, and the caption read, *'Vous vous promenez très tard ce soir, mon vieux!'* This remained my favourite line until I saw one

'Vous vous promenez très tard ce soir, mon vieux!'

night in Paris an old W. S. Hart movie called *Le Roi du Far-Ouest*, in which Hart, insulted by a drunken ruffian, turned upon him and said, in his grim, laconic way, *'Et puis, après?'*

I first became interested in the French tales of the Far West when, one winter in Nice, a French youngster of fifteen, who, it turned out, devoted all his spending money to them, asked me if I had ever seen a 'wishtonwish.' This meant nothing to me, and I asked him where he had heard about the wishton-wish. He showed me a Far West paperback he was reading. There was a passage in it which recounted an adventure of Buffalo Bill and Wild Bill, during the course of which Buffalo Bill signalled to Wild Bird 'in the voice of the wishtonwish.' Said the author in a parenthesis which at that time gave me as much trouble as Mr Forster's sentence about the platinum eyebrows does now, 'The wishtonwish was seldom heard west of Philadelphia.' It was some time – indeed, it was not until I got back to America – before I traced the wishtonwish to its lair, and in so doing discovered the influence of James Fenimore Cooper on all these French writers of Far West tales. Cooper, in his novels, frequently mentioned the wishtonwish, which was a Caddoan Indian name for the prairie dog. Cooper erroneously applied it to the whip-poor-will. An animal called the 'ouapiti' also figured occasionally in the French stories, and this turned out to be the wapiti, or American elk, also mentioned in Cooper's tales. The French writer's parenthetical note on the habitat of the wishton-wish only added to the delightful confusion and inaccuracy which threaded these wondrous stories.

There were, in my lost and lamented collection, a hundred other fine things, which I have forgotten, but there is one that will forever remain with me. It occurred in a book in which, as I remember it, Billy the Kid, alias Billy the Boy, was the central figure. At any rate, two strangers had turned up in a small Western town and their actions had aroused the suspicions of a group of respectable citizens, who forthwith called on the sheriff to complain about the newcomers. The sheriff listened gravely for a while, got up and buckled on his gun belt, and said, '*Alors, je vais demander ses cartes d'identité!*' There are few things, in any literature, that have ever given me a greater thrill than coming across that line.

Doc Marlowe

I WAS too young to be other than awed and puzzled by Doc Marlowe when I knew him. I was only sixteen when he died. He was sixty-seven. There was that vast difference in our ages and there was a vaster difference in our backgrounds. Doc Marlowe was a medicine-show man. He had been a lot of other things, too: a circus man, the proprietor of a concession at Coney Island, a saloon-keeper; but in his fifties he had travelled around with a tent-show troupe made up of a Mexican named Chickalilli, who threw knives, and a man called Professor Jones, who played the banjo. Doc Marlowe would come out after the entertainment and harangue the crowd and sell bottles of medicine for all kinds of ailments. I found out all this about him gradually, towards the last, and after he died. When I first knew him, he represented the Wild West to me, and there was nobody I admired so much.

I met Doc Marlowe at old Mrs Willoughby's rooming-house. She had been a nurse in our family, and I used to go and visit her over week-ends sometimes, for I was very fond of her. I was about eleven years old then. Doc Marlowe wore scarred leather leggings, a bright-coloured bead vest that he said he got from the Indians, and a ten-gallon hat with kitchen matches stuck in the band, all the way around. He was about six feet four inches tall, with big shoulders, and a long, drooping moustache. He let his hair grow long, like General Custer's. He had a wonderful collection of Indian relics and six-shooters, and he used to tell me stories of his adventures in the Far West. His favourite expressions were 'Hay, boy!' and 'Hay, boy-gie!' which he used the way some people now use 'Hot dog!' or 'Doggone!' He told me once that he had killed an Indian chief named Yellow Hand in a tomahawk duel on horseback. I thought he was the greatest man I had ever seen. It wasn't until he died and his son came on from New Jersey for the funeral that I found out he had never been in the Far West in his life. He had been born in Brooklyn.

Doc Marlowe had given up the road when I knew him, but he still dealt in what he called 'medicines.' His stock in trade was a liniment that he had called Snake Oil when he travelled around. He changed the name to Blackhawk Liniment when he settled in Columbus. Doc didn't always sell enough of it to pay for his bed and board, and old Mrs Willoughby would sometimes have to 'trust' him for weeks at a time. She didn't mind, because his liniment had taken a bad kink out of her right limb that had bothered her for thirty years. I used to see people whom Doc had massaged with Blackhawk Liniment move arms and legs that they hadn't been able to move before he 'treated' them. His patients were day labourers, wives of tramcar conductors and people like that.

Sometimes they would shout and weep after Doc had massaged them and several got up and walked around who hadn't been able to walk before. One man hadn't turned his head to either side for seven years before Doc soused him with Blackhawk. In half an hour he could move his head as easily as I could move mine. 'Glory be to God!' he shouted. 'It's the secret qualities in the ointment, my friend,' Doc Marlowe told him, suavely. He always called the liniment ointment.

News of his miracles got around by word of mouth among the poorer classes of town – he was not able to reach the better people (the 'tony folks,' he called them) – but there was never a big enough sale to give Doc a steady income. For one thing, people thought there was more magic in Doc's touch than in his liniment, and, for another, the ingredients of Blackhawk cost so much that his profits were not very great. I know, because I used to go to the wholesale chemical company once in a while for him and buy his supplies. Everything that went into the liniment was standard and expensive (and well known, not secret). A man at the company told me he didn't see how Doc could make much money on it at thirty-five cents a bottle. But even when he was very low in funds Doc never cut out any of the ingredients or substituted cheaper ones. Mrs Willoughby had suggested it to him once, she told me, when she was helping him 'put up a batch,' and he had got mad. 'He puts a heap of store by that liniment being right up to the mark,' she said.

Doc added to his small earnings, I discovered, by money he made gambling. He used to win quite a few dollars on Saturday nights at Freck's saloon, playing poker with the marketmen and the railwaymen who dropped in there. It wasn't for several years that I found out Doc cheated. I had never heard about marked cards until he told me about them and showed me his. It was one rainy afternoon, after he had played seven-up with Mrs Willoughby and old Mr Peiffer, another roomer of hers. They had played for small stakes (Doc wouldn't play cards unless there was some money up, and Mrs Willoughby wouldn't play if very much was up). Only twenty or thirty cents had changed hands in the end. Doc had won it all. I remember my astonishment and indignation when it dawned on me that Doc had used the marked cards in playing the old lady and the old man. 'You didn't cheat *them*, did you?' I asked him. 'Jimmy, my boy,' he told me, 'the man that calls the turn wins the money.' His eyes twinkled and he seemed to enjoy my anger. I was outraged, but I was helpless. I knew I could never tell Mrs Willoughby about how Doc had cheated her at seven-up. I liked her, but I liked him, too. Once he had given me a whole dollar to buy fireworks with on the Fourth of July.

I remember once, when I was staying at Mrs Willoughby's, Doc Marlowe was roused out of bed in the middle of the night by a poor woman who was frantic because her little girl was sick. This woman had had the sciatica driven out of her by his liniment, she reminded Doc. He placed her then. She had never been able to pay him a cent for his liniment or his 'treatments,' and he had given her a great many. He got up and dressed, and went over to her house. The child had colic, I suppose. Doc couldn't have had any idea what was the matter, but he sopped on liniment; he sopped on a whole bottle. When he came back home, two hours later, he said he had 'relieved the distress.' The little girl had gone to sleep and was all right the next day, whether on account of Doc Marlowe or in spite of him I don't know. 'I want to thank you, doctor,' said the mother, tremulously, when she called on him that afternoon. He gave her another bottle of liniment, and he didn't charge her for it or for his 'professional call.' He used to massage, and give liniment to, a lot of sufferers who were too poor to pay. Mrs Willoughby told him once that he was too generous and too easily taken in. Doc laughed – and winked at me, with the twinkle in his eye that he had had when he told me how he had cheated the old lady at cards.

Once I went for a walk with him out Town Street on a Saturday afternoon. It was a warm day, and after a while I said I wanted a soda. Well, he said, he didn't care if he took something himself. We went into a drugstore, and I ordered a chocolate soda and he had a lemon phosphate. When we had finished, he said, 'Jimmy, my son, I'll match you to see who pays for the drinks.' He handed me a quarter and he told me to toss the quarter and he would call the turn. He called heads and won. I paid for the drinks. It left me with a dime.

I was fifteen when Doc got out his pamphlets, as he called them. He had eased the misery of the wife of a small-time printer and the grateful man had given him a special price on two thousand advertising pamphlets. There was very little in them about Blackhawk Liniment. They were mostly about Doc himself and his *Life in the Far West*. He had gone out to Franklin Park one day with a photographer – another of his numerous friends – and there the photographer took dozens of pictures of Doc, a lariat in one hand, a six-shooter in the other. I had gone along. When the pamphlets came out, there were the pictures of Doc, peering around trees, crouching behind bushes, whirling the lariat, aiming the gun. 'Dr H. M. Marlowe Hunting Indians' was one of the captions. 'Dr H. M. Marlowe after Hoss-Thieves' was another one. He was very proud of the pamphlets and always had a sheaf with him. He would pass them out to people on the street.

Two years before he died Doc got hold of an ancient wheezy Cadillac somewhere. He aimed to start travelling around again, he said, but he never did, because the old automobile was so worn out it wouldn't hold up for more than a mile or so. It was about this time that a man named Hardman and his wife came to stay at Mrs Willoughby's. They were farm people from around Lancaster who had sold their place. They got to like Doc because he was so jolly, they said, and they enjoyed his stories. He treated Mrs Hardman for an old complaint in the small of her back and wouldn't take any money for it. They thought he was a fine gentleman. Then there came a day when they announced that they were going to St Louis, where they had a son. They talked some of settling in St Louis. Doc Marlowe told them they ought to buy a nice auto cheap and drive out, instead of going by train – it wouldn't cost much and they could see the country, give themselves a treat. Now, he knew where they could pick up just such a car.

Of course, he finally sold them the decrepit Cadillac – it had been stored away somewhere in the back of a garage whose owner kept it there for nothing because Doc had relieved his mother of a distress in the groins, as Doc explained it. I don't know just how the garage man doctored up the car, but he did. It actually chugged along pretty steadily when Doc took the Hardmans out for a trial spin. He told them he hated to part with it, but he finally let them have it for a hundred dollars. I knew, of course, and so did Doc, that it couldn't last many miles.

A Man Called Professor Jones

Doc got a letter from the Hardmans in St Louis, ten days later. They had had to abandon the old junk pile in West Jefferson, some fifteen miles out of Columbus. Doc read the letter aloud to me, peering over his glasses, his eyes twinkling, every now and then punctuating the lines with 'Hay, boy!' and 'Hay, boy-gie!' 'I just want you to know, Dr Marlowe,' he read, 'what I think of low-life swindlers like you [Hay, boy!] and that it will be a long day before I put my trust in a two-faced lyer and imposture again [Hay, boy-gie!]. The garrage man in W. Jefferson told us your old rattle-trap had been doctored up just to fool us. It was a low-down dirty trick as no swine would play on a white man [Hay, boy!].' Far from being disturbed by the letter, Doc Marlowe was plainly amused. He took off his glasses after he had finished it and laughed, his hand to his brow and his eyes closed. I was pretty mad, because I had liked the Hardmans, and because they had liked him. Doc Marlowe put the letter carefully back into its envelope and tucked it away in his inside pocket, as if it were something precious. Then he picked up a pack of cards and began to lay out a solitaire hand. 'Want to set in a little seven-up game, Jimmy?' he asked me. I was furious. 'Not with a cheater like you!' I shouted, and stamped out of the room, slamming the door. I could hear him chuckling to himself behind me.

The last time I saw Doc Marlowe was just a few days before he died. I didn't know anything about death, but I knew that he was dying when I saw him. His voice was very faint and his face was drawn; they told me he had a lot of pain. When I got ready to leave the room, he asked me to bring him a tin box that was on his bureau. I got it and handed it to him. He poked around in it for a while with unsteady fingers and finally found what he wanted. He handed it to me. It was a quarter, or rather it looked like a quarter, but it had heads on both sides. 'Never let the other fella call the turn, Jimmy, my boy,' said Doc, with a shadow of his old twinkle and the echo of his old chuckle. I still have the two-headed quarter. For a long time I didn't like to think about it, or about Doc Marlowe, but I do now.

The Wood Duck

MR KREPP, our vegetable man, had told us we might find some cider out the New Milford road a way – we would come to a sign saying 'Morris Plains Farm' and that would be the place. So we got into the car and drove down the concrete New Milford road, which is black in the centre with the dropped oil of a million cars. It's a main-trunk highway; you can go fifty miles an hour on it except where warning signs limit you to forty or, near towns, thirty-five, but nobody ever pays any attention to these signs. Even then, in November, dozens of cars flashed past us with a high, ominous whine, their tyres roaring rubberly on the concrete. We found Morris Plains Farm without any trouble. There was a big white house to the left of the highway; only a few yards off the road a small barn had been made into a roadside stand, with a dirt driveway curving up to the front of it. A spare, red-cheeked man stood in the midst of baskets and barrels of red apples and glass jugs of red cider. He was waiting on a man and a woman. I turned into the driveway – and put the brakes on hard. I had seen, just in time, a duck.

It was a small, trim duck, and even I, who know nothing about wild fowl, knew that this was no barnyard duck, this was a wild duck. He was all alone. There was no other bird of any kind around, not even a chicken. He was immensely solitary. With none of the awkward waddling of a domestic duck, he kept walking busily around in the driveway, now and then billing up water from a dirty puddle in the middle of the drive. His obvious contentment, his apparently perfect adjustment to his surroundings, struck me as something of a marvel. I got out of the car and spoke about it to a man who had driven up behind me in a rattly sedan. He wore a leather jacket and high, hard boots, and I figured he would know what kind of duck this was. He did. 'That's a wood duck,' he said. 'It dropped in here about two weeks ago, Len says, and's been here ever since.'

The proprietor of the stand, in whose direction my informant had nodded as he spoke, helped his customers load a basket of apples into their car and walked over to us. The duck stepped, with a little flutter of its wings, into the dirty puddle, took a small, unconcerned swim, and got out again, ruffling its feathers. 'It's rather an odd place for a wood duck, isn't it?' asked my wife. Len grinned and nodded; we all watched the duck. 'He's a banded duck,' said Len. 'There's a band on his leg. The state game commission sends out a lot of 'em. This'n lighted here two weeks ago – it was on a Saturday – and he's been around ever since.' 'It's funny he wouldn't be frightened away, with all the cars going by and all the people driving in,' I said. Len chuckled. 'He seems to like it here,' he said. The duck wandered over to some sparse grass at the edge of the road, aimlessly, but with an air of settled satisfaction. 'He's tame as anything,' said Len. 'I guess they get tame when them fellows band 'em.' The man in the leather jacket said, ' 'Course they haven't let you shoot wood duck for a long while and that might make 'em tame, too.' 'Still,' said my wife (we forgot about the cider for the moment), 'it's strange he would stay here, right on the road almost.' 'Sometimes,' said Len, reflectively, 'he goes round back o' the barn. But mostly he's here in the drive.' 'But don't they,' she asked, 'let them loose in the woods after they're banded ? I mean, aren't they supposed to stock up the forests ?' 'I guess they're supposed to,' said Len, chuckling again. 'But 'pears this'n didn't want to.'

An old Ford truck lurched into the driveway and two men in the seat hailed the proprietor. They were hunters, big, warmly-dressed, heavily-shod men.

In the back of the truck was a large bird dog. He was an old pointer and he wore an expression of remote disdain for the world of roadside commerce. He took no notice of the duck. The two hunters said something to Len about cider, and I was just about to chime in with my order when the accident happened. A car went by the stand at fifty miles an hour, leaving something scurrying in its wake. It was the duck, turning over and over on the concrete. He turned over and over swiftly, but lifelessly, like a thrown feather duster, and then he lay still. 'My God,' I cried, 'they've killed your duck, Len!' The accident gave me a quick feeling of anguished intimacy with the bereaved man. 'Oh, now,' he wailed. 'Now, that's awful!' None of us for a moment moved. Then the two hunters walked toward the road, slowly, self-consciously, a little embarrassed in the face of this quick incongruous ending of a wild fowl's life in the middle of a concrete highway. The pointer stood up, looked after the hunters, raised his ears briefly, and then lay down again.

It was the man in the leather jacket finally who walked out to the duck and tried to pick it up. As he did so, the duck stood up. He looked about him like a person who has been abruptly wakened and doesn't know where he is. He didn't ruffle his feathers. 'Oh, he isn't quite *dead*!' said my wife. I knew how she felt. We were going to have to see the duck die; somebody would have to kill him, finish him off. Len stood beside us. My wife took hold of his arm. The man in the leather jacket knelt down, stretched out a hand, and the duck moved slightly away. Just then, out from behind the barn, limped a setter dog, a lean white setter dog with black spots. His right back leg was useless and he kept it off the ground. He stopped when he saw the duck in the road and gave it a point, putting his head out, lifting his left front leg, maintaining a wavering, marvellous balance on two legs. He was like a drunken man drawing a bead with a gun. This new menace, this anticlimax, was too much. I think I yelled.

What happened next happened as fast as the automobile accident. The setter made his run, a limping, wobbly run, and he was in between the men and the bird before they saw him. The duck flew, got somehow off the ground a foot or two, and tumbled into the grass of the field across the road, the dog after him. It seemed crazy, but the duck could fly – a little, anyway. 'Here, here,' said Len, weakly. The hunters shouted, I shouted, my wife screamed, 'He'll kill him! He'll *kill* him!' The duck flew a few yards again, the dog at his tail. The dog's third plunge brought his nose almost to the duck's tail, and then one of the hunters tackled the animal and pulled him down and knelt in the grass, holding him. We all breathed easier. My wife let go Len's arm.

Len started across the road after the duck, who was fluttering slowly, waveringly, but with a definite purpose, towards a wood that fringed the far side of the field. The bird was dazed, but a sure, atavistic urge was guiding him; he was going home. One of the hunters joined Len in his pursuit. The other came back across the road, dragging the indignant setter; the man in the leather jacket walked beside them. We all watched Len and his companion reach the edge of the wood and stand there, looking; they had followed the duck through the grass slowly, so as not to alarm him; he had been alarmed enough. 'He'll never come back,' said my wife. Len and the hunter finally turned and came back through the grass. The duck had got away from them. We walked out to meet them at the edge of the concrete. Cars began to whizz by in both directions. I realized, with wonder, that all the time the duck, and the hunters, and the setter were milling around in the road, not one had passed. It was as if traffic had been held up so that our little drama could go on. 'He couldn't o' been much hurt,' said Len. 'Likely just grazed and pulled along in the wind of the car. Them fellows don't look out for anything. It's a sin.' My wife had a question for him. 'Does your dog always chase the duck?' she asked. 'Oh, that ain't my dog,' said Len. 'He just comes around.' The hunter who had been holding the setter now let him go, and he slunk away. The pointer, I noticed, lay with his eyes closed. 'But doesn't the duck mind the dog?' persisted my wife. 'Oh, he minds him,' said Len. 'But the dog's never really hurt him none yet. There's always somebody around.'

We drove away with a great deal to talk about (I almost forgot the cider). I explained the irony, I think I explained the profound symbolism, of a wild duck's becoming attached to a roadside stand. My wife strove simply to understand the duck's viewpoint. She didn't get anywhere. I knew even then, in the back of my mind, what would happen. We decided, after a cocktail, to drive back and find out if the duck had returned. My wife hoped it wouldn't be there, on account of the life it led in the driveway; I hoped it wouldn't because I felt that would be, somehow, too pat an ending. Night was falling when we started off again for Morris Plains Farm. It was a five-mile drive and I had to put my bright lights on before we got there. The barn door was closed for the night. We didn't see the duck anywhere. The only thing to do was to go up to the house and inquire. I knocked on the door and a young man opened it. 'Is – is the proprietor here?' I asked. He said no, he had gone to Waterbury. 'We wanted to know,' my wife said, 'whether the duck came back.' 'What?' he asked, a little startled, I thought. Then, 'Oh, the duck. I saw him around the driveway when my father drove off.' He stared at us, waiting. I thanked him and started back to the car. My wife lingered, explaining, for a moment. 'He thinks we're crazy,' she said, when she got into the car. We drove on a little distance. 'Well,' I said, 'he's back.' 'I'm glad he is, in a way,' said my wife. 'I hated to think of him all alone out there in the woods.'

The Admiral on the Wheel

W HEN the coloured maid stepped on my glasses the other morning, it was the first time they had been broken since the late Thomas A. Edison's seventy-ninth birthday. I remember that day well, because I was working for a newspaper then and I had been assigned to go over to West Orange that morning and interview Mr Edison. I got up early and, in reaching for my glasses under the bed (where I always put them), I found that one of my more sober and reflective Scotch terriers was quietly chewing them. Both tortoiseshell temples (the pieces that go over your ears) had been eaten and Jeannie was toying with the lenses in a sort of jaded way. It was in going over to Jersey that day, without my glasses, that I realized that the disadvantages of defective vision (bad eyesight) are at least partially compensated for by its peculiar advantages. Up to that time I had been in the habit of going to bed when my glasses were broken and lying there until they were fixed again. I had believed I could not go very far without them, not more than a block, anyway, on account of the danger of bumping into things, getting a headache, losing my way. None of those things happened, but a lot of others did. I saw the Cuban flag flying over a national bank, I saw a gay old lady with a grey parasol walk right through the side of a truck, I saw a cat roll across a street in a small striped barrel, I saw bridges rise lazily into the air, like balloons.

I suppose you have to have just the right proportion of sight to encounter such phenomena: I seem to remember that oculists have told me I have only two-fifths vision without what one of them referred to as 'artificial compensation' (glasses). With three-fifths vision or better, I suppose the Cuban flag would have been an American flag, the gay old lady a garbage man with a garbage can on his back, the cat a piece of butcher's paper blowing in the wind, the floating bridges smoke from tugs, hanging in the air. With perfect vision, one is extricably trapped in the workaday world, a prisoner of reality, as lost in the commonplace America of 1937 as Alexander Selkirk was lost on his lonely island. For the hawk-eyed person life has none of those soft edges which for me blur into fantasy; for such a person an electric welder is merely an electric welder, not a radiant fool setting off a sky-rocket by day. The kingdom of the partly blind is a little like Oz, a little like Wonderland, a little like Poictesme. Anything you can think of, and a lot you never would think of, can happen there.

For three days after the maid, in cleaning the apartment, stepped on my glasses – I had not put them far enough under the bed – I worked at home and did not go uptown to have them fixed. It was in this period that I made the acquaintance of a remarkable Chesapeake spaniel. I looked out of my window and after a moment spotted him, a noble, silent dog lying on a ledge above the entrance to a brownstone house in lower Fifth Avenue. He lay there, proud and austere, for three days and nights, sleepless, never eating, the perfect watchdog. No ordinary dog could have got up on the high ledge above the doorway, to begin with; no ordinary people would have owned such an animal. The ordinary people were the people who walked by the house and did not see the dog. Oh, I got my glasses fixed finally and I know that now the dog has gone, but I haven't looked to see what prosaic object occupies the spot where he so staunchly stood guard over one of the last of the old New York houses on Fifth Avenue; perhaps an unpainted flower-box or a cleaning cloth dropped from an upper window by a careless menial. The moment of disenchantment would be too hard; I never look out of that particular window any more.

Sometimes at night, even with my glasses on, I see strange and unbelievable sights, mainly when I am riding in an automobile which somebody else is driving (I never drive myself at night out of fear that I might turn up at the portals of some mystical monastery and never return). Only last summer I was riding with someone along a country road when suddenly I cried at him to look out. He slowed down and asked me sharply what was the matter. There is no worse experience than to have someone shout at you to look out for something you don't see. What this driver didn't see and I did see (two-fifths vision works a kind of magic in the night) was a little old admiral in full-dress uniform riding a bicycle at right angles to the car I was in. He might have been starlight behind a tree, or a billboard advertising Moxie; I don't know – we were quickly past the place he rode out of; but I would recognize him if I saw him again. His beard was blowing in the breeze and his hat was set at a rakish angle, like Admiral Beatty's. He was having a swell time. The gentleman who was driving the car has been, since that night, a trifle stiff and distant with me. I suppose you can hardly blame him.

To go back to my daylight experiences with the naked eye, it was me, in case you have heard the story, who once killed fifteen white chickens with small stones. The poor beggars never had a chance. This happened many years ago when I was living at Jay, New York. I had a vegetable garden some seventy feet behind the house, and the lady of the house had asked me to keep an eye on it in my spare moments and to chase away any chickens from neighbouring farms that came pecking around. One morning, getting up from my type-writer, I wandered out behind the house and saw that a flock of white chickens had invaded the garden. I had, to be sure, misplaced my glasses for the moment, but I could still see well enough to let the chickens have it with ammunition from a pile of stones that I kept handy for the purpose. Before I could be stopped, I had riddled all the tomato plants in the garden, over the tops of which the lady of the house had, the twilight before, placed newspapers and paper bags to ward off the effects of frost. It was one of the darker ex-periences of my dimmer hours.

Some day, I suppose, when the clouds are heavy and the rain is coming down and the pressure of realities is too great, I shall deliberately take my glasses off and go wandering out into the streets. I dare say I may never be heard of again (I have always believed it was Ambrose Bierce's vision and not his whim that caused him to wander into oblivion). I imagine I'll have a remarkable time, wherever I end up.

Fables for Our Time

&

Famous Poems Illustrated

FOR HERMAN AND DOROTHY

The Mouse Who Went to the Country

ONCE upon a Sunday there was a city mouse who went to visit a country mouse. He hid away on a train the country mouse had told him to take, only to find that on Sundays it did not stop at Beddington. Hence the city mouse could not get off at Beddington and catch a bus for Sibert's Junction, where he was to be met by the country mouse. The city mouse, in fact, was carried on to Middleburg, where he waited three hours for a train to take him back. When he got back to Beddington he found that the last bus for Sibert's Junction had just left, so he ran and he ran and he ran and he finally caught the bus and crept aboard, only to find that it was not the bus for Sibert's Junction at all, but was going in the opposite direction through Pell's Hollow and Grumm to a place called Wimberby. When the bus finally stopped, the city mouse got out into a heavy rain and found that there were no more buses that night going anywhere. 'To the hell with it,' said the city mouse, and he walked back to the city.

Moral: Stay where you are, you're sitting pretty.

The Little Girl and the Wolf

ONE afternoon a big wolf waited in a dark forest for a little girl to come along carrying a basket of food to her grandmother. Finally a little girl did come along and she was carrying a basket of food. 'Are you carrying that basket to your grandmother?' asked the wolf. The little girl said yes, she was. So the wolf asked her where her grandmother lived and the little girl told him and he disappeared into the wood.

When the little girl opened the door of her grandmother's house she saw that there was somebody in bed with a nightcap and nightgown on. She had approached no nearer than twenty-five feet from the bed when she saw that it was not her grandmother but the wolf, for even in a nightcap a wolf does not look any more like your grandmother than the Metro-Goldwyn lion looks like Calvin Coolidge. So the little girl took an automatic out of her basket and shot the wolf dead.

Moral: It is not so easy to fool little girls nowadays as it used to be.

The Two Turkeys

ONCE upon a time there were two turkeys, an old turkey and a young turkey. The old turkey had been cock of the walk for many years and the young turkey wanted to take his place. 'I'll knock that old buzzard cold one of these days,' the young turkey told his friends. 'Sure you will, Joe, sure you will,' his friends said, for Joe was treating them to some corn he had found. Then the friends went and told the old turkey what the young turkey had said. 'Why, I'll have his gizzard!' said the old turkey, setting out some corn for his visitors. 'Sure you will, Doc, sure you will,' said the visitors.

One day the young turkey walked over to where the old turkey was telling tales of his prowess in battle. 'I'll bat your teeth into your crop,' said the young turkey. 'You and who else?' said the old turkey. So they began to circle around each other, sparring for an opening. Just then the farmer who owned the turkeys swept up the young one and carried him off and wrung his neck.

Moral: Youth will be served, frequently stuffed with chestnuts.

The Tiger Who Understood People

ONCE upon a time there was a tiger who escaped from a zoo in the United States and made his way back to the jungle. During his captivity the tiger had learned a great deal about how men do things and he thought he would apply their methods to life in the jungle. The first day he was home he met a leopard and he said, 'There's no use in you and me hunting for food; we'll make the other animals bring it to us.' 'How will we do that?' asked the leopard. 'Easy,' said the tiger, 'you and I will tell everybody that we are going to put on a fight and that every animal will have to bring a freshly killed boar in order to get in and see the fight. Then we will just spar around and not hurt each other. Later you can say you broke a bone in your paw during the second round and I will say I broke a bone in my paw during the first round. Then we will announce a return engagement and they'll have to bring us more wild boars.' 'I don't think this will work,' said the leopard. 'Oh, yes it will,' said the tiger. 'You just go around saying that you can't help winning because I am a big palooka and I will go around saying I can't lose because you are a big palooka, and everybody will want to come and see the fight.'

So the leopard went around telling everybody that he couldn't help winning because the tiger was a big palooka and the tiger went around telling everybody he couldn't lose because the leopard was a big palooka. The night of the fight came and the tiger and the leopard were very hungry because they hadn't gone out and done any hunting at all; they wanted to get the fight over as soon as possible and eat some of the freshly killed wild boars which all the animals would bring to the fight. But when the hour of the combat came none of the animals at all showed up. 'The way I look at it,' a fox had told them, 'is this: if the leopard can't help winning and the tiger can't lose, it will be a draw and a draw is a very dull thing to watch, particularly when fought by fighters who are both big palookas.' The animals all saw the logic of this and stayed away from the arena. When it got to be midnight and it was obvious that none of the animals would appear and that there wouldn't be any wild-boar meat to devour, the tiger and the leopard fell upon each other in a rage. They were both injured so badly and they were both so worn out by hunger that a couple of wild boars who came wandering along attacked them and killed them easily.

Moral: If you live as humans do, it will be the end of you.

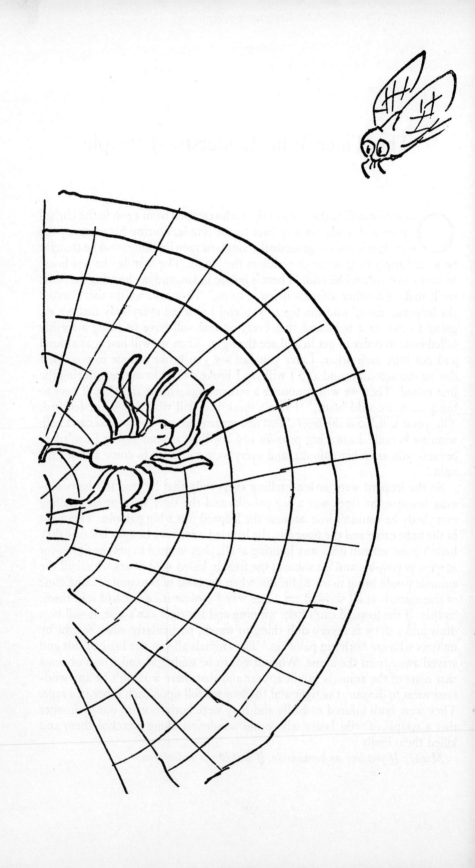

The Fairly Intelligent Fly

A LARGE spider in an old house built a beautiful web in which to catch flies. Every time a fly landed on the web and was entangled in it the spider devoured him, so that when another fly came along he would think the web was a safe and quiet place in which to rest. One day a fairly intelligent fly buzzed around above the web so long without lighting that the spider appeared and said, 'Come on down.' But the fly was too clever for him and said, 'I never light where I don't see other flies and I don't see any other flies in your house.' So he flew away until he came to a place where there were a great many other flies. He was about to settle down among them when a bee buzzed up and said, 'Hold it, stupid, that's flypaper. All those flies are trapped.' 'Don't be silly,' said the fly, 'they're dancing.' So he settled down and became stuck to the flypaper with all the other flies.

Moral: There is no safety in numbers, or in anything else.

The Lion Who Wanted to Zoom

THERE was once a lion who coveted an eagle's wings. So he sent a message to the eagle asking him to call, and when the eagle came to the lion's den the lion said, 'I will trade you my mane for your wings.' 'Keep talking, brother,' said the eagle. 'Without my wings I could no longer fly.' 'So what?' said the lion. 'I can't fly now, but that doesn't keep me from being king of beasts. I became king of beasts on account of my magnificent mane.' 'All right,' said the eagle, 'but give me your mane first.' 'Just approach a little nearer,' said the lion, 'so that I can hand it to you.' The eagle came closer and the lion clapped a huge paw on him, pinning him to the ground. 'Come across with those wings!' he snarled.

So the lion took the eagle's wings but kept his own mane. The eagle was very despondent for a while and then he had an idea. 'I bet you can't fly off the top of that great rock yonder,' said the eagle. 'Who, me?' said the lion, and he walked to the top of the rock and took off. His weight was too great for the eagle's wings to support, and besides he did not know how to fly, never having tried it before. So he crashed at the foot of the rock and burst into flames. The eagle hastily climbed down to him and regained his wings and took off the lion's mane, which he put about his own neck and shoulders. Flying back to the rocky nest where he lived with his mate, he decided to have some fun with her. So, covered with the lion's mane, he poked his head into the nest and in a deep, awful voice said '*Harrrooo!*' His mate, who was very nervous anyway, grabbed a pistol from a bureau drawer and shot him dead, thinking he was a lion.

Moral: Never allow a nervous female to have access to a pistol, no matter what you're wearing.

The Very Proper Gander

NOT so very long ago there was a very fine gander. He was strong and smooth and beautiful and he spent most of his time singing to his wife and children. One day somebody who saw him strutting up and down in his yard and singing remarked, 'There is a very proper gander.' An old hen overheard this and told her husband about it that night in the roost. 'They said something about propaganda,' she said. 'I have always suspected that,' said the rooster, and he went around the barnyard next day telling everybody that the very fine gander was a dangerous bird, more than likely a hawk in gander's clothing. A small brown hen remembered a time when at a great distance she had seen the gander talking with some hawks in the forest. 'They were up to no good,' she said. A duck remembered that the gander had once told him he did not believe in anything. 'He said to hell with the flag, too,' said the duck. A guinea hen recalled that she had once seen somebody who looked very much like the gander throw something that looked a great deal like a bomb. Finally everybody snatched up sticks and stones and descended on the gander's house. He was strutting in his front yard, singing to his children and his wife. 'There he is!' everybody cried. 'Hawk-lover! Unbeliever! Flag-hater! Bomb-thrower!' So they set upon him and drove him out of the country.

Moral: Anybody who you or your wife thinks is going to overthrow the government by violence must be driven out of the country.

The Moth and the Star

A YOUNG and impressionable moth once set his heart on a certain star.
He told his mother about this and she counselled him to set his heart
on a bridge lamp instead. 'Stars aren't the thing to hang around,' she
said; 'lamps are the thing to hang around.' 'You get somewhere that way,'
said the moth's father. 'You don't get anywhere chasing stars.' But the moth
would not heed the words of either parent. Every evening at dusk when the
star came out he would start flying toward it and every morning at dawn he
would crawl back home worn out with his vain endeavour. One day his father
said to him, 'You haven't burned a wing in months, boy, and it looks to me
as if you were never going to. All your brothers have been badly burned flying
around street lamps and all your sisters have been terribly singed flying around
house lamps. Come on, now, get out of here and get yourself scorched! A big
strapping moth like you without a mark on him!'

The moth left his father's house, but he would not fly around street lamps
and he would not fly around house lamps. He went right on trying to reach
the star, which was four and one-third light years, or twenty-five trillion
miles, away. The moth thought it was just caught in the top branches of an
elm. He never did reach the star, but he went right on trying, night after night,
and when he was a very, very old moth he began to think that he really had
reached the star and he went around saying so. This gave him a deep and
lasting pleasure, and he lived to a great old age. His parents and his brothers
and his sisters had all been burned to death when they were quite young.

*Moral: Who flies afar from the sphere of our sorrow is here today and here
tomorrow.*

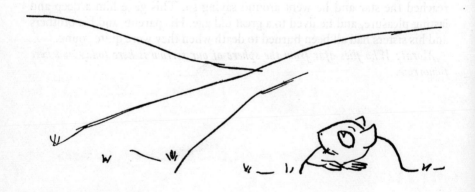

The Shrike and the Chipmunks

ONCE upon a time there were two chipmunks, a male and a female. The male chipmunk thought that arranging nuts in artistic patterns was more fun than just piling them up to see how many you could pile up. The female was all for piling up as many as you could. She told her husband that if he gave up making designs with the nuts there would be room in their large cave for a great many more and he would soon become the wealthiest chipmunk in the woods. But he would not let her interfere with his designs, so she flew into a rage and left him. 'The shrike will get you,' she said, 'because you are helpless and cannot look after yourself.' To be sure, the female chipmunk had not been gone three nights before the male had to dress for a banquet and could not find his studs or shirt or suspenders. So he couldn't go to the banquet, but that was just as well, because all the chipmunks who did go were attacked and killed by a weasel.

The next day the shrike began hanging around outside the chipmunk's cave, waiting to catch him. The shrike couldn't get in because the doorway was clogged up with soiled laundry and dirty dishes. 'He will come out for a walk after breakfast and I will get him then,' thought the shrike. But the chipmunk slept all day and did not get up and have breakfast until after dark. Then he came out for a breath of air before beginning work on a new design. The shrike swooped down to snatch up the chipmunk, but could not see very well on account of the dark, so he batted his head against an alder branch and was killed.

A few days later the female chipmunk returned and saw the awful mess the house was in. She went to the bed and shook her husband. 'What would you do without me?' she demanded. 'Just go on living, I guess,' he said. 'You wouldn't last five days,' she told him. She swept the house and did the dishes and sent out the laundry, and then she made the chipmunk get up and wash and dress. 'You can't be healthy if you lie in bed all day and never get any exercise,' she told him. So she took him for a walk in the bright sunlight and they were both caught and killed by the shrike's brother, a shrike named Stoop.

Moral: Early to rise and early to bed makes a male healthy and wealthy and dead.

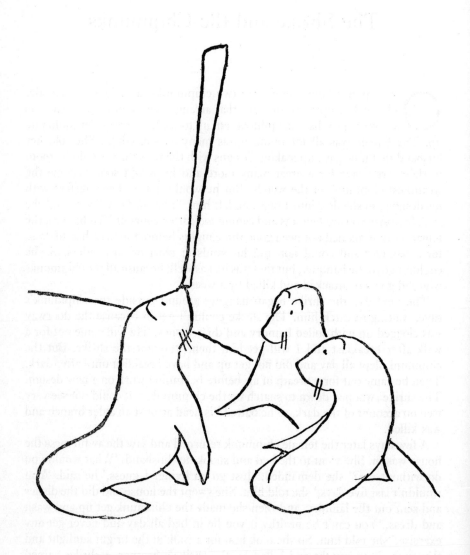

The Seal Who Became Famous

A SEAL who lay basking on a large, smooth rock said to himself: all I ever do is swim. None of the other seals can swim any better than I can, he reflected, but, on the other hand, they can all swim just as well. The more he pondered the monotony and uniformity of his life, the more depressed he became. That night he swam away and joined a circus.

Within two years the seal had become a great balancer. He could balance lamps, billiard cues, medicine balls, hassocks, taborets, dollar cigars, and anything else you gave him. When he read in a book a reference to the Great Seal of the United States, he thought it meant him. In the winter of his third year as a performer he went back to the large, smooth rock to visit his friends and family. He gave them the Big Town stuff right away: the latest slang, liquor in a golden flask, zippers, a gardenia in his lapel. He balanced for them everything there was on the rock to balance, which wasn't much. When he had run through his repertory, he asked the other seals if they could do what he had done and they all said no. 'O.K.,' he said. 'Let's see you do something I can't do.' Since the only thing they could do was swim, they all plunged off the rock into the sea. The circus seal plunged right after them, but he was so hampered by his smart city clothes, including a pair of seventeen-dollar shoes, that he began to founder at once. Since he hadn't been in swimming for three years, he had forgot what to do with his flippers and tail, and he went down for the third time before the other seals could reach him. They gave him a simple but dignified funeral.

Moral: Whom God has equipped with flippers should not monkey around with zippers.

The Hunter and the Elephant

ONCE upon a time there was a hunter who spent the best years of his life looking for a pink elephant. He looked in Cathay and he looked in Africa; he looked in Zanzibar and he looked in India; but he couldn't find one. The longer he looked, the more he wanted a pink elephant. He would trample black orchids and he would walk right past purple cows, so intent was he on his quest. Then one day in a far corner of the world he came upon a pink elephant and he spent ten days digging a trap for it and he hired forty natives to help him drive the elephant into the trap. The pink elephant was finally captured and tied up and taken back to America.

When the hunter got home, he found that his farm was really no place for an elephant. It trampled his wife's dahlias and peonies, it broke his children's toys, it crushed the smaller animals around the place, and it smashed pianos and kitchen cabinets as if they were berry boxes. One day, when the hunter had had the elephant for about two years, he woke up to find that his wife had left his bed and his children had left his board and all the animals on the estate were dead except the elephant. The elephant was the same as ever except that it had faded. It wasn't pink any more. It was white.

Moral: A burden in the bush is worth two on your hands.

The Scotty Who Knew Too Much

SEVERAL summers ago there was a Scotty who went to the country for a visit. He decided that all the farm dogs were cowards, because they were afraid of a certain animal that had a white stripe down its back. 'You are a pussy-cat and I can lick you,' the Scotty said to the farm dog who lived in the house where the Scotty was visiting. 'I can lick the little animal with the white stripe, too. Show him to me.' 'Don't you want to ask any questions about him?' said the farm dog. 'Naw,' said the Scotty. '*You* ask the questions.'

So the farm dog took the Scotty into the woods and showed him the white-striped animal and the Scotty closed in on him, growling and slashing. It was all over in a moment and the Scotty lay on his back. When he came to, the farm dog said, 'What happened?' 'He threw vitriol,' said the Scotty, 'but he never laid a glove on me.'

A few days later the farm dog told the Scotty there was another animal all the farm dogs were afraid of. 'Lead me to him,' said the Scotty. 'I can lick anything that doesn't wear horseshoes.' 'Don't you want to ask any questions about him?' said the farm dog. 'Naw,' said the Scotty. 'Just show me where he hangs out.' So the farm dog led him to a place in the woods and pointed out the little animal when he came along. 'A clown,' said the Scotty, 'a pushover,' and he closed in, leading with his left and exhibiting some mighty fancy footwork. In less than a second the Scotty was flat on his back, and when he woke up the farm dog was pulling quills out of him. 'What happened?' said the farm dog. 'He pulled a knife on me,' said the Scotty, 'but at least I have learned how you fight out here in the country, and now I am going to beat *you* up.' So he closed in on the farm dog, holding his nose with one front paw to ward off the vitriol and covering his eyes with the other front paw to keep out the knives. The Scotty couldn't see his opponent and he couldn't smell his opponent and he was so badly beaten that he had to be taken back to the city and put in a nursing home.

Moral: It is better to ask some of the questions than to know all the answers.

The Bear Who Let It Alone

IN THE woods of the Far West there once lived a brown bear who could take it or let it alone. He would go into a bar where they sold mead, a fermented drink made of honey, and he would have just two drinks. Then he would put some money on the bar and say, 'See what the bears in the back room will have,' and he would go home. But finally he took to drinking by himself most of the day. He would reel home at night, kick over the umbrella stand, knock down the bridge lamps, and ram his elbows through the windows. Then he would collapse on the floor and lie there until he went to sleep. His wife was greatly distressed and his children were very frightened.

At length the bear saw the error of his ways and began to reform. In the end he became a famous teetotaller and a persistent temperance lecturer. He would tell everybody that came to his house about the awful effects of drink, and he would boast about how strong and well he had become since he gave up touching the stuff. To demonstrate this, he would stand on his head and on his hands and he would turn cartwheels in the house, kicking over the umbrella stand, knocking down the bridge lamps, and ramming his elbows through the windows. Then he would lie down on the floor, tired by his healthful exercise, and go to sleep. His wife was greatly distressed and his children were very frightened.

Moral: You might as well fall flat on your face as lean over too far backward.

The Owl Who Was God

ONCE upon a starless midnight there was an owl who sat on the branch of an oak tree. Two ground moles tried to slip quietly by, unnoticed. 'You!' said the owl. 'Who?' they quavered, in fear and astonishment, for they could not believe it was possible for anyone to see them in that thick darkness. 'You two!' said the owl. The moles hurried away and told the other creatures of the field and forest that the owl was the greatest and wisest of all animals because he could see in the dark and because he could answer any question. 'I'll see about that,' said a secretary bird, and he called on the owl one night when it was again very dark. 'How many claws am I holding up?' said the secretary bird. 'Two,' said the owl, and that was right. 'Can you give me another expression for "that is to say" or "namely"?' asked the secretary bird. 'To wit,' said the owl. 'Why does a lover call on his love?' asked the secretary bird. 'To woo,' said the owl.

The secretary bird hastened back to the other creatures and reported that the owl was indeed the greatest and wisest animal in the world because he could see in the dark and because he could answer any question. 'Can he see in the daytime, too?' asked a red fox. 'Yes,' echoed a dormouse and a French poodle. 'Can he see in the daytime, too?' All the other creatures laughed loudly at this silly question, and they set upon the red fox and his friends and drove them out of the region. Then they sent a messenger to the owl and asked him to be their leader.

When the owl appeared among the animals it was high noon and the sun was shining brightly. He walked very slowly, which gave him an appearance of great dignity, and he peered about him with large, staring eyes, which gave him an air of tremendous importance. 'He's God!' screamed a Plymouth Rock hen. And the others took up the cry 'He's God!' So they followed him wherever he went and when he began to bump into things they began to bump into things, too. Finally he came to a concrete highway and he started up the middle of it and all the other creatures followed him. Presently a hawk, who was acting as outrider, observed a truck coming toward them at fifty miles an hour, and he reported to the secretary bird and the secretary bird reported to the owl. 'There's danger ahead,' said the secretary bird. 'To wit?' said the owl. The secretary bird told him. 'Aren't you afraid?' he asked. 'Who?' said the owl calmly, for he could not see the truck. 'He's God!' cried all the creatures again, and they were still crying 'He's God!' when the truck hit them and ran them down. Some of the animals were merely injured, but most of them, including the owl, were killed.

Moral: You can fool too many of the people too much of the time.

The Sheep in Wolf's Clothing

NOT very long ago there were two sheep who put on wolf's clothing and went among the wolves as spies, to see what was going on. They arrived on a fête day, when all the wolves were singing in the taverns or dancing in the street. The first sheep said to his companion, 'Wolves are just like us, for they gambol and frisk. Every day is fête day in Wolfland.' He made some notes on a piece of paper (which a spy should never do) and he headed them 'My Twenty-Four Hours in Wolfland,' for he had decided not to be a spy any longer but to write a book on Wolfland and also some articles for the *Sheep's Home Companion*. The other sheep guessed what he was planning to do, so he slipped away and began to write a book called 'My Ten Hours in Wolfland.' The first sheep suspected what was up when he found his friend had gone, so he wired a book to his publisher called 'My Five Hours in Wolfland,' and it was announced for publication first. The other sheep immediately sold his manuscript to a newspaper syndicate for serialization.

Both sheep gave the same message to their fellows: wolves were just like sheep, for they gambolled and frisked, and every day was fête day in Wolfland. The citizens of Sheepland were convinced by all this, so they drew in their sentinels and they let down their barriers. When the wolves descended on them one night, howling and slavering, the sheep were as easy to kill as flies on a windowpane.

Moral: Don't get it right, just get it written.

The Stork Who Married a Dumb Wife

A DANISH stork was in the habit of spending six nights a week out on the town with the boys, drinking and dicing and playing the match game. His wife had never left their nest, which was on a chimney top, since he married her, for he did not want her to get wise to the ways of the male. When he got home, which was usually at four o'clock in the morning – unless the party had gone on to Reuben's – he always brought her a box of candy and handed it to her together with a stork story, which is the same as a cock-and-bull story. 'I've been out delivering babies,' he would say. 'It's killing me, but it is my duty to go on.' 'Who do you deliver babies for?' she asked one morning. 'Human beings,' he said. 'A human being cannot have a baby without help from someone. All the other animals can, but human beings are helpless. They depend on the other animals for everything from food and clothing to companionship.' Just then the phone rang and the stork answered it. 'Another baby on the way,' he said when he had hung up. 'I'll have to go out again tonight.' So that night he went out again and did not get home until seven-thirty in the morning. 'Thish was very special case,' he said, handing his wife a box of candy. 'Five girls.' He did not add that the five girls were all blondes in their twenties.

After a while the female stork got to thinking. Her husband had told her never to leave the nest, because the world was full of stork traps, but she began to doubt this. So she flew out into the world, looking and listening. In this way she learned to tell time and to take male talk with a grain of salt; she found out that candy is dandy, as the poet has said, but that licker is quicker; she discovered that the offspring of the human species are never brought into the world by storks. This last discovery was a great blow to her, but it was a greater blow to Papa when he came home the next morning at a quarter to six. 'Hello, you phony obstetrician,' said his wife coldly. 'How are all the blonde quintuplets today?' And she crowned him with a chimney brick.

Moral: The male was made to lie and roam, but woman's place is in the home.

The Green Isle in the Sea

ONE sweet morning in the Year of Our Lord, Nineteen hundred and thirty-nine, a little old gentleman got up and threw wide the windows of his bedroom, letting in the living sun. A black widow spider, who had been dozing on the balcony, slashed at him, and although she missed, she did not miss very far. The old gentleman went downstairs to the dining-room and was just sitting down to a splendid breakfast when his grandson, a boy named Burt, pulled the chair from under him. The old man's hip was strained but it was fortunately not broken.

Out in the street, as he limped toward a little park with many trees, which was to him a green isle in the sea, the old man was tripped up by a gaily-coloured hoop sent rolling at him, with a kind of disinterested deliberation, by a grim little girl. Hobbling on a block farther, the old man was startled, but not exactly surprised, when a bold daylight robber stuck a gun in his ribs. 'Put 'em up, Mac,' said the robber, 'and come across.' Mac put them up and came across with his watch and money and a gold ring his mother had given him when he was a boy.

When at last the old gentleman staggered into the little park, which had been to him a fountain and a shrine, he saw that half the trees had been killed by a blight, and the other half by a bug. Their leaves were gone and they no longer afforded any protection from the skies, so that the hundred planes which appeared suddenly overhead had an excellent view of the little old gentleman through their bombing-sights.

Moral: The world is so full of a number of things, I am sure we should all be as happy as kings, and you know how happy kings are.

The Crow and the Oriole

ONCE upon a time a crow fell in love with a Baltimore oriole. He had seen her flying past his nest every spring on her way North and every autumn on her way South, and he had decided that she was a tasty dish. He had observed that she came North every year with a different gentleman, but he paid no attention to the fact that all the gentlemen were Baltimore orioles. 'Anybody can have that mouse,' he said to himself. So he went to his wife and told her that he was in love with a Baltimore oriole who was as cute as a cuff link. He said he wanted a divorce, so his wife gave him one simply by opening the door and handing him his hat. 'Don't come crying to me when she throws you down,' she said. 'That fly-by-season hasn't got a brain in her head. She can't cook or sew. Her upper register sounds like a streetcar taking a curve. You can find out in any dictionary that the crow is the smartest and most capable of birds – or was till you became one.' 'Tush!' said the male crow. 'Pish! You are simply a jealous woman.' He tossed her a few dollars. 'Here,' he said, 'go buy yourself some finery. You look like the bottom of an old tea-kettle.' And off he went to look for the oriole.

This was in the springtime and he met her coming North with an oriole he had never seen before. The crow stopped the female oriole and pleaded his cause – or should we say cawed his pleas? At any rate, he courted her in a harsh, grating voice, which made her laugh merrily. 'You sound like an old window shutter,' she said, and she snapped her fingers at him. 'I am bigger and stronger than your gentleman friend,' said the crow. 'I have a vocabulary larger than his. All the orioles in the country couldn't even lift the corn I own. I am a fine sentinel and my voice can be heard for miles in case of danger.' 'I don't see how that could interest anybody but another crow,' said the female oriole, and she laughed at him and flew on toward the North. The male oriole tossed the crow some coins. 'Here,' he said, 'go buy yourself a blazer or something. You look like the bottom of an old coffee-pot.'

The crow flew back sadly to his nest, but his wife was not there. He found a note pinned to the front door. 'I have gone away with Bert,' it read. 'You will find some arsenic in the medicine chest.'

Moral: Even the llama should stick to mamma.

The Elephant Who Challenged the World

AN ELEPHANT who lived in Africa woke up one morning with the conviction that he could defeat all the other animals in the world in single combat, one at a time. He wondered that he hadn't thought of it before. After breakfast he called first on the lion. 'You are only the King of Beasts,' bellowed the elephant, 'whereas I am the Ace!' and he demonstrated his prowess by knocking the lion out in fifteen minutes, no holds barred. Then in quick succession he took on the wild boar, the water buffalo, the rhinoceros, the hippopotamus, the giraffe, the zebra, the eagle, and the vulture, and he conquered them all. After that the elephant spent most of his time in bed eating peanuts, while the other animals, who were now his slaves, built for him the largest house any animal in the world had ever had. It was five stories high, solidly made of the hardest woods to be found in Africa. When it was finished, the Ace of Beasts moved in and announced that he could pin back the ears of any animal in the world. He challenged all comers to meet him in the basement of the big house, where he had set up a prize ring ten times the regulation size.

Several days went by and then the elephant got an anonymous letter accepting his challenge. 'Be in your basement tomorrow afternoon at three o'clock,' the message read. So at three o'clock the next day the elephant went down to the basement to meet his mysterious opponent, but there was no one there, or at least no one he could see. 'Come out from behind whatever you're behind!' roared the elephant. 'I'm not behind anything,' said a tiny voice. The elephant tore around the basement, upsetting barrels and boxes, banging his head against the furnace pipes, rocking the house on its foundations, but he could not find his opponent. At the end of an hour the elephant roared that the whole business was a trick and a deceit – probably ventriloquism – and that he would never come down to the basement again. 'Oh, yes you will,' said the tiny voice. 'You will be down here at three o'clock tomorrow and you'll end up on your back.' The elephant's laughter shook the house. 'We'll see about that,' he said.

The next afternoon the elephant, who slept on the fifth floor of the house, woke up at two-thirty o'clock and looked at his wristwatch. 'Nobody I can't see will ever get me down to the basement again,' he growled, and went back to sleep. At exactly three o'clock the house began to tremble and quiver as if an earthquake had it in its paws. Pillars and beams bent and broke like reeds, for they were all drilled full of tiny holes. The fifth floor gave way completely and crashed down upon the fourth, which fell upon the third, which fell upon the second, which carried away the first as if it had been the floor of a berry basket. The elephant was precipitated into the basement, where he fell heavily upon the concrete floor and lay there on his back, completely unconscious. A tiny voice began to count him out. At the count of ten the elephant came to, but he could not get up. 'What animal are you?' he demanded of the mysterious voice in a quavering tone which had lost its menace. 'I am the termite,' answered the voice.

The other animals, straining and struggling for a week, finally got the elephant lifted out of the basement and put him in jail. He spent the rest of his life there, broken in spirit and back.

Moral: The battle is sometimes to the small, for the bigger they are the harder they fall.

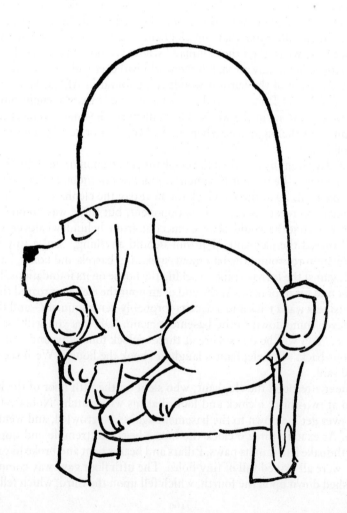

The Birds and the Foxes

ONCE upon a time there was a bird sanctuary in which hundreds of Baltimore orioles lived together happily. The refuge consisted of a forest entirely surrounded by a high wire fence. When it was put up, a pack of foxes who lived nearby protested that it was an arbitrary and unnatural boundary. However, they did nothing about it at the time because they were interested in civilizing the geese and ducks on the neighbouring farms. When all the geese and ducks had been civilized, and there was nothing else left to eat, the foxes once more turned their attention to the bird sanctuary. Their leader announced that there had once been foxes in the sanctuary but that they had been driven out. He proclaimed that Baltimore orioles belonged in Baltimore. He said, furthermore, that the orioles in the sanctuary were a continuous menace to the peace of the world. The other animals cautioned the foxes not to disturb the birds in their sanctuary.

So the foxes attacked the sanctuary one night and tore down the fence that surrounded it. The orioles rushed out and were instantly killed and eaten by the foxes.

The next day the leader of the foxes, a fox from whom God was receiving daily guidance, got upon the rostrum and addressed the other foxes. His message was simple and sublime. 'You see before you,' he said, 'another Lincoln. We have liberated all those birds!'

Moral: Government of the orioles, by the foxes, and for the foxes, must perish from the earth.

The Courtship of Arthur and Al

ONCE upon a time there was a young beaver named Al and an older beaver named Arthur. They were both in love with a pretty little female. She looked with disfavour upon the young beaver's suit because he was a harum-scarum and a ne'er-do-well. He had never done a single gnaw of work in his life, for he preferred to eat and sleep and to swim lazily in the streams and to play Now-I'll-Chase-You with the girls. The older beaver had never done anything but work from the time he got his first teeth. He had never played anything with anybody.

When the young beaver asked the female to marry him, she said she wouldn't think of it unless he amounted to something. She reminded him that Arthur had built thirty-two dams and was working on three others, whereas he, Al, had never even made a bread-board or a pin tray in his life. Al was very sorry, but he said he would never go to work just because a woman wanted him to. Thereupon she offered to be a sister to him, but he pointed out that he already had seventeen sisters. So he went back to eating and sleeping and swimming in the streams and playing Spider-in-the-Parlour with the girls. The female married Arthur one day at the lunch hour – he could never get away from work for more than one hour at a time. They had seven children and Arthur worked so hard supporting them he wore his teeth down to the gum line. His health broke in two before long and he died without ever having had a vacation in his life. The young beaver continued to eat and sleep and swim in the streams and play Unbutton-Your-Shoe with the girls. He never Got Anywhere, but he had a long life and a Wonderful Time.

Moral: It is better to have loafed and lost than never to have loafed at all.

The Hen Who Wouldn't Fly

IN ONE of the Midwestern states there lived a speckled hen who was opposed to aviation. In her youth, watching a flight of wild geese going north, she had seen two fall (shot by hunters), go into a nose dive, and crash into the woods. So she went about the countryside saying that flying was very dangerous and that any fowl with any sense would stick to the solid earth. Every time she had to cross a concrete highway near her farm she ran on foot, screaming and squawking; sometimes she made it easily, at other times she was almost tagged by passing cars. Five of her sisters and three of her daughters' husbands were killed trying to cross the road in one month (July).

Before long an enterprising wood duck set up an airways service across the road and back. He charged five grains of corn to take a hen or a rooster across, two grains for a chick. But the speckled hen, who was a power in the community, went around clucking and cut-cutting and cadawcutting and telling everybody that air travel was not safe and never would be. She persuaded the chickens not to ride on the duck's back, and he failed in business and returned to the forests. Before the year was out, the speckled hen, four more of her sisters, three of her sons-in-law, four aunts, and a grandfather had been killed trying to cross the road on foot.

Moral: Use the wings God gave you, or nothing can save you.

The Glass in the Field

A SHORT time ago some builders, working on a studio in Connecticut, left a huge square of plate glass standing upright in a field one day. A goldfinch flying swiftly across the field struck the glass and was knocked cold. When he came to he hastened to his club, where an attendant bandaged his head and gave him a stiff drink. 'What the hell happened?' asked a sea-gull. 'I was flying across a meadow when all of a sudden the air crystallized on me,' said the goldfinch. The sea-gull and a hawk and an eagle all laughed heartily. A swallow listened gravely. 'For fifteen years, fledgling and bird, I've flown this country,' said the eagle, 'and I assure you there is no such thing as air crystallizing. Water, yes; air, no.' 'You were probably struck by a hailstone,' the hawk told the goldfinch. 'Or he may have had a stroke,' said the sea-gull. 'What do you think, swallow?' 'Why, I – I think maybe the air crystallized on him,' said the swallow. The large birds laughed so loudly that the goldfinch became annoyed and bet them each a dozen worms that they couldn't follow the course he had flown across the field without encountering the hardened atmosphere. They all took his bet; the swallow went along to watch. The sea-gull, the eagle, and the hawk decided to fly together over the route the goldfinch indicated. 'You come, too,' they said to the swallow. 'I—I—well, no,' said the swallow. 'I don't think I will.' So the three large birds took off together and they hit the glass together and they were all knocked cold.

Moral: He who hesitates is sometimes saved.

The Tortoise and the Hare

THERE was once a wise young tortoise who read in an ancient book about a tortoise who had beaten a hare in a race. He read all the other books he could find but in none of them was there any record of a hare who had beaten a tortoise. The wise young tortoise came to the natural conclusion that he could outrun a hare, so he set forth in search of one. In his wanderings he met many animals who were willing to race him: weasels, stoats, dachshunds, badger-boars, short-tailed field mice and ground squirrels. But when the tortoise asked if they could outrun a hare, they all said no, they couldn't (with the exception of a dachshund named Freddy, and nobody paid any attention to him). 'Well, I can,' said the tortoise, 'so there's no use wasting my time on you.' And he continued his search.

After many days, the tortoise finally encountered a hare and challenged him to a race. 'What are you going to use for legs?' asked the hare. 'Never mind that,' said the tortoise. 'Read this.' He showed the hare the story in the ancient book, complete with moral about the swift not always being so terribly fast. 'Tosh,' said the hare. 'You couldn't go fifty feet in an hour and a half, whereas I can go fifty feet in one and a fifth seconds.' 'Posh,' said the tortoise. 'You probably won't even finish second.' 'We'll see about that,' said the hare. So they marked off a course fifty feet long. All the other animals gathered around. A bull-frog set them on their marks, a gun dog fired a pistol, and they were off.

When the hare crossed the finish line, the tortoise had gone approximately eight and three-quarter inches.

Moral: A new broom may sweep clean, but never trust an old saw.

The Patient Bloodhound

IN MAY, 1937, a bloodhound who lived in Wapokoneta Falls, Ohio, was put on the trail of a man suspected of a certain crime. The bloodhound followed him to Akron, Cleveland, Buffalo, Syracuse, Rochester, Albany, and New York. The Westminster dog show was going on at the time but the bloodhound couldn't get to the garden because the man got on the first ship for Europe. The ship landed at Cherbourg and the bloodhound followed the man to Paris, Beauvais, Calais, Dover, London, Chester, Llandudno, Bettws-y-Coed, and Edinburgh, where the dog wasn't able to take in the international sheep trials. From Edinburgh, the bloodhound trailed the man to Liverpool, but since the man immediately got on a ship for New York, the dog didn't have a chance to explore the wonderful Liverpool smells.

In America again, the bloodhound traced the man to Teaneck, Tenafly, Nyack, and Peapack – where the dog didn't have time to run with the Peapack beagles. From Peapack the hound followed the man to Cincinnati, St Louis, Kansas City, St Louis, Cincinnati, Columbus, Akron, and finally back to Wapokoneta Falls. There the man was acquitted of the crime he had been followed for.

The bloodhound had developed fallen paw-pads and he was so worn out he could never again trail anything that was faster than a turtle. Furthermore, since he had gone through the world with his eyes and nose to the ground, he had missed all its beauty and excitement.

Moral: The paths of glory at least lead to the Grave, but the paths of duty may not get you Anywhere.

The Unicorn in the Garden

ONCE upon a sunny morning a man who sat in a breakfast nook looked up from his scrambled eggs to see a white unicorn with a golden horn quietly cropping the roses in the garden. The man went up to the bedroom where his wife was still asleep and woke her. 'There's a unicorn in the garden,' he said. 'Eating roses.' She opened one unfriendly eye and looked at him. 'The unicorn is a mythical beast,' she said, and turned her back on him. The man walked slowly downstairs and out into the garden. The unicorn was still there; he was now browsing among the tulips. 'Here, unicorn,' said the man, and he pulled up a lily and gave it to him. The unicorn ate it gravely. With a high heart, because there was a unicorn in his garden, the man went upstairs and roused his wife again. 'The unicorn,' he said, 'ate a lily.' His wife sat up in bed and looked at him, coldly. 'You are a booby,' she said, 'and I am going to have you put in the booby-hatch.' The man, who had never liked the words 'booby' and 'booby-hatch,' and who liked them even less on a shining morning when there was a unicorn in the garden, thought for a moment. 'We'll see about that,' he said. He walked over to the door. 'He has a golden horn in the middle of his forehead,' he told her. Then he went back to the garden to watch the unicorn; but the unicorn had gone away. The man sat down among the roses and went to sleep.

As soon as the husband had gone out of the house, the wife got up and dressed as fast as she could. She was very excited and there was a gloat in her eye. She telephoned the police and she telephoned a psychiatrist; she told them to hurry to her house and bring a strait-jacket. When the police and the psychiatrist arrived they sat down in chairs and looked at her, with great interest. 'My husband,' she said, 'saw a unicorn this morning.' The police looked at the psychiatrist and the psychiatrist looked at the police. 'He told me it ate a lily,' she said. The psychiatrist looked at the police and the police looked at the psychiatrist. 'He told me it had a golden horn in the middle of its forehead,' she said. At a solemn signal from the psychiatrist, the police leaped from their chairs and seized the wife. They had a hard time subduing her, for she put up a terrific struggle, but they finally subdued her. Just as they got her into the strait-jacket, the husband came back into the house.

'Did you tell your wife you saw a unicorn?' asked the police. 'Of course not,' said the husband. 'The unicorn is a mythical beast.' 'That's all I wanted to know,' said the psychiatrist. 'Take her away. I'm sorry, sir, but your wife is as crazy as a jay bird.' So they took her away, cursing and screaming, and shut her up in an institution. The husband lived happily ever after.

Moral: Don't count your boobies until they are hatched.

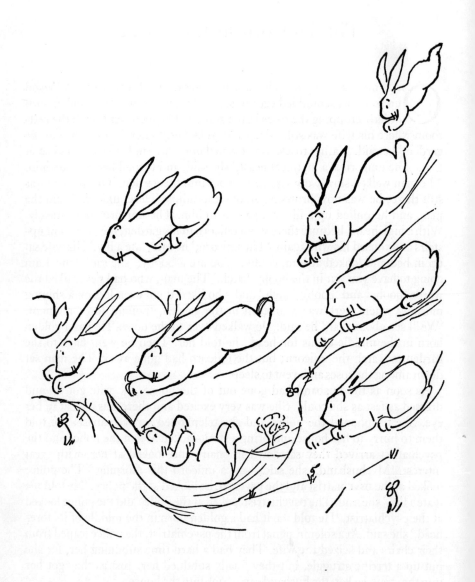

The Rabbits Who Caused All the Trouble

WITHIN the memory of the youngest child there was a family of rabbits who lived near a pack of wolves. The wolves announced that they did not like the way the rabbits were living. (The wolves were crazy about the way they themselves were living, because it was the only way to live.) One night several wolves were killed in an earthquake and this was blamed on the rabbits, for it is well known that rabbits pound on the ground with their hind legs and cause earthquakes. On another night one of the wolves was killed by a bolt of lightning and this was also blamed on the rabbits, for it is well known that lettuce-eaters cause lightning. The wolves threatened to civilize the rabbits if they didn't behave, and the rabbits decided to run away to a desert island. But the other animals, who lived at a great distance, shamed them, saying, 'You must stay where you are and be brave. This is no world for escapists. If the wolves attack you, we will come to your aid, in all probability.' So the rabbits continued to live near the wolves and one day there was a terrible flood which drowned a great many wolves. This was blamed on the rabbits, for it is well known that carrot-nibblers with long ears cause floods. The wolves descended on the rabbits, for their own good, and imprisoned them in a dark cave, for their own protection.

When nothing was heard about the rabbits for some weeks, the other animals demanded to know what had happened to them. The wolves replied that the rabbits had been eaten and since they had been eaten the affair was a purely internal matter. But the other animals warned that they might possibly unite against the wolves unless some reason was given for the destruction of the rabbits. So the wolves gave them one. 'They were trying to escape,' said the wolves, 'and, as you know, this is no world for escapists.'

Moral: Run, don't walk, to the nearest desert island.

The Hen and the Heavens

ONCE upon a time a little red hen was picking up stones and worms and seeds in a barnyard when something fell on her head. 'The heavens are falling down!' she shouted, and she began to run, still shouting, 'The heavens are falling down!' All the hens that she met and all the roosters and turkeys and ducks laughed at her, smugly, the way you laugh at one who is terrified when you aren't. 'What did you say?' they chortled. 'The heavens are falling down!' cried the little red hen. Finally a very pompous rooster said to her, 'Don't be silly, my dear, it was only a pea that fell on your head.' And he laughed and laughed and everybody else except the little red hen laughed. Then suddenly with an awful roar great chunks of crystallized cloud and huge blocks of icy blue sky began to drop on everybody from above, and everybody was killed, the laughing rooster and the little red hen and everybody else in the barnyard, for the heavens actually *were* falling down.

Moral : It wouldn't surprise me a bit if they did.

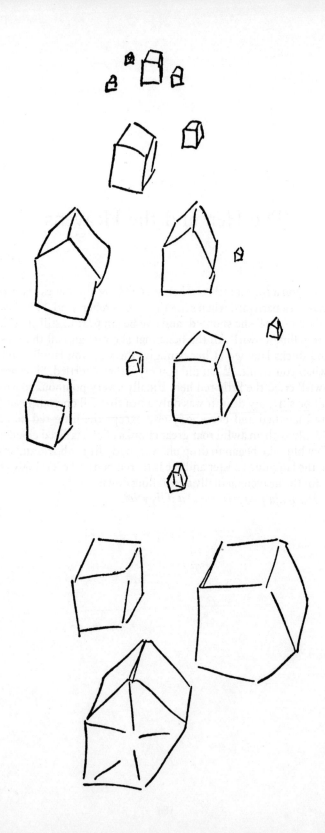

Excelsior

By HENRY WADSWORTH LONGFELLOW

The shades of night were falling fast,
As through an Alpine village passed
A youth, who bore, 'mid snow and ice,
A banner with the strange device –
Excelsior!

'Try not the pass,' the old man said;
'Dark lowers the tempest overhead;
The roaring torrent is deep and wide!'
And loud that clarion voice replied,
        Excelsior!

'O stay,' the maiden said, 'and rest
Thy weary head upon this breast!'
A tear stood in his bright blue eye,
But still he answered, with a sigh,
Excelsior!

'Beware the pine-tree's withered branch!
Beware the awful avalanche!'
This was the peasant's last good night:
A voice replied, far up the height,
       Excelsior!

At break of day, as heavenward
The pious monks of Saint Bernard
Uttered the oft-repeated prayer,
A voice cried through the startled air,
             Excelsior!

A traveller, by the faithful hound,
Half-buried in the snow was found,
Still grasping in his hand of ice
That banner with the strange device,
       Excelsior!

There in the twilight cold and grey,
Lifeless, but beautiful, he lay,
And from the sky, serene and far,
A voice fell, like a falling star –
       Excelsior!

The Sands o' Dee

By CHARLES KINGSLEY

'O Mary, go and call the cattle home,
    And call the cattle home,
    And call the cattle home,
    Across the sands o' Dee!'
The western wind was wild and dank wi' foam,
    And all alone went she.

The creeping tide came up along the sand,
   And o'er and o'er the sand,
   And round and round the sand,
  As far as eye could see;
The blinding mist came down and hid the land:
  And never home came she.

'O, is it weed, or fish, or floating hair –
    A tress o' golden hair,
     O' drownèd maiden's hair –
   Above the nets at sea?
Was never salmon yet that shone so fair
   Among the stakes on Dee.'

They rowed her in across the rolling foam,
   The cruel, crawling foam,
   The cruel, hungry foam,
  To her grave beside the sea;
But still the boatmen hear her call the cattle home
  Across the sands o' Dee.

Lochinvar

By Sir Walter Scott

O, young Lochinvar is come out of the west,
Through all the wide Border his steed was the best;
And, save his good broadsword, he weapon had none,
He rode all unarmed, and he rode all alone.
So faithful in love, and so dauntless in war,
There never was knight like the young Lochinvar.

But, ere he alighted at Netherby gate,
The bride had consented, the gallant came late;
For a laggard in love, and a dastard in war,
Was to wed the fair Ellen of brave Lochinvar.

So boldly he entered the Netherby Hall,
Among bridesmen, and kinsmen, and brothers, and all.
Then spoke the bride's father, his hand on his sword
(For the poor craven bridegroom said never a word),
'O come ye in peace here, or come ye in war,
Or to dance at our bridal, young Lord Lochinvar?'

'I long wooed your daughter, my suit you denied –
Love swells like the Solway, but ebbs like its tide –
And now I am come, with this lost love of mine,
To lead but one measure, drink one cup of wine.
There are maidens in Scotland more lovely by far,
That would gladly be bride to the young Lochinvar.'

The bride kissed the goblet; the knight took it up,
He quaffed off the wine, and threw down the cup.
She looked down to blush, and she looked up to sigh,
With a smile on her lips, and a tear in her eye.
He took her soft hand, ere her mother could bar –
'Now tread we a measure,' said young Lochinvar.

So stately his form, and so lovely her face,
That never a hall such a galliard did grace;
While her mother did fret, and her father did fume,
And the bridegroom stood dangling his bonnet and plume . . .

One touch to her hand, and one word in her ear,
When they reached the hall door, and the charger stood near;
So light to the croupe the fair lady he swung,
So light to the saddle before her he sprung;
'She is won! we are gone! Over bank, bush, and scaur;
They'll have fleet steeds that follow,' quoth young Lochinvar.

There was mounting 'mong Graemes of the Netherby clan;
Forsters, Fenwicks, and Musgraves, they rode and they ran;
There was racing and chasing on Cannobie Lee,
But the lost bride of Netherby ne'er did they see.
So daring in love, and so dauntless in war,
Have ye e'er heard of gallant like young Lochinvar?

Locksley Hall

By ALFRED, LORD TENNYSON

Comrades, leave me here a little, while as yet 'tis early morn;
Leave me here, and when you want me, sound upon the bugle horn.

'Tis the place, and all around it, as of old, the curlews call,
Dreary gleams about the moorland, flying over Locksley Hall.

208

In the spring a livelier iris changes on the burnished dove;
In the spring a young man's fancy lightly turns to thoughts of love.

O my cousin, shallow-hearted! O, my Amy, mine no more!
O the dreary, dreary moorland! O the barren, barren shore!

Is it well to wish thee happy? – having known me; to decline
On a range of lower feelings and a narrower heart than mine!

As the husband is, the wife is; thou art mated with a clown,
And the grossness of his nature will have weight to drag thee down.

Like a dog, he hunts in dreams; and thou art staring at the wall,
Where the dying night-lamp flickers, and the shadows rise and fall.

Then a hand shall pass before thee, pointing to his drunken sleep,
To thy widowed marriage-pillows, to the tears that thou wilt weep.

Hark! my merry comrades call me, sounding on the bugle-horn, –
They to whom my foolish passion were a target for their scorn.

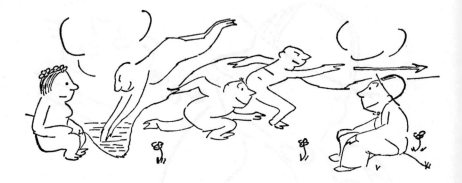

. . . I will take some savage woman, she shall rear my dusky race.

Iron-jointed, supple-sinewed, they shall dive, and they shall run,
Catch the wild goat by the hair, and hurl their lances in the sun.

Fool, again the dream, the fancy! but I *know* my words are wild . . .

O, I see the crescent promise of my spirit hath not set;
Ancient founts of inspiration well through all my fancy yet.

. . . a long farewell to Locksley Hall!
Now for me the woods may wither, now for me the roof-tree fall.

Comes a vapour from the margin, blackening over heath and holt,
Cramming all the blast before it, in its breast a thunderbolt.

Let it fall on Locksley Hall, with rain or hail, or fire or snow;
For the mighty wind arises, roaring seaward, and I go.

'Oh When I Was . . . ,'[1]

By A. E. HOUSMAN

Oh when I was in love with you,
Then I was clean and brave,
And miles around the wonder grew
How well did I behave.

[1] From *A Shropshire Lad*, by A. E. Housman, by permission of Jonathan Cape Ltd.

And now the fancy passes by,
And nothing will remain,
And miles around they'll say that I
Am quite myself again.

Curfew Must Not Ring Tonight

By ROSE HARTWICK THORPE

'Sexton,' Bessie's white lips faltered, pointing to the prison old,
With its turrets tall and gloomy, with its walls dark, damp, and cold,
'I've a lover in that prison, doomed this very night to die,
At the ringing of the Curfew, and no earthly help is nigh;
Cromwell will not come till sunset,' and her lips grew strangely white
As she breathed the husky whisper: –

'Curfew must not ring tonight.'

'Bessie,' calmly spoke the sexton – every word pierced her young heart
Like the piercing of an arrow, like a deadly poisoned dart –
'Long, long years I've rung the Curfew from that gloomy, shadowed tower;
Every evening, just at sunset, it has told the twilight hour;
I have done my duty ever, tried to do it just and right,
Now I'm old I will not falter –
                                        Curfew, it must ring tonight.'

With quick step she bounded forward, sprang within the old church door,
Left the old man treading slowly paths so oft he'd trod before;
Not one moment paused the maiden, but with eye and cheek aglow
Mounted up the gloomy tower, where the bell swung to and fro:
As she climbed the dusty ladder, on which fell no ray of light,
Up and up – her white lips saying: –

'Curfew must not ring tonight.'

She has reached the topmost ladder; o'er her hangs the great dark bell;
Awful is the gloom beneath her, like the pathway down to hell.
Lo, the ponderous tongue is swinging – 'tis the hour of Curfew now,
And the sight has chilled her bosom, stopped her breath, and paled her brow.
Shall she let it ring? No, never! flash her eyes with sudden light,
As she springs and grasps it firmly –

                        'Curfew shall not ring tonight!'

Out she swung – far out; the city seemed a speck of light below,
There 'twixt heaven and earth suspended as the bell swung to and fro,
And the sexton at the bell rope, old and deaf, heard not the bell,
Sadly thought, 'That twilight Curfew rang young Basil's funeral knell.'
Still the maiden clung more firmly and with trembling lips so white,
Said to hush her heart's wild throbbing: –

'Curfew shall not ring tonight!'

O'er the distant hills came Cromwell; Bessie sees him, and her brow,
Lately white with fear and anguish, has no anxious traces now.
At his feet she tells her story, shows her hands all bruised and torn;
And her face so sweet and pleading, yet with sorrow pale and worn,
Touched his heart with sudden pity, lit his eyes with misty light:
'Go! your lover lives,' said Cromwell,
                            'Curfew shall not ring tonight.'

Wide they flung the massive portal; led the prisoner forth to die –
All his bright young life before him. 'Neath the darkening English sky
Bessie comes with flying footsteps, eyes aglow with love-light sweet;
Kneeling on the turf beside him, lays his pardon at his feet.
In his brave, strong arms he clasped her, kissed the face upturned and white,
Whispered, 'Darling, you have saved me –

                    Curfew will not ring tonight!'

Barbara Frietchie

By JOHN GREENLEAF WHITTIER

On that pleasant morn of the early fall
When Lee marched over the mountain wall;

Over the mountains winding down,
Horse and foot, into Frederick town,

Forty flags with their silver stars,
Forty flags with their crimson bars,

Flapped in the morning wind . . .

. . . the sun
Of noon looked down, and saw not one.

Up rose old Barbara Frietchie then,
Bowed with her fourscore years and ten;

Bravest of all in Frederick town,
She took up the flag the men hauled down;

In her attic window the staff she set,
To show that one heart was loyal yet.

Up the street came the rebel tread,
Stonewall Jackson riding ahead.

Under his slouched hat left and right
He glanced; the old flag met his sight.

'Halt!' – the dust-brown ranks stood fast;
'Fire!' – out blazed the rifle-blast.

It shivered the window, pane and sash;
It rent the banner with seam and gash.

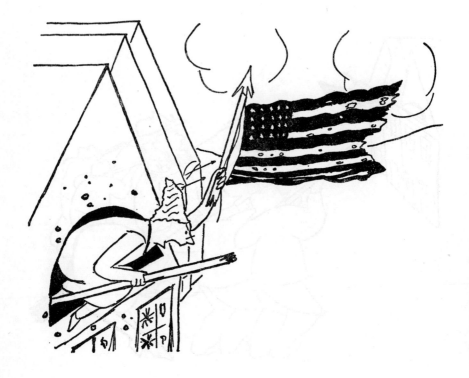

Quick, as it fell, from the broken staff
Dame Barbara snatched the silken scarf.

She leaned far out on the window-sill,
And shook it forth with a royal will.

'Shoot, if you must, this old grey head,
But spare your country's flag,' she said.

A shade of sadness, a blush of shame,
Over the face of the leader came;

The nobler nature within him stirred
To life at that woman's deed and word;

'Who touches a hair of yon grey head
Dies like a dog! March on!' he said.

All day long through Frederick street
Sounded the tread of marching feet:

All day long that free flag tossed
Over the heads of the rebel host.

Ever its torn folds rose and fell
On the loyal winds that loved it well;

And through the hill-gaps sunset light
Shone over it with a warm good-night . . .

The Glove and the Lions

By LEIGH HUNT

King Francis was a hearty king, and loved a royal sport,
And one day, as his lions fought, sat looking at the court.
The nobles filled the benches, and the ladies in their pride,
And 'mongst them sat the Count de Lorge, with one for whom he sighed:
And truly 'twas a gallant thing to see that crowning show,
Valour and love, and a king above, and the royal beasts below.

Ramped and roared the lions, with horrid laughing jaws;
They bit, they glared, gave blows like beams, a wind went with their paws;
With wallowing might and stifled roar they rolled on one another,
Till all the pit with sand and mane was in a thunderous smother.

The bloody foam above the bars came whisking through the air;
Said Francis then, 'Faith, gentlemen, we're better here than there.'

234

De Lorge's love o'erheard the King, a beauteous lively dame,
With smiling lips and sharp bright eyes, which always seemed the same;
She thought, 'The Count, my lover, is brave as brave can be;
He surely would do wondrous things to show his love of me;
King, ladies, lovers, all look on; the occasion is divine;
I'll drop my glove, to prove his love; great glory will be mine.'
She dropped her glove, to prove his love, then looked at him and smiled;

He bowed, and in a moment leaped among the lions wild;

The leap was quick, return was quick, he has regained his place,
Then threw the glove, but not with love, right in the lady's face.
'By Heaven,' said Francis, 'rightly done!' and he rose from where he sat;
'No love,' quoth he, 'but vanity, sets love a task like that.'

Ben Bolt

By THOMAS DUNN ENGLISH

Don't you remember sweet Alice, Ben Bolt –
  Sweet Alice whose hair was so brown,
Who wept with delight when you gave her a smile,

And trembled with fear at your frown?

In the old churchyard in the valley, Ben Bolt,
  In a corner obscure and alone,
They have fitted a slab of the granite so grey
  And Alice lies under the stone.

I

And don't you remember the school, Ben Bolt,
  With the master so cruel and grim,
And the shaded nook in the running brook
  Where the children went to swim?

241

Grass grows on the master's grave, Ben Bolt,
The spring of the brook is dry,

And of all the boys who were schoolmates then
There are only you and I.

Men, Women and Dogs

Preface

I had long ago made my design for what was to become of me when the Reaper had swung his scythe through my neck. I was to be cremated after death — at least, I always trusted it would be after death. I even left instructions to this effect in my will, a document that might otherwise have been writ in a large, schoolgirl backhand on the head of a pin. Now, with the publication of this book, I must change those words, and with them my plans for the long, long rest. Now I want to be left as approximately is, so I may be buried in a prominent place on a travelled thoroughfare through a wildly popular cemetery. Above me I want a big white stone – you will see why it must be big – on which I want carven in clear letters: 'Uncover before this dust, for when it was a woman, it was doubly honoured. Twice in life, it was given to her below to introduce the work of James Thurber.* Reader, who around here, including you, can tie that record?'

I like to think of my shining tombstone. It gives me, as you might say, something to live for.

It gives me, also, a lovely diversion with which to while away eternity. I have always found it best to be quiet and alone with a Thurber drawing, that I may seek to fathom what went on in the lives of the characters depicted, before the artist chose his moment for setting them down for ever. Sometimes I wonder if eternity is going to be half long enough for me to make anything near a reasonable guess.

Consider, for instance, the picture showing a man, his wife, and a male guest. They are standing in a something less than gracious enclosure, furnished mainly with a bookcase apparently ordered by mail from the company that did such notable work in Pisa. And on top of the bookcase is a woman on all fours. So help me God, there is a woman on all fours on top of the bookcase. And the host is saying, 'That's my first wife up there, and this is the *present* Mrs Harris.'†

Well, what would you do about that? I worked for a while on the theory that the first Mrs Harris, the one on top of the bookcase, was dead and stuffed, but my heart was never really in it. In the first place, she doesn't look stuffed; she looks limp. She looks limp and resigned and only a trifle bewildered. She has the look of having been where she is for a long time. How do they feed her? Do they put a cover over her at night? And what made her

*See Volume Two, Introduction to *The Seal in the Bedroom*
†See page 418

husband dispose of her and take his present mate? The new spouse is no more sweetly shaped, no more elegantly clothed, no more carefully coiffed than the old one. They look equally terrible. Could it be that the first wife had a habit of crouching on top of bookcases, and one day he could stand it no longer and said, 'Oh, all right, if *that's* what you want to do,' and flung out and got married again? What does the new wife, that *present* Mrs Harris, think of the arrangement? She looks not too sensitive, luckily for her, but she must know, when her friends come in for bridge, that her household is not overly conventional. And the bookcase is full of books. What books, in heaven's name, what books do such people read?

You understand what I mean when I say that eternity will not be long enough for my figuring?

Or take again, for instance, the fine drawing of the court scene – the mild judge, the cocksure lawyer, and the aghast witness. 'Perhaps *this* will refresh your memory,' the lawyer is saying in his nasty way, as he produces, no doubt with a flourish, a kangaroo – a tender, young, innocent, wistful kangaroo. What, I ask you, what can lie back of that?

I give up such things; or at least I say I do. But I find I keep on working at them through the white nights.

I cannot say that James Thurber's work has progressed. No more could I say that the new moon is more exquisite than the last one. I will not be so illiterate as to expand the perfect into the more perfect.

But I do say I see certain changes in his characters. The men seem to me, in the main, a little smaller, even a little more innocent, even a little more willing to please than before. Also, the *pince nez*, superbly done by a slanted line across the nose, seems to be more widely worn by them. It is to be hoped they do not turn to glasses to obtain a better view of their women. Because the ladies are increasingly awful. They get worse and worse, as we sit here. And there they are behaving, with never a moment's doubt, like *femmes fatales*.

It is hard for me to comment on The War Between Men and Women, for naturally I am partisan because of my sex. It is tough going for me to see the women in retreat, routed; finally to witness the woman general, mounted on that curious horse, doubtless a spy, surrendering her baseball bat to the late enemy. I comforted myself with the fact that no man had equalled the strange wild daring of Mrs Pritchard's Leap. Then I realized I needed no such comfort. For if you study this glorious battle sequence closely, you will realize that the women, rout or no rout, surrender or no surrender, are the real winners. I suppose I understand that we are licked only when I say I doubt if our victory is for the best.

Mr Thurber's animals have not changed with his new work; they have just got more so. My heart used to grow soft at the sight of his dogs; now it turns completely liquid. I give you, for the third time in instance, that darling who looks cautiously out his door, curves his paw to the snowstorm, and turns his poor, bewildered head up to the spewing heavens. There is nowhere else existent an innocence like to that of Thurber animals. . . . Even that strange, square beast, beside which lie the neat hat, the cold pipe, the empty shoe, and in front of which stands the stern woman, her hands on her hips, demanding, 'What have you done with Dr Millmoss?' . . .*

You see how easy it is to say 'Thurber animals.' The artist has gone into the language. How often we say, 'He's a Thurber man' or 'Look at that woman – she's a perfect Thurber,' and, God help us and them, we are always understood. We need say no more about them. We have been taught to recognize them by the master. Possibly Thurber humans and animals existed before the artist drew them. I am willing to concede that they may have, but I am strong to say that I doubt it. I believe that Nature again has been shown her place, and has gone into her old specialty of imitating art.

Two of my best friends are dogs of a whirling mélange of ancestry. They are short in the paw, long and wavering in the body, heavy and worried in the head. They are willing, useless, and irresistible. Nobody ever asks their breed. 'Oh, look at the Thurber dogs,' people say who see them for the first time. . . . If I were Mr Thurber, I should rather have my name used that way even than have it bracketed, as it has so often been, with that of Matisse. . . .

I think you must know how I feel to be in the same book with a fine artist, to be standing here, this moment and forever, presenting his finest work. That is why I choke a little when I say, and with doubled privilege and doubled pride that I may say it again: Ladies and gentlemen, Mr James Thurber.

DOROTHY PARKER

New York, 1943

*See page 421

'*Well*, don't *come and look at the rainbow then, you big ape!*'

'She has the true Emily Dickinson spirit except that she gets fed
up occasionally.'

'All right, all right, try it that way! Go ahead and try it that way!'

'They were shot by George's uncle – the one that lost his mind.'

'Have you no code, man?'

'It's a naïve domestic Burgundy without any breeding, but I think you'll be amused by its presumption.'

252

'You're going a bit far, Miss Blanchard.'

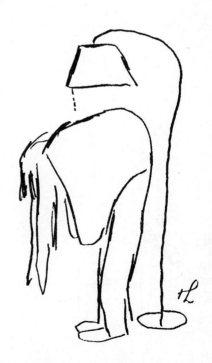

'*Bang! Bang! Bang!*'

'You gah dam pussy cats!'

'It's Lida Bascom's husband – he's frightfully unhappy.'

'*What do you want to be inscrutable* for, *Marcia?*'

'*Look out! Here they come again!*'

'*I'm afraid you are in the wrong apartment, Madam.*'

'*Why do you keep raising me when you* know *I'm bluffing?*'

'Why don't you wait and see what becomes of your own generation
before you jump on mine?'

'*There's no use you trying to save* me, *my good man.*'

'*I'm wearing gloves because I don't want to leave any fingerprints around.*'

'*I come from haunts of coot and hern!*'

'I was voted the biggest heel in school, Mamma!'

'You and your premonitions!'

'She's reading some novel that's breaking her heart, but we don't
know where she hides it.'

'They're going to put you away if you don't quit acting like this.'

'You were wonderful at the Gardners' last night, Fred, when you turned on the charm.'

'*Oh, Doctor* Conroy – look*!*'

'You haven't got the face for it, for one thing.'

'*Of course he's terribly nervous, but I'm sure he meant it as a pass at me.*'

'Here! Here! There's a place for that, sir!'

'*Maybe you don't have charm, Lily, but you're enigmatic.*'

'One of you men in the kitchen give the officer another drink!'

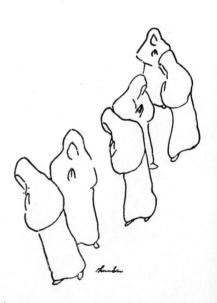

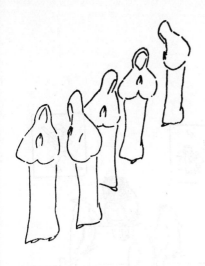

'What do four ones beat?'

'*Good* morning, *my feathered friends!*'

'I can't get in touch with your uncle, but there's a horse here that wants to say hello.'

'I'm so glad you're a writer – I'm just full of themes and ideas.'

'I drew three more clubs and filled my flush!'

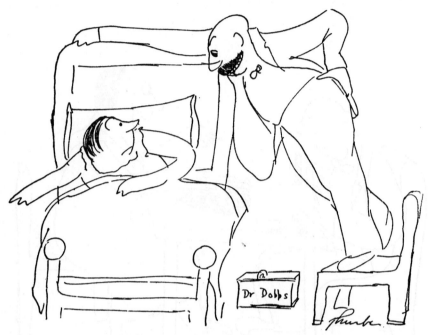

'You're not my patient, you're my meat, Mrs Quist!'

'Why don't you let me know what it is, if it's so pleasant?'

'*I'll thank you to keep your mother's name out of this!*'

'. . . and keep me a normal, healthy girl.'

'That martyred look won't get you anywhere with me!'

'This is Miss Jones, Doctor – I want you to cheer her up. She's
been through hell recently.'

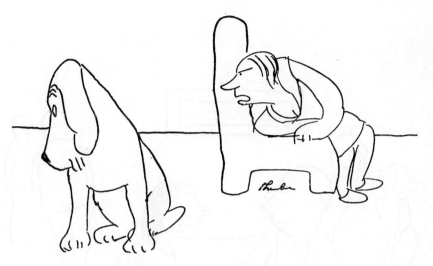

'*For Heaven's sake, why don't you go outdoors and trace something?*'

'I think of you as being enormously alive.'

'*Ooooo*, guesties!'

'*If you can keep a secret, I'll tell you how my husband died.*'

'*What's come over you since Friday, Miss Schemke?*'

'Here's to m' first wife, darling – she only wore one hat, God bless 'er!'

'The trouble with me is I can never say no.'

'I'm Virgo with the moon in Aries, if that will help you any.'

'There go the most intelligent of all animals.'

'*My wife always has me shadowed on Valentine's Day.*'

'*Why did I ever marry below my emotional level!*'

'One of us ought to be a Boswell, taking this all down.'

'I'd feel a great deal easier if her husband hadn't gone to bed.'

'And this is Tom Weatherby, an old beau of your mother's. He
never got to first base.'

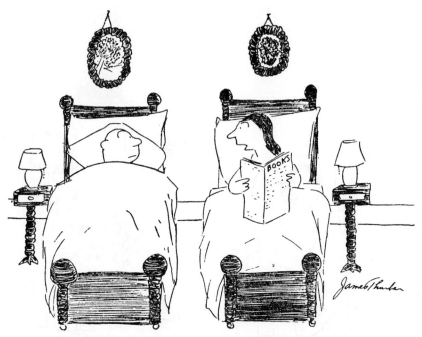

'What the hell ever happened to the old-fashioned love story?'

'Shut up, Prince! What's biting you?'

'I want you to know Mr Thrawn, Mr Simms. Mr Thrawn claims
to be a werewolf.'

'My heart has been a stick of wood since May, 1927, Miss Prentice.'

'*Darling, I seem to have this rabbit.*'

'He's just heard about the changes that are taking place in civilization.'

Destinations

'I don't know them either, dear, but there may be some very simple
explanation.'

'I love the idea of there being two sexes, don't you?'

304

'Yoo-hoo – George! Chanticleer!'

The enemies

'*And* this *is my* father, *Mr Williams* – *home from the wars or something.*'

'*I don't want him to be comfortable if he's going to look too funny.*'

'*I can't* stand *to have my pulse felt, Doctor!*'

'*You wait here and I'll bring the etchings down.*'

'*Unhappy woman!*'

'*See you at the barricades, Mr Whitsonby!*'

'*Have you seen my pistol, Honey-bun?*'

'I wouldn't rent this room to everybody, Mr Spencer. This is where my husband lost his mind.'

'I don't want any part of it!'

'I'd dread falling under your spell, Mr Pierson.'

'I said the hounds of Spring are on Winter's traces – but let it pass,
let it pass!'

'*I wonder what dark flowers grow in the mysterious caverns of your soul.*'

'I thought you'd enjoy Miss Perrish, darling. She has a constant ringing in her ears, too.'

'I brought a couple of midgets – do you mind?'

'What do you want me to do with your remains, George?'

'*He knows all about art, but he doesn't know what he likes.*'

'*Father would be much happier if you wouldn't.*'

'This gentleman was kind enough to see me home, darling.'

'Well, it makes a difference to me!'

319

'*It's our own story exactly! He bold as a hawk, she soft as the dawn.*'

'*Miss Gorce is in the embalming game.*'

'I beg to differ with you!'

'*Every day is Arbor Day to Mr Chisholm.*'

'*I never really rallied after the birth of my first child.*'

'Other end, Mr Pemberton.'

'Welcome back to the old water hole, Mrs Bixby!'

324

'Well, who made *the magic go out of our marriage – you or me?*'

'*Le cœur a ses raisons, Mrs Bence, que la raison ne connaît pas.*'

'Well, if I called the wrong number, why did you answer the phone?'

'Would you step over here a second, Waldo? This one's bearing cotton.'

'He doesn't believe a single word he's read in the past ten years.'

'I do love you. I just don't feel like talking military tactics with you.'

'Now I'm going to go in over your horns!'

'*Alice can be a little* girl *Commando in your game, Donald.*'

'Dr Livingstone, I presume?'

'Yoo-hoo, it's me and the ape man.'

'*I tell you there isn't going to* be *any insurrection.*'

355

'*Mother, this is Tristram.*'

'I'm offering you sanctuary, Dr Mason.'

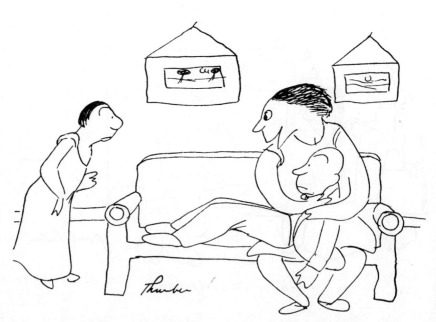

'Your husband has talked about nothing but you, Mrs Miller.'

'*With a hey-nonny-nonny and a nuts to you!*'

'*Which you am I talking to now?*'

'*You can't* make *me* go home!'

'You can tell me if I bend my knees, Sugar.'

'The party's breaking up, darling.'

338

'*Look out, Harry!*'

'*Tell her she's afraid to come out and fight!*'

'This is not the real me you're seeing, Mrs Clisbie.'

'And this is the little woman.'

'She's been this way ever since she saw "Camille." '

'I assume then, that you regard yourself as omniscient. If I am
wrong, correct me!'

'He's given up everything for a whole year.'

'George! If that's you I'll never forgive you!'

'*My wife wants to spend Hallowe'en with her first husband.*'

'*My analyst is crazy to meet you, darling.*'

'She predicts either war or the end of the world in October.'

'Perhaps this will refresh your memory.'

'Why, Mr Spears, how cute you look!'

'It's a strange mood she's in, kind of a cross between Baby Doll
and Elizabeth Barrett Browning'

'*Dance with the nice man's little boy, dear.*'

'He's so charming it gives you the creeps.'

'Well, you see, the story really goes back to when I was a teensy-
weensy little girl.'

'Do you people mind if I take off some of these hot clothes?'

'Will you please cease calling me Sweetie Pie in public?'

'It goes, "Build thee some stately mansions, O my soul."'

'Hello, darling – woolgathering?'

'He doesn't know anything except facts.'

'Laissez faire and let laissez faire is what *I* believe in.'

'Why, I never dreamed your union had been blessed with issue!'

351

'She built up her personality but she's undermined her character.'

'*He hates people.*'

'I say she used to be no better than she ought to be, but she is now.'

'Sorry, partner!'

'It's Parkins, sir; we're 'aving a bit of a time below stairs.'

'*I suppose all that you men think about is war.*'

The Hound and The Hat

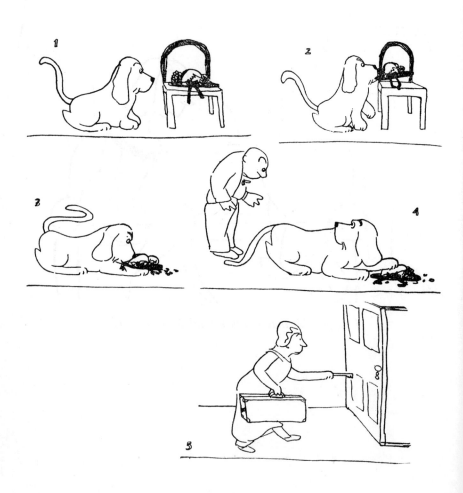

The Masculine Approach

The Candy-and-Flowers Campaign

*The I'm-Drinking-Myself-to-Death-and-Nobody-Can-Stop-Me
Method*

The Strong, Silent System

The Pawing System

The Strange-Fascination Technique

The You'll-Never-See-Me-Again Tactics

The Heroic, or Dangers-I-Have-Known, Method

The Let-'Em-Wait-and-Wonder Plan

The Unhappy-Childhood Story

The Indifference Attitude

The Letter-Writing Method

The Man-of-the-World, or Ordering-in-French, Manœuvre

The Sweep-'Em-Off-Their-Feet Method

The Her-Two-Little-Hands-in-His-Huge-Ones Pass

The Sudden Onslaught

The Continental-Manners Technique

The I'm-Not-Good-Enough-for-You Announcement

The Just-a-Little-Boy System

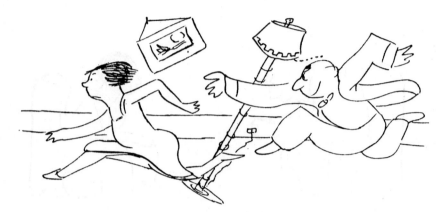

The Harpo Marx Attack

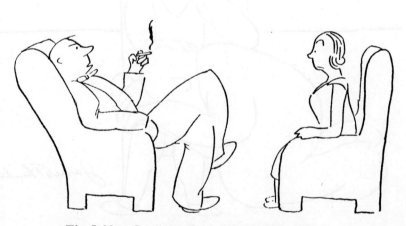

The I-May-Go-Away-for-a-Year-or-Two Move

First Aid

First Aid

'*In first-aid class today we learned eleven different ways to poison people.*'

'Well, you're not going to try the fireman's lift on me!'

'I think he's stopped breathing. What do I do now?'

'How's about going somewhere and trying traction splints on each
other, Miss Bryson?'

The War Between Men and Women

I. *The Overt Act*

II. *The Battle on the Stairs*

III. The Fight in the Grocery

IV. Men's G.H.Q.

V. Women's G.H.Q.

VI. Capture of three physics professors

VII. Surrender of three blondes

VIII. The Battle of Labrador

IX. The Spy

X. Mrs Pritchard's Leap

XI. Zero Hour – Connecticut

XII. *The Sniper*

XIII. *Parley*

XIV. Gettysberg

XV. Retreat

XVI. Rout

XVII. Surrender

The Beast in Me and Other Animals

A COLLECTION OF PIECES AND
DRAWINGS ABOUT HUMAN BEINGS
AND LESS ALARMING CREATURES

FOR RONNIE AND JANEY WILLIAMS
IN MEMORY OF THE SERENE HOURS
AT FELICITY HALL

Am Not I Your Rosalind?

'"A RARE find is an able wife",' George Thorne recited. 'There are cigarettes in that box, Fred.'
'I got some right here.' Fred Stanton pulled a pack from his pocket.
Thorne walked over, snapped his lighter, and held the flame for his guest.
' "A rare find is an able wife",' he began again. 'She rises early and pays off the
servants, and so on, but she invariably mucks up the cocktail hour. I'll stir up
some more Martinis for us.' He went over to the bar. 'They'll be up there a
good half hour. Let 'em catch up.'

Stanton watched his host's ritual with bottles, ice, and shaker. 'Lydia
always shows her friends over the house, too,' he said, 'even if they've seen
everything a hundred times.'

'Pride of possession.' Thorne stirred his mixture thoughtfully. 'These are
my jewels, and so on. I gave Ann an old lace fan when we were in Rome before
the war. Too fragile to handle, so she's just had it shadow-boxed. That'll take
up a good fifteen minutes. Then, there's the Landeck drypoint in the hall up
there.

'Thanks.' Stanton studied the cocktail pouring into his glass.

Thorne filled his own glass, set it and the shaker down, and went out into
the hall and frowned up the stairs.

'I wouldn't yell at 'em,' Stanton said. 'Women don't like to be yelled at.'

'Ann!' Thorne called. There was no answer, no sound from upstairs.
Thorne came back into the room and picked up his glass. 'To the ladies!' he
declaimed. 'We can drink with 'em or without 'em.'

'Women like to do things in the house their own way,' Stanton brought out
after some thought. 'That's a good cocktail.'

Thorne walked over and filled his guest's glass again. 'O.K.?'

'Perfect.'

Thorne refilled his own glass. 'You're oversimplifying a pretty profound
difference, Fred. Did you ever see directors at a board meeting exclaiming over
a perfectly darling new water cooler or a desk calendar just too cunning for
words?'

Stanton stirred uneasily and recrossed his legs. 'How do you shadow-box
a fan?' he asked after an obvious search for something to turn the conversation.

'You set it in a deep frame against a rose-coloured background,' Thorne
explained. 'Effective and expensive.' He glanced at his wristwatch and went
out again to the bottom of the stairs. 'Hey! Girls!' he yelled. 'Ann! It's seven-
thirty, for heaven's sake!'

A faint 'Shut up' drifted down from somewhere above. Stanton was sitting on the edge of his chair looking unhappy when his host came back, saying, 'A woman should be yelled at regularly, like an umpire – to paraphrase Noël Coward. Clears the air. Here.'

'Thanks,' said Stanton.

'Ann snaps back – I'll mix some more – but what the hell. Are they dry enough for you? She's got temperament – you know that – but I like it.' He went to the bar after swallowing his drink.

'Lydia's got temperament, too,' Stanton said defensively.

'Seems awful calm and levelheaded.' Thorne poured the last measure of gin into the shaker.

'Lydia's got a lot – a lot of variety,' Stanton said, sitting up straighter.

'Oh, sure, sure,' Thorne said, stirring. 'Lydia's a swell gal.'

'Lydia, you know, Lydia' – Stanton's left hand seemed to be trying to pull out of the air an instance of his wife's variety – 'Lydia played Rosalind in her senior-class play when she was in high school,' he said loudly. And, apparently surprised at his outburst, and embarrassed, he lit a cigarette with unnecessary care. 'Oh, that was twenty, twenty-one years ago, in Binghamton. Played only one performance, of course. Every class –'

'For God's sake, this is wonderful!' Thorne cut in. 'This is really wonderful! Ann was Rosalind, too, in *her* senior-class play, in a high school in Nebraska. For God's sake! Hold out your glass.'

'Thanks,' said Stanton. He had the expression of a man who has unwarily touched something old and precious, like an heirloom, and seen it suddenly fall apart.

'Both the girls were born in 1919, so they must have been ranting and posturing at practically the same time,' Thorne cried.

'I don't know that we better mention it,' Stanton said. 'You know how women are.'

Thorne laughed gleefully. 'What I want to find out is how women *were*, and I got just exactly the right thing. Do you know what a sound mirror is?'

'Have you got one of those wire recorders?' Stanton asked apprehensively. 'You could never get Lydia to talk into it. She'd never do that.'

'Look, you get a hambo high, any hambo, and he'll act.' Thorne chortled.

'After all, this was years ago,' Stanton said.

'Here they come. Leave it to me.' Thorne winked at him.

'If I were you –' Stanton began.

The two women came down the stairs and into the room laughing and talking.

'You don't know what you got coming to you,' Thorne said.

'Fred, you simply *must* see the perfectly lovely fan George got Ann in Rome!' Lydia cried.

'What's the matter – are the drinks that bad?' Ann asked her husband.

'The drinks are excellent,' Stanton said. 'Excellent.'

Thorne went to the bar, chuckling.

'Has he rigged up a booby trap, or is he just merry and gay?' Ann said to Stanton.

'What's the matter with *you*, Fred?' his wife demanded. 'You look worried. Did Mickey Mantle die, or something?'

'George has been showing off, probably,' Ann said.

Thorne gave each of the women a glass and filled it up.

'No more for me,' Stanton said, raising his hand.

'Come on, we're going to have toasts, old boy. Here.'

'Thanks.' Stanton sighed.

'I was doing that big scene of mine from "A Night at an Inn",' Thorne told his wife.

'George was all over the stage in college,' Ann said. 'He was picked as the man most likely to flop out of town.' The two women laughed, Thorne grinned, and Stanton shifted in his chair.

'We are poor little hams that have lost our way,' Thorne said, bowing to the women. 'Raise glasses.' Lydia and Ann looked at him. Stanton stared at the floor.

'What are you mumbling about?' Ann said.

'To the two fairest Rosalinds who ever strutted their little hour!'

'George!' Ann made a gavel rap of the name.

Then, suddenly, the two women looked at each other. There was a swift, almost reflex interchange of appraisal. It was as if each had clicked on and off the searching beam of a flashlight.

'Did you play Rosalind, too?' Ann cried.

'I'm afraid I did.' Lydia laughed. They laughed together.

'I think Rosalind is really horribly boring,' Lydia said. She looked at her husband, but he wouldn't meet her eyes.

'It's terribly hard to make her *appealing*,' Ann said. 'She's like Diana of the Crossways in a way. Didn't you *hate* Diana of the Crossways?'

Thorne went around draining the shaker, and moved tentatively to the bar. He could tell that it was all right to mix another round when Ann didn't say anything.

'Mickey Mantle isn't any Tris Speaker, but he's better than Di Maggio for my money,' said Stanton.

'Rosalind is one of the first ten aggressive ladies in literature.' Thorne had no intention of letting Diana or Mantle sidetrack the topic of conversation. 'That's what makes her a hell of a challenge to an actress. Being aggressive, she's also gabby, and that makes it a fat part.'

'George's descriptions are always so charming,' Ann said.

'Any child in her teens could enchant the Parent-Teacher Association by being cute as a little red wagon,' Thorne said.

'Oh, for God's sake, George!' Ann spanked out a cigarette she had just lighted.

'Anybody can be precocious,' Thorne went on. 'The real test comes in the years of maturity.'

'I know what you're up to, but it isn't going to work.' Ann turned to Lydia. 'He has one of those damn recorders, and he thinks he'll get us a little tight and make us perform.'

'You talk into it, turn a gadget, and – zip! – your voice comes out clear and perfect as a bell,' George explained.

'Really?' Lydia said.

'They used 'em in the Air Corps,' Stanton put in. 'Combat reports. Invented for that purpose.'

'George'll do Jeeter Lester for you at the drop of a hat,' Ann said. 'And that big going-to-pieces scene from "What Price Glory?" '

Lydia, holding out her glass, laughed in a higher key than before. 'Goodness,' she said, 'I haven't done a thing since college.'

'College?' Ann gave her the appraising glance again.

'I don't know why Fred didn't bring it *all* out, in his cups.' Lydia gave a little disparaging laugh. 'Yes, I did Nora in "A Doll's House," and Candida.'

'Well!' Ann made a polite quaver of the exclamation. She held out her glass. A white-coated coloured man appeared at the dining-room door.

'Herbert, would you ask Florence if she'll give us fifteen minutes more?' Ann said. He nodded and went away.

'There are several makes, all of them hard to get,' Stanton said, and coughed.

'I simply didn't have the time for it in college.' Ann waved it all away lightly with her left hand. 'So many *other* outside activities.'

Lydia brushed from her skirt a thread that was not there. 'Of course,' she said quietly.

Thorne stood grinning at his wife.

'We'll have time for another quick round,' she said. She looked coolly at Lydia. 'The wine can stand a bit more chilling.'

The two women smiled at each other, brightly. Thorne, mixing the Martinis, began to hum, 'I can do anything better than you. Anything you can do, I can do better...'

Over the soup, Stanton wrenched the talk away from acting by launching into a vehement attack on Rube Marquard's record of nineteen straight victories on the mound, attributing the old pitcher's success to the dead baseball of his period. This led into an argument with Thorne as to the exact date of the Oeschger-Cadore twenty-six-inning pitching duel, during which the ladies discovered that they saw precisely eye to eye in the case of an enormous mutual friend who had let herself go with shocking results not only in girth but in intelligence. They were both reminded, in the same instant, of their common incredulity upon encountering a certain blonde whose youth and beauty had been utterly destroyed in less than a year of marriage. The talk joined when the women attacked and the men defended the blonde's husband – a heel, a swell guy, a lush, a drinker of incomparable moderation. It was all amiable enough. Thorne repeated a witticism about marriage that Ann had heard a dozen times but she laughed merrily with the others.

Over the coffee and brandy in the living room, the men revealed their secret knowledge of what was going on in the mind of Bulganin, and pointed out how any child could have avoided the blunders of Eden and Mollet. The women, meanwhile, were exchanging candid praises of each other's subtlety of taste in flower arrangement, working in a fleeting counterpoint of small self-deprecations.

Thorne gave one ear to Stanton's fluent breakdown of the first ten ballots that would be cast at the 1960 National Conventions. With the other ear, he sounded the temper of the women, the strength of whose mutual esteem he decided to test with further applications of brandy.

"It'll be a flurry, all right, but it won't be a trend," Stanton said.

"Hmm?" Thorne had lost the thread of his guest's argument.

"The Kennedy bid," Stanton explained. "It'll be like one of those wide end runs that get everybody in the stands to yelling but don't go anywhere."

The women did not protest when Thorne refilled their glasses. They were now shrewdly exploring the possibility that the enormous woman's vapid stare and slow mental activity might be the result, in part, of persistent overdoses of barbiturates.

'My dear,' Thorne said mockingly, grinning at each one in turn, 'if I were married to *that* man, I should *certainly* take – '

'Shut up,' said Ann.

Although the conversation took a dozen different turns, Thorne was careful not to let the mouse of Rosalind get too far away from the cat of his stubborn intention. He filled four or five lulls in the talk with interested questions. How many lines of the play, if any, could they remember? Had there been reviews? Had they saved the programmes? How large were their audiences? Why had neither of the girls gone in seriously for a stage career when so many inconsiderable talents had achieved undeserved success? Ann and Lydia waved it all away with little laughs and 'Oh, for heaven's sake!' and 'I haven't the faintest idea,' but Thorne thought he saw the embers of pride glow again in the ashes of old dreams.

Between eleven o'clock and midnight, Stanton made several abortive moves to go, but he finally gave up. One o'clock found him sitting uncomfortably in his chair with the strained expression of a man who has resigned himself to a sleepless night in a hotel taken over by a convention of surgeons. Furthermore, his attempts to rise and his repeated 'Lydia, dear' had had the disturbing effect of bringing out, one after another, George Thorne's imitations of W. C. Fields, Ed Wynn, Al Jolson, Peter Lorre, and Henry Hull as Jeeter Lester.

During these sporadic performances, the smooth surface of Ann Thorne's dutiful attention had developed cracks obvious to her husband's trained eye, which had also discerned Lydia Stanton's polite amusement changing to brave tolerance and deteriorating at last into the restlessness of posture and precise dreaminess of eye that Thorne had been so energetically working to produce. During it all, Thorne had managed to keep the highball glasses constantly refreshed, and the success of this phase of his strategy showed in a glowing relaxation of manner, except in the case of Stanton, and a tendency in the women to use each other's name in every sentence.

'What do you say we run off my Chevalier recording?' Thorne said suddenly.

'He really does do a very good imitation of Chevalier, Lydia,' Ann said.

'We had about six of us here one night after a big party broke up,' Thorne explained. 'Everybody read or recited something into the recorder mike. I remember Tom Sessions read an editorial from the Phi Psi *Shield* – I had one lying around. Well, everybody shot off his mouth except Dot Gardner and Julia Reid. Oh, no – no, indeed – not for them! You wouldn't catch *them* making a fool of themselves. Of course, at three o'clock they elbowed the other hambos aside and took over the mike.'

Stanton cleared his throat. 'Lydia, dear,' he said.

'It was really too wonderful, Lydia,' Ann said, laughing.

'Dot read that Cornford poem – uh – "Autumn Morning in Cambridge",' Thorne said. 'I had a first edition lying around.'

'And what was it Julia did, George?' Ann giggled.

'Lizette Woodworth Reese's, as God is my judge, "Tears".'

'Oh, no!' Lydia shouted. 'That tiny voice, Ann, coming out of that enormous hulk!'

'It was rich,' Thorne said. 'What the hell, it *is* rich! The goddam thing is preserved for lucky people of the future, digging around in the atomic rubble. Let's play it. My Chevalier imitation, a perfect gem, is thrown in for good measure.'

'Lydia,' Stanton said.

'It's in the library, the recorder is in the library,' Thorne said.

'Come on, Fred.' Lydia took his arm, smiled, and whispered savagely, 'For God's sake, keep your eyes open!'

'Bring your drink, Fred,' Thorne said. 'Let me put some more ice in it.'

'No, thanks,' said Stanton. 'It's fine.' He saw, first, the small microphone on the table in the library, and his reluctant eyes followed the cord attached to it as if it were a lighted fuse glittering toward the ominous box at the other end.

'I think you better get Herbert to do it, George,' Ann said. 'Or maybe Fred could –'

Her husband scowled. 'For God's sake, Ann, I've worked this thing a hundred times.'

'I know,' she said, with the look of a woman riding in a car driven by a little boy.

'It's a perfectly wonderful-looking thing,' Lydia said. 'Was it terribly expensive?'

'Around two hundred and fifty bucks,' Thorne said. 'We're in luck. That spool's on here now.'

Stanton was gazing with tidy disapproval at the reproduction of Dufy's 'Marne' over the fireplace.

'Are you sure you can make it go without breaking it?' Ann asked.

Thorne did not look at her. 'Here we go!' he yelled.

The machine began to hum, low and menacingly. There was a loud electric whine, a sudden roar, and George's recorded voice bawled from the machine, 'O.K., Herbert? Is it O.K.?'

'Yes, sir, you can go ahead, sir,' the butler's voice bellowed.

'Turn down the volume! For the love of heaven, turn it down!' Ann screamed.

Thorne succeeded at last in finding the knob that controlled the volume. They listened while the solemn voice of Tom Sessions turgidly read an editorial from the Phi Psi *Shield* entitled 'The Meaning of Fraternity in Wartime.' Lydia began to squirm in her chair. She turned on a frosty smile when the voice of her host began a burlesque of Chevalier explaining in English the meaning of 'Auprès de Ma Blonde.' During this performance, Thorne modestly left the room, carrying the four highball glasses. He spiked the women's drinks, shooting in only two squirts of soda. He came back in time to hear the voice of Dorothy Gardner reciting, in a curiously uneven mixture of eloquence and uncertainty, the Cornford lyric.

'Sounds like a crippled half back running through a broken field,' Thorne said.

'Sh-h,' said Lydia. She put her tongue out at the first taste of the powerful highball.

'Go get that seltzer bottle,' Ann commanded.

Thorne grinned and went out to the bar.

'Don't miss this coming now!' Ann cried.

The voice of Julia Reid, exalted, abnormally low, got by 'A rose choked in the grass . . .' and then died. There was a long pause. 'What the hell comes next?' the diseuse demanded. A dim voice that had spoken far from the microphone prompted her. The voice of the unseen, elated lady then went on to finish Miss Reese's sonnet in a tone of almost sepulchral dignity.

'I really think, Lydia –' Stanton said.

Ann took the seltzer bottle from Thorne and diluted Lydia's drink and her own. 'Turn it off,' she said. The reel was still unwinding, but no voices came from it.

'Wait a second,' Thorne said. 'Don't you want to hear Mark and Ken sing "I Had a Dream, Dear"?' Two male voices began a ragged rendition of the old song in a key too low for them. Ann went over and shut off the machine.

'Well, sir, that was very fine,' Stanton proclaimed loudly. He stood up.

'I'm going to put on a new spool for the gals,' Thorne said. 'Sit down, Fred.'

Ann and Lydia protested quickly, but not, Thorne's ear told him, with sharpness or finality. There was a hint of excitement, an unmistakable eagerness in their chimed 'Oh, no, you're not!'

'I can put on a new one faster than you can say Sarah Bernhardt,' he said.

'I've never heard my own voice,' Lydia said. 'They say you never recognize your own voice.'

'It's because you hear the sound internally, inside your mouth,' Ann explained. 'It's really fascinating.'

o

"As You Like It" is right there on the second shelf, Volume Two, the collected comedies,' Thorne said.

'Oh, for heaven's sake,' Ann squealed. 'I haven't looked at that damn play for twenty years!'

Lydia quietly finished her drink.

'There we are,' Thorne said, stepping back and scowling at the sound mirror. 'All ready to shoot. Here, I'll get the book.'

Stanton, eyes closed, hands gripping his chair arms, seemed to be awaiting the impact of a dentist's drill. The women made little arrangements of their hair and skirts. Thorne flipped through the pages of the Shakespeare volume. 'May the best Rosalind win!' He grinned. 'How about this?'

Stanton tightened his grip on the chair. Ann examined her wedding ring. Lydia studied the floor.

' "A lean cheek, which you have not, a blue eye and sunken, which you have not, an unquestionable spirit, which you have not –" '

'For heaven's sake, George, read it straight,' Ann broke in. 'Don't act it.'

' "A beard neglected, which you have not; but I pardon you for that, for simply your having in beard is a younger brother's revenue: then your hose should be ungartered, your bonnet unbanded, your sleeve unbuttoned, your shoe untied and everything about you demonstrating a careless desolation; but you are no such man; you are rather point-device in your accoutrements as loving yourself than seeming the lover of any other." '

'That *awful* speech,' Ann said. 'I hated it.'

'You don't happen to have a copy of "Candida"?' Lydia asked.

'No fear,' Thorne said. 'Ann never did Candida. How about this passage? "Yes, one, and in this manner. He was to imagine me his love, his mistress; and I set him every day to woo me: at which time would I, being but a moonish youth, grieve, be effeminate, changeable, longing and liking, proud, fantastical, apish, shallow, inconstant, full of tears, full of smiles, for every passion something and for no passion truly anything, as boys and women are for the most part cattle of this colour; would now like him, now loathe him; then entertain him, then forswear him; now weep for him, then spit at him; that I drave my suitor from his mad humour of love to a living humour of madness; which was, to forswear the full stream of the world and to live in a nook merely monastic. And thus I cured him; and this way will I take upon me to wash your liver as clean as a sound sheep's heart, that there shall not be one spot of love in't".'

'Wouldn't you just *know* a man wrote that?' Ann lifted her hands hopelessly.

'It has to be thrown away, you know – parts of that speech.' Lydia sighed, as if it were impossible to explain how to attack this particular passage.

'Oh, let's do it and get it over with, Lydia,' Ann said. 'Do you want to go first?'

'You go ahead, darling.' Lydia waved at Thorne, and he handed his wife the book, pointing at the selected speech. Ann's eyebrows went up when she looked at the page. 'The type is funny,' she announced.

'Read it over a couple of times while I fix a nightcap.' Thorne gathered up all the glasses.

'Just one sip,' Ann said when, a few minutes later, he brought in the fresh highballs.

'Ready?' asked Thorne.

'Roll 'em,' she said.

The machine began to hum. Ann leaned toward the microphone on the edge of the table. Then she leaned back with a shy little run of laughter. 'Heavens, I can't do it in front of people!' Her girlish ripple coagulated when she caught the professional glint of amusement in Lydia's eye. 'All right, George,' Ann said. 'Start the damn thing.'

She seemed to her watchful husband to lunge suddenly, like an unwary boxer. She gave the speech at the very beginning a brisk blow from which it never recovered. The swiftness of her attack was too much for the old lines, and although she slowed down halfway through, the passage could not regain its balance. It faded, brightened unexpectedly, faded again, and collapsed with a dignified whisper at the end. Thorne repressed a wild impulse to jump over and raise his wife's right hand.

Stanton applauded loudly, and all three of her audience called out 'Fine!' and 'Wonderful!'

Ann showed charming dismay. 'Mercy! I was *horrible!*' she wailed. 'You'll murder me, Lydia.'

'You were perfectly fine,' Lydia said.

'Here we go, Lydia!' Thorne shouted. 'Your time has come.'

'Oh, dear, I hate to follow Ann,' Lydia almost whispered. She made an elaborate rite of lifting her highball glass and taking a final sip, and then began to read.

Fred Stanton turned a slow, wondering head toward the source of a voice he had never heard before. It was low, resonant, and strange.

Closing his eyes and pursuing his image of the prize ring, Thorne saw Lydia circle cautiously about the lines, waiting for an opening. She did not find one. Her slow, monotonous tactics went on to the end. It reminded Thorne of the first few rounds of the second Louis-Conn fight.

Thorne led the loud applause this time, Ann shrieked with delight, Stanton said, 'Well, well, well!', and Lydia sat back, covered her eyes with her hand, and shook her head despondently, like a frustrated prima donna whose trunks have gone astray in a small town.

'Well, well, well,' Stanton said again. He got to his feet.

'Sit down, Fred,' Thorne said. 'We got to play it back.' Worrying the machine as if it were a tangled fishing line, he finally made the necessary shifts and adjustments. 'Quiet! Here we go!' he yelled. The volume was stepped up as high as it would go. 'I set him every day to woo me!' Ann howled from the machine. Thorne made a wild leap and cut the volume down.

'Goddam it!' Ann said, glaring at him. Then, 'Oh, no,' she whispered, her startled stare disowning the unfamiliar voice that mocked her from the sound mirror. Stanton started to applaud at the end, but Thorne cut him off with 'Sh-h, here comes Lydia!' and moved quickly to the recorder and, as if in an innocent effort to ensure perfection of reproduction, shot up the volume on Lydia's opening line, so that she also bawled it. He turned it down instantly. 'Well,' Lydia said. Then, 'That's not me!' 'Perfect,' Stanton said. Everybody stared fixedly at the machine.

When it was over, Stanton broke through the chatter with a determined 'Very fine, very fine! We must go, Lydia.' 'Can't I sell a nightcap, one nightcap?' Thorne kept saying. But the others moved out of the library, Stanton firmly leading the way. Five minutes later, a high tide of gaiety flooded the front hallway and bore out into the night a bright flotsam of pledge and promise, praise and disclaimer, regrets at parting, and wonder at the swiftness of time.

The Stantons drove in silence until they were a good three hundred yards from the house.

'Well.' Lydia sighed with tired satisfaction, ran up the window, and settled back comfortably. 'I've heard some strange performances in my life, but I never heard anything like that. I sat there biting my lip.' She made a Jane Cowl gesture.

'Yeah,' Stanton said.

'That silly little singsong voice,' she went on. 'Why, she can barely *read*. And the way she kept batting her eyes, trying to look cute and appealing.'

'She doesn't drink very well,' Stanton said. 'She had an awful lot to drink.'

Lydia laughed harshly. ' "Imitation of Chevalier!" I thought I would *scream*. I really thought I would *scream!*'

'What was that?' Stanton asked.

'Oh, you didn't get it, of course, sitting there with your eyes closed, a million miles away. You didn't say one word, one single, solitary word, from ten o'clock until we left that house, except "Lydia, dear – Lydia, dear – Lydia, dear," until I thought I would go *out* of my mind.'

'Aw,' Stanton said. He reached for the pack of cigarettes in his pocket.

'I'll light it for you. Keep your hands on the wheel.'

'Light the match toward you,' he said. 'Don't strike it away from you. You always strike it away from you.'

She wasted three matches striking them away from her. 'Slow down,' she said.

He stopped the car. 'I'll light it,' he told her. 'That guy always gets me down. He won't sit still and he won't stop talking. Yammering all over the place.'

'At least he stays awake, at least he knows what's going on.'

'Anyway, you were wonderful,' Stanton said quickly. 'You made Ann look like an amateur. You were marvellous.'

She sighed a hopeless little sigh. 'Well, you either have talent, Fred, or you haven't. She must have been the only girl in that Wyoming school, or wherever it was. You went past that turn again.'

Stanton stopped the car and began to back up. 'What was that goddam fan like?' he asked.

'It was awful,' she told him. 'And if she said "George got it for me in Rome" once, she said it fifty times. George obviously got it from some Italian street pedlar for a few francs. Eighteenth century, my foot!'

They drove awhile in silence. 'Lire,' Stanton said.

Lydia sniffed. 'I doubt it,' she said.

Back in their living room, the Thornes were having a short nightcap. 'I wish the hell you wouldn't always act as if I couldn't make anything work,' Thorne said. 'I can do more with my feet than that big dolt can do with his hands. "Better let Fred do it, George. Better get Herbert to do it." For God's sake, lay off, will you? I made the thing work. I always make it work.'

'Shut up, George, and give me some more ice,' Ann said. 'The thing that really got me, though, was that horrible affectation. She sounded like a backward child just learning to read.' She paused and put on a frown that her husband recognized. She wore it when she was hunting for a grievance. She found one. 'If you can make it work so well, why did you turn it up so high people could hear me yelling for three blocks?'

'I cut it down right away, didn't I, and I made her yell even louder.'

Ann laughed. 'That was wonderful. That was really wonderful, George.'

'At your service.' Thorne bowed. 'Come on, let's go with unlighted candle dark to bed. The light that breaks through yonder Eastern window is not the setting sun, my pet.'

They got up and Thorne turned out the lights. 'Does he know *anything*? Has he got a brain in his head?' she demanded.

'Fred? God, no! He has the mind of a turtle.'

'If he'd only yawn and get it over with, instead of working his mouth that way.'

Halfway up the stairs, Ann turned suddenly. Thorne stopped and looked up at her. 'Do you know the most ghastly thing about her?' she asked.

'That moo-cow voice?'

'No. Heaven knows that's bad enough, but can you possibly imagine her in doublet and *hose*? Those *legs*, George, those *legs*!'

Thorne jumped a step, caught up with her, and they went the rest of the way to their bedroom arm in arm.

The Princess and the Tin Box

ONCE UPON a time, in a far country, there lived a king whose daughter was the prettiest princess in the world. Her eyes were like the cornflower, her hair was sweeter than the hyacinth, and her throat made the swan look dusty.

From the time she was a year old, the princess had been showered with presents. Her nursery looked like Cartier's window. Her toys were all made of gold or platinum or diamonds or emeralds. She was not permitted to have wooden blocks or china dolls or rubber dogs or linen books, because such materials were considered cheap for the daughter of a king.

When she was seven, she was allowed to attend the wedding of her brother and throw real pearls at the bride instead of rice. Only the nightingale, with his lyre of gold, was permitted to sing for the princess. The common blackbird, with his boxwood flute, was kept out of the palace grounds. She walked in silver-and-samite slippers to a sapphire-and-topaz bathroom and slept in an ivory bed inlaid with rubies.

On the day the princess was eighteen, the king sent a royal ambassador to the courts of five neighbouring kingdoms to announce that he would give his daughter's hand in marriage to the prince who brought her the gift she liked the most.

The first prince to arrive at the palace rode a swift white stallion and laid at the feet of the princess an enormous apple made of solid gold which he had taken from a dragon who had guarded it for a thousand years. It was placed on a long ebony table set up to hold the gifts of the princess's suitors. The second prince, who came on a grey charger, brought her a nightingale made of a thousand diamonds, and it was placed beside the golden apple. The third prince, riding on a black horse, carried a great jewel box made of platinum and sapphires, and it was placed next to the diamond nightingale. The fourth prince, astride a fiery yellow horse, gave the princess a gigantic heart made of rubies and pierced by an emerald arrow. It was placed next to the platinum-and-sapphire jewel box.

Now the fifth prince was the strongest and handsomest of all the five suitors, but he was the son of a poor king whose realm had been overrun by mice and locusts and wizards and mining engineers so that there was nothing much of value left in it. He came plodding up to the palace of the princess on a plough horse and he brought her a small tin box filled with mica and feldspar and hornblende which he had picked up on the way.

The other princes roared with disdainful laughter when they saw the tawdry gift the fifth prince had brought to the princess. But she examined it with great interest and squealed with delight, for all her life she had been glutted with precious stones and priceless metals, but she had never seen tin before or mica or feldspar or hornblende. The tin box was placed next to the ruby heart pierced with an emerald arrow.

'Now,' the king said to his daughter, 'you must select the gift you like best and marry the prince that brought it.'

The princess smiled and walked up to the table and picked up the present she liked the most. It was the platinum-and-sapphire jewel box, the gift of the third prince.

'The way I figure it,' she said, 'is this. It is a very large and expensive box, and when I am married, I will meet many admirers who will give me precious gems with which to fill it to the top. Therefore, it is the most valuable of all the gifts my suitors have brought me and I like it the best.'

The princess married the third prince that very day in the midst of great merriment and high revelry. More than a hundred thousand pearls were thrown at her and she loved it.

Moral: All those who thought the princess was going to select the tin box filled with worthless stones instead of one of the other gifts will kindly stay after class and write one hundred times on the blackboard 'I would rather have a hunk of aluminium silicate than a diamond necklace.'

The Waters of the Moon

I HAD BROKEN away from an undulant discussion of kinetic dimen-
sionalism and was having a relaxed moment with a slender woman I had
not seen before, who described herself as a chaoticist, when my hostess, an
avid disturber of natural balances and angles of repose, dragged me off to meet
the guest of honour, a Mr Peifer, editor of a literary review. 'Holds his liquor
beautifully,' my hostess said. 'Burns it up, I guess. He's terribly intense.'
Peifer was pacing back and forth on a rug, haranguing a trapped etcher whose
reluctant eyes kept following him as if he were a tennis rally.

'No, I'm not interested in the ageing American *female* author,' Peifer was
saying. 'That's a phenomenon that confounds analysis. The female writer's
fertility of invention and glibness of style usually survive into senility, just as
her artistic gestation frequently seems to be independent of the nourishment
of thought.'

Peifer made three turns of the rug in silence. He had the expression of a
chemist absorbed in abstruse formulae. 'I am interested in the male American
writer who peters out in his fifties, who has the occupational span of a hockey
player. The tempo of our American life may have something to do with it, but
there must be a dozen other factors that dry up the flow of ideas and transform
a competent prose style into the meagre iterations of a train announcer.'

My hostess finally broke in, and Peifer stopped pacing to shake hands. The
etcher seized the opportunity to disappear. 'Mr Thurber is fifty-three,' my
hostess said. 'He hasn't written anything since last April.' Peifer looked at me
as if I were the precipitate of a moderately successful test-tube experiment. My
first name suddenly reminded him of a tangent of his theme. 'Take Henry
James,' he said. 'If he had lived in this country, he would probably have spent
his middle years raising collies or throwing darts. It is preposterous to assume,
however, that region or climate is the important factor. There must be something, though, in the American way of life and habit of thought. I want to get
Wylie or De Voto or somebody to do a comprehensive treatise on the subject,
looking at it from the viewpoints of marriage, extramarital relations, the educa-
tional system, home environment, the failure of religion, the tyranny of
money, and the rich breeding ground of decomposition which I believe is to
be found in syphilophobia, prostatitis, early baldness, peptic ulcer, edentulous
cases, true and hysterical impotence, and spreading of the metatarsals.' I tried
to wrench a tray of Martinis from a man in a white coat, but he would only let
me have one. 'Let's go over and sit down on that sofa,' Peifer said. I followed
him, glancing ruefully over my shoulder at my lost chaoticist. 'It's a difficult

article,' I said. 'If you use names, it's dangerous, and if you don't, it won't be interesting. You can't very well say that Joseph Doakes, after petering out on page 73 of his unfinished novel, "Whatever Gods," a childlike and feathery permutation of his first book, "Fear Set Free," is living in sin with his cook and spends his time cutting the pips out of playing cards.'

Peifer took my olive. 'The article is not to be a gossip column,' he said. 'It's to be a scholarly treatise. I am interested in exploring the causes of literary collapse, not in collecting scandalous post-disintegration case histories of quixotic individuals who would no doubt have gone to pieces in precisely the same way had they been milliners or pharmacists' mates.'

'Then, unhappily,' I said, 'you cannot follow the old codgers past the hour of their deterioration, and in so doing you will omit a great deal of fascinating sequelae. You are interested only in causation. You would trace the career of, let us say, Bruce Balliol up to that afternoon in June when he abruptly began to write the middle section of "Love Not the Wind" in the manner of the late Senator Albert J. Beveridge, and realized to his dismay that he was washed up at fifty-six. I would take him through his divorce, his elopement with the hairdresser, and those final baffling years on the peacock ranch.'

A grim man I had never seen before walked up to us, dribbling his Manhattan. 'Cora in the bells and grass,' he said. 'Cora with a cherry halfway to her lips.' The man walked away. 'I like Eve better than Cora,' I said. Peifer apparently didn't know the poem the man had paraphrased. 'You do?' he said, with his laboratory glint. 'You were talking,' I said. 'Go on.' Peifer took a curved briar pipe out of his pocket and rubbed the bowl on his pants leg. He began to chew on the stem of his pipe.

'That was poor old Greg Selby,' I said, 'a perfect specimen for your analysis. He stopped writing suddenly, a fortnight after his fifty-fourth birthday. Bang!' Peifer started. 'Like that,' I said. 'His felicity of style was the envy and despair of us all, and then abruptly one day he began to write like a doorman cockeyed on cooking sherry.' 'I never heard of any writer named Greg Selby,' Peifer said. I lifted a Martini from a passing tray. 'He has never published anything,' I said. 'He is going to leave all his work to Harvard, to be published a thousand years from now. Greg's writing has what he calls Projected Meaning. He feels that in another millennium the intellectuals will understand it readily enough. I have never made head or tail of any of his stuff myself, but there is no missing the unique quality of the most exquisite English prose of our time.'

Peifer made figure eights in the air with his pipe. 'He seems a little special,' he said. 'I'm not interested in idiosyncratic variables, except, perhaps, as footnotes.'

'He is a male American writer who petered out in his middle fifties,' I insisted. 'He fits in perfectly.'

'What I have in mind is the published writer of established merit,' my companion said as I stopped another Martini tray, 'but go on. What happened to this man Selby?'

'His first wife, Cora,' I began, 'claimed to have discovered that his last book,

"Filiring Gree," was his next-to-last book, "Saint Tomany's Rain," written backward. It was insupportable to Greg that his wife should go through his books like a public accountant investigating a bank ledger. He threw her and her Siamese cats out of the house – the macaw wouldn't go. He had not heard the last of her, however. She called him up every few days and in the falsetto of a little child asked him why he didn't dramatize the Little Colonel stories for Margaret O'Brien. She divorced him, finally, and married a minor-league outfielder.'

'This is really terribly special,' Peifer complained, signalling a tray of highballs.

'Cora was ordinary enough. It was Eve who was special. She was the author of a number of mystery books. You probably remember "Pussy Wants a Coroner." ' Peifer replied, a little pettishly, that he did not read mysteries.

'After her marriage to Greg,' I went on, 'Eve's books took on a curiously Gothic tone; the style was cold and blocky, and the plots had all the flexibility of an incantation. She explained to her alarmed publishers that she was trying to write for the understanding of intellectuals a thousand years ago.' Peifer put his drink on the floor and stood up. 'I presume you would consider Douglas Bryce a published author of established merit, wouldn't you ?' I demanded. I had thought the name up fast. 'Well,' Peifer said uneasily. He sat down again.

'Doug,' I said, 'ran out of ideas and his command of sentence construction at the same time, on a Wednesday. He was fifty-eight. That was a long time ago. He died in 1932, on his chinchilla farm, and only the hat-check girl, Dolores, was at his bedside. Nell left him after the Lawrence Stone incident.'

Peifer recrossed his legs restlessly and reached for another highball. 'It would be as hard to find a copy of "The Tenant of the Room" now as it would be to turn up a first edition of "V.V.'s Eyes," ' I told him. ' "The Tenant" was Doug's last book. It was a flimsy rehash of his earlier "A Piece in Bloom." The love story was a little more disgusting, but in general it was a slight rearrangement of the well-worn characters and incidents. Doug had once had a facile and effective style, but the writing in "The Tenant" fell well within the capabilities of a shrewd pin boy.'

I took another Martini. 'Get on with it,' Peifer said.

'Nell once told me that after the failure of "The Tenant," Doug spent his days making cryptic and vainglorious notes on pieces of Kleenex, doorjambs, the flyleaves of books, and shirt fronts. He would jot down such things as "Translate Lippmann into Latin," "Reply to Shelburne Essays," "Refute Toynbee," "Collaborate with G.B.S. ?", "Call Gilbert Miller." Other notes indicated that he planned a history of the New York, New Haven & Hartford in verse, an account of women in sports, to be called "Atalanta to Babe Didrikson," and a pageant based on the Tristram legends, in which he proposed to star the late Devereux Milburn.'

'I really must go,' Peifer said. He stood up and then resumed his seat. 'What was the Lawrence Stone incident?' he asked.

'Just before he bought the chinchilla farm, Nell found, scribbled on the bathroom wall, "The Shore; The Plain; The Mountain, a trilogy by Douglas Bryce." Under that he had written "A monumental achievement," which he had signed "Van Wyck Brooks." But he was onto himself at last; he was tired and he was through and he knew it. The reservoir of his natural talent had run dry and he had been reaching for the waters of the moon. But as I say, he was onto himself. Under it all he had scrawled, almost illegibly, "a trilogy wilogy by Brycey-Wycey." '

'Who was this man Stone? And then I must go,' Peifer said. 'People are beginning to sing.'

'Doug had one more project,' I said. 'He conceived the idea of writing a long biography of a man picked at random in the street. The book was to be called "Let Twenty Pass." He stood one day at the corner of Fifth Avenue and Forty-fourth Street, counted off twenty men who walked by going north, and accosted the twenty-first. The twenty-first was a large, preoccupied mining engineer named Lawrence Stone. He called the police and a rather nasty fuss was kicked up in the papers. It came out, you remember, that Stone was quite deaf, and his functional disability had twisted Doug's proposal into a shockingly complex plan to seize the major networks. Dolores was passing when Doug accosted Stone, and her testimony as to what was actually said cleared Bryce. It was a near thing, though.'

Peifer twisted around on the sofa, slowly and with difficulty, as if invisible blankets hampered his legs. I saw that his unfriendly stare glittered frostily in almost imperceptibly crossed eyes. I wondered I had not noticed before that his liquor, much of it unburned, had left him, in spite of a fluent grasp on his subject, balanced precariously between command and dissolution. His expression took away all my pride of invention in the garish show of figures I had conjured up to ornament his theme. I had been careless, too, in the name of the mining engineer, and Peifer had caught me out. 'I happen to be familiar with Browning,' he said with shrewd dignity, 'and I happen to know how the line that begins "Let twenty pass" ends.'

I was conscious of a figure at my shoulder. Someone had come to save me. It was the slender lady, my dark lady of chaos, grown a little mistier with the passing of the afternoon and possessed now of the posture of the rose in a summer wind. I stood up, and Peifer managed it, too. 'Nell,' I said, 'may I present Mr Peifer?' He bowed stiffly. 'This is Nell Bryce,' I told him. The game was up, but here I was, kicking field goals by moonlight. 'Peifer here,' I said, 'would not have followed Bierce beyond the Rio Grande or Villon through the *porte* of St Denis to see in what caprice or rondeaux their days came to an end.'

'Let's phone the police and plague 'em till hell won't have it,' the lady said. It seemed to hurt Peifer like a slap. He bowed, almost too low to sustain the moral advantage he undoubtedly held over both of us. 'It is a great pity, Madam,' he said, tightly, 'that your mythical husband had the misfortune to encounter an engineer named Stone. Ah, what a flaw in the verisilimitude was there! It is a great pity your husband did not have the luck to encounter an engineer named Costello or McKelway or Shapiro.' The dark lady listened to him with the expression of one who is receiving complicated directions in a great, strange town.

Peifer turned a cold, uncertain eye on me. 'Let twenty pass,' he snarled, 'and stone the twenty-first.' The dark lady watched him, on a quick opening play, break between guard and centre of a mixed quartet. 'Now, how in the God's name' – she had a charming diaphragmatic convulsion – 'did he know my husband was mythical?' It was too long a story to go into. I took her arm and, in silence, led her to the telephone to call the police.

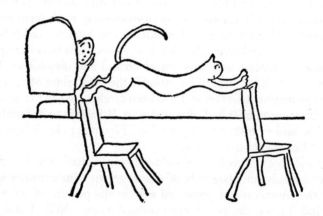

Exhibit X

I HAD BEEN a code clerk in the State Department in Washington for four months during the first World War before my loyalty was investigated, if you could call my small, pleasant interview with Mr Shand an investigation. He had no dossier on Thurber, James Grover, except a birth certificate and draft-board deferment papers. In 1918, Americans naïvely feared the enemy more than they feared one another. There was no F.B.I. to speak of, and I had neither been followed nor secretly photographed. A snooping photographer could have caught me taking a code book home to study one night and bringing it back the next day – an act that was indiscreet, and properly regretted when I learned the rules – but a pictorial record of my activities outside the Bureau of Indexes and Archives in Washington would actually have been as innocent as it might have *looked* damning.

It would have shown me in the company of Mrs Nichols, head of the information desk at the State, War, and Navy Building (a psychic lady I had known since I was six); George P. Martin, proprietor of the Post Café, and Mrs Rabbit, his assistant; Frank Farrington, a movie actor who had played the part of a crook named Braine in 'The Million Dollar Mystery'; and Jack Bridges, a Los Angeles air-mail flier and Hispano-Suiza expert. I doubt if any such photographs, even one showing me borrowing twenty dollars from Bridges half an hour after meeting him for the first time in my life, would have shaken Mr Shand's confidence in me.

Mr Shand called me to his office about a week before I was to sail for France and the Paris Embassy. He was a tall, quiet, courteous gentleman, and he had only one question to ask me. He wanted to know if all my grandparents had been born in the United States. I said yes, he wished me Godspeed, we shook hands, and I left. That's all there was to it. Waking up at night now and looking back on it, I sometimes wonder how I would have come out of one of those three-men inquisitions the Department was caught conducting last year. Having as great a guilt sense as any congressman, and a greater tendency to confession, it might have taken me hours to dredge up out of my mind and memory all the self-indictments that must have been there. I believed then, and still do, that generals of the Southern Confederacy were, in the main, superior to generals of the Northern armies; I suspected there were flaws in the American political system; I doubted the virgin birth of United States senators; I thought that German cameras and English bicycles were better than ours; and I denied the existence of actual proof that God was exclusively a citizen of the United States. But, as I say, Mr Shand merely asked me about my grandparents, and that was all. I realize now that, as a measure of patriotism, the long existence of my ancestors on American soil makes me more loyal than Virginia Dare or even George Washington, but I didn't give it any thought at the time.

Before I sailed on the S.S. *Orizaba*, a passenger ship converted into an Army transport and looking rather sheepish about it, I was allowed to spend four days in Columbus, Ohio, and my mother has preserved, for reasons known only to mothers, a snapshot taken of me on the last day of my leave. The subject of the photograph is obviously wearing somebody else's suit, which not only convicts him of three major faults in a code clerk – absent-mindedness, carelessness, and peccability – but gives him the unwonted appearance of a saluki who, through some egregious mischance of nature, has exchanged his own ears for those of a barn owl. If this would not be enough to cause a special agent to phone Hoover personally, *regardez*, as the French Sûreté would say excitedly, the *figure* of this alarming *indiscret*. His worried expression indicates that he has just mislaid a code book or, what is worse, has sold one. Even Mr Hoover's dullest agent could tell that the picture is that of a man who would be putty in the hands of a beautiful, or even a dowdy, female spy. The subject's curious but unmistakable you-ask-me-and-I'll-tell-you look shows that he would babble high confidences to low companions on his third *pernod à l'eau*. This man could even find some way to compromise the Department of Agriculture, let alone the Department of State.

The picture would have aroused no alarm in the old days, however, for it was almost impossible to be a security risk in the State Department in 1918, no matter how you looked. All our code books except one were quaint transparencies dating back to the time when Hamilton Fish was Secretary of State, under President Grant, and they were intended to save words and cut telegraph costs, not to fool anybody. The new code book had been put together so hastily that the word 'America' was left out, and code groups so closely paralleled true readings that 'LOVVE,' for example, was the symbol for 'love.'

Whatever slight illusion of secrecy we code clerks may have had was dispelled one day by a dour gentleman who announced that the Germans had all our codes. It was said that the Germans now and then got messages through to Washington taunting us about our childish ciphers, and suggesting on one occasion that our clumsy device of combining two codes, in a desperate effort at deception, would have been a little harder if we had used two other codes, which they named. This may have been rumour or legend, like the story, current at the time, that six of our code books were missing and that a seventh, neatly wrapped, firmly tied, and accompanied by a courteous note, had been returned to one or another of our embassies by the Japanese, either because they had finished with it or because they already had one.

A system of deception as easy to see through as the passing attack of a grammar-school football team naturally produces a cat's-out-of-the-bag attitude. In enciphering messages in one code, in which the symbol for 'quote' was (to make up a group) 'ZOXIL,' we were permitted to use 'UNZOXIL' for

Exhibit X 4I3

'unquote,' an aid to perspicuity that gave us code clerks the depressing feeling that our tedious work was merely an exercise in block lettering. The Department may have comforted itself with the knowledge that even the most ingenious and complex codes could have been broken down by enemy cipher experts. Unzoxilation just made it a little easier for them.

Herbert O. Yardley, one-time chief cryptographer of the War Department, warned the government in a book published nearly twenty years ago that the only impregnable codes are those whose pattern is mechanically jumbled in transmission by a special telegraphic method that reassembles the pattern at the point of reception. To prove his point, Yardley revealed how he had broken the toughest Japanese code five years before. The government must have taken his advice. I doubt that we could have got through a second world war shouting, 'zoxil Here we come, ready or not UNZOXIL.'

The State Department, in the happy-go-lucky tradition of the time, forgot to visa my special diplomatic passport, and this was to cause a tremendous *brouhaha* later on, when the French discovered I was loose in their country without the signs, seals, and signatures they so devoutly respect. The captain of the *Orizaba* wanted nothing to do with me when I boarded his ship, whether my passport was visaed or not. He had no intention of taking orders from the State Department or carrying its code clerks, and who the hell was Robert Lansing, anyway? He finally let me stay on board after I had bowed and scraped and touched my forelock for an hour, but he refused to monkey around getting my trunk on board. When I received it in Paris, more than a year later, everything in it was covered with the melted chocolate of a dozen Hershey bars I had tucked in here and there.

I had been instructed to report to Colonel House at the Hotel Crillon when I got to Paris, but I never saw him. I saw instead an outraged gentleman named Auchincloss, who plainly regarded me as an unsuccessfully comic puppet in a crude and inexcusable practical joke. He said bitterly that code clerks had been showing up for days, that Colonel House did not want even one code clerk, let alone twelve or fifteen, and that I was to go on over to the Embassy, where I belonged. The explanation was, I think, as simple as it was monumental. Several weeks before, the State Department in Washington had received a cablegram from Colonel House in Paris urgently requesting the immediate shipment of twelve or fifteen code clerks to the Crillon, where headquarters for the American Peace Delegation had been set up. It is plain to me now what must have happened. Colonel House's cablegram must have urgently requested the immediate shipment of twelve or fifteen code books, not code clerks. The cipher groups for 'books' and 'clerks' must have been nearly identical, say 'DOGEC' and 'DOGED,' and hence a setup for the telegraphic garble. Thus, if my theory is right, the single letter 'D' sent me to Paris, when I had originally been slated for Berne. Even after thirty years, the power of that minuscule slip of the alphabet gives me a high sense of insecurity. A 'D' for a 'C' sent Colonel House clerks instead of books, and sent me to France instead of Switzerland. On the whole, I came off far better, as events proved, than the

Colonel did. There I was in Paris, with a lot of jolly colleagues, and there was Colonel House, up to his ears in code clerks, but without any code books, or at least not enough to handle the flow of cablegrams to and from the Crillon when the Peace Conference got under way.

That tiny 'D' was to involve the State Department, the Paris Embassy, the Peace Conference, and, in a way that would have delighted Gilbert and Sullivan, the United States Navy in a magnificent comic opera of confusion. An admiral of the Navy, for some reason (probably because he had a lot of Navy code books), arbitrarily took over, at the Crillon, the State Department's proud prerogative of diplomatic communication, and a code shambles that might have perplexed Herbert Yardley himself developed when cablegrams in Navy codes were dispatched to the State Department in Washington, which could not figure them out and sent back bewildered and frantic queries in State Department codes, which the admiral and his aides could not unravel. The Navy has always been proud of its codes, and the fact that they couldn't be broken by the State Department only went to show how strong they were, but when communication between the Peace Conference and Washington came to a dead stop, the admiral agreed to a compromise. His clerks, young and eager junior lieutenants, would use the State Department codes. This compounded the confusion, since the lieutenants didn't know how to use the strange codes. The dozen State Department clerks Colonel House had turned away and now needed badly were finally sent for, after a month, but even then they were forced to work under the supervision of the Navy. The Great Confusion was at last brought to an end when the desperate State Department finally turned to a newspaperman for help, and assigned him to go and get its stolen power of diplomatic communication and bring it back where it belonged. Not since an American battleship, many years before, in firing a twenty-one-gun salute in honour of the President of France, had accidentally used real shells and blown the bejeezus out of the harbour of Le Havre had the American Navy so royally loused up a situation. And think of it – a 'DOGEC' for a 'DOGED' would have sent me to Berne, where nothing at all ever happened.

The last time I saw the old building, at 5 Rue de Chaillot, that housed the chancery of the American Embassy when I was a code clerk was in 1937. Near the high, grilled door, a plaque proclaimed that Myron T. Herrick was our Ambassador during the first World War, thus perpetuating a fond American misconception and serving as a monument to the era of the Great Confusion. The truth is that Herrick served during only the first four months of the war, and from December, 1914, until after the war, in 1919, an unsung man named William Sharp was our Ambassador to France. This note of bronze fuzziness cheered me in a peculiar way. It was a brave, cockeyed testament to the enduring strength of a nation that can get more ingloriously mixed up than any other and somehow gloriously come out of it in the end.

As I stood there before the old chancery, I remembered another visit I had made to 5 Rue de Chaillot, in 1925, and for the convenience of the F.B.I., who must already have twenty-three exhibits to fling at me when I am called up

Exhibit X 415

before some committee or other, I offer my adventure in 1925 as Exhibit X. Myron Herrick was once more our Ambassador to France, and I was granted an interview with him, or, as Counsellor Sheldon Whitehouse insisted on calling it, an audience. I had given up diplomacy for journalism, as I used to explain it, and I needed material for an article I was writing about Herrick for an American newspaper. I decided I ought to have a little 'art' to go along with the story, such as a photograph of the Ambassador's office, a large, bright, well-appointed room on the second floor, facing the street. I knew I couldn't get official permission to take a picture of the room, but this didn't discourage me. I had discovered that the same old French *concierge* lived in the same rooms on the ground floor of the chancery and controlled the opening of the great, grilled door. Remembering that Sunday had always been an off day, with a skeleton staff in charge, I picked out a clear, sunny Sabbath for my exploit. I went to the chancery and pushed the bell, and the *concierge* clicked the lock from her room. I went in, said '*Bonjour, Madame,*' went upstairs, photographed the Ambassador's office, came down again, having been challenged by nobody, said '*Bonjour, Madame*' to the *concierge*, raised my hat politely, and went away.

The Republicans were in charge of the Embassy then, not the Democrats, as in my code-clerk days, but things hadn't changed much. I am a pretty good hand at time exposures, and the photograph came out well. There is still a print of it in the art morgue of an American newspaper, or ought to be, but it is merely a view of a room in the home of whatever French family now lives at 5 Rue de Chaillot.

We probably learned a lot during the recent war, and I doubt if tourists with cameras could get into any of our Embassies today. If this belated confession makes it a bit harder for them, anyway, I shall be very happy indeed. I must close now, since somebody is knocking at the door. Why, it's a couple of strange men! Now, what in the world could *they* want with me?

The Lady on the Bookcase

NE DAY twelve years ago an outraged cartoonist, four of whose drawings had been rejected in a clump by *The New Yorker*, stormed into
the office of the late Harold Ross, editor of the magazine. 'Why is it,'
demanded the cartoonist, 'that you reject my work and publish drawings by a
fifth-rate artist like Thurber?' Ross came quickly to my defence like the true

'With you I have known peace, Lida, and now you say you're going crazy.'

friend and devoted employer he was. 'You mean third-rate,' he said quietly,
but there was a warning glint in his steady grey eyes that caused the discom-
fited cartoonist to beat a hasty retreat.

With the exception of Ross, the interest of editors in what I draw has been
rather more journalistic than critical. They want to know if it is true that I
draw by moonlight, or under water, and when I say no, they lose interest until
they hear the rumour that I found the drawings in an old trunk or that I do
the captions while my nephew makes the sketches.

The other day I was shoving some of my originals around on the floor (I do
not draw on the floor; I was just shoving the originals around) and they fell, or
perhaps I pushed them, into five separate and indistinct categories. I have
never wanted to write about my drawings, and I still don't want to, but it

occurred to me that it might be a good idea to do it now, when everybody is busy with something else, and get it over quietly.

Category No. 1, then, which may be called the Unconscious or Stream of Nervousness category, is represented by 'With you I have known peace, Lida, and now you say you're going crazy' and the drawing entitled with simple dignity, 'Home.' These drawings were done while the artist was thinking of

Home

something else (or so he has been assured by experts) and hence his hand was guided by the Unconscious which, in turn, was more or less influenced by the Subconscious.

Students of Jung have instructed me that Lida and the House-Woman are representations of the *anima*, the female essence or directive which floats around in the ageless universal Subconscious of Man like a tadpole in a cistern. Less intellectual critics insist that the two ladies are actual persons I have consciously known. Between these two schools of thought lies a discouragingly large space of time extending roughly from 1,000,000 B.C. to the middle nineteen thirties.

Whenever I try to trace the true identity of the House-Woman, I get to thinking of Mr Jones. He appeared in my office one day twelve years ago, said he was Mr Jones, and asked me to lend him 'Home' for reproduction in an art

'*All right, have it your way – you heard a seal bark.*'

'*That's my first wife up there, and this is the* present *Mrs Harris.*'

magazine. I never saw the drawing again. Tall, well-dressed, kind of sad-looking chap, and as well spoken a gentleman as you would want to meet.

Category No. 2 brings us to Freud and another one of those discouragingly large spaces – namely, the space between the Concept of the Purely Accidental and the Theory of Haphazard Determination. Whether chance is capricious or we are all prisoners of pattern is too long and cloudy a subject to go into here. I shall consider each of the drawings in Category No. 2, explaining

'For the last time, you and your horsie get away from me and stay away!'

what happened and leaving the definition of the forces involved up to you. The seal on top of the bed, then ('All right, have it your way – you heard a seal bark'), started out to be a seal on a rock. The rock, in the process of being drawn, began to look like the head of a bed, so I made a bed out of it, put a man and wife in the bed, and stumbled onto the caption as easily and unexpectedly as the seal had stumbled into the bedroom.

The woman on top of the bookcase ('That's my first wife up there, and this is the *present* Mrs Harris') was originally designed to be a woman crouched on the top step of a staircase, but since the tricks and conventions of perspective and planes sometimes fail me, the staircase assumed the shape of a bookcase and was finished as such, to the surprise and embarrassment of the first Mrs Harris, the present Mrs Harris, the lady visitor, Mr Harris and me. Before *The New Yorker* would print the drawing, they phoned me long distance to inquire whether the first Mrs Harris was alive or dead or stuffed. I replied that my taxidermist had advised me that you cannot stuff a woman, and that my physician had informed me that a dead lady cannot support herself on all fours. This meant, I said, that the first Mrs Harris was unquestionably alive.

The man riding on the other man's shoulders in the bar ('For the last time, you and your horsie get away from me and stay away!') was intended to be standing alongside the irate speaker, but I started his head up too high and

'The father belonged to some people who were driving through in a Packard.'

made it too small, so that he would have been nine feet tall if I had completed his body that way. It was but the work of thirty-two seconds to put him on another man's shoulders. As simple or, if you like, as complicated as that. The psychological factors which may be present here are, as I have indicated, elaborate and confused. Personally, I like Dr Claude Thornway's theory of the Deliberate Accident or Conditioned Mistake.

Category No. 3 is perhaps a variant of Category No. 2; indeed, they may even be identical. The dogs in 'The father belonged to some people who were driving through in a Packard' were drawn as a captionless spot, and the interior with figures just sort of grew up around them. The hippopotamus in 'What have you done with Dr Millmoss?' was drawn to amuse my small daughter. Something about the creature's expression when he was completed convinced me that he had recently eaten a man. I added the hat and pipe and Mrs Millmoss, and the caption followed easily enough. Incidentally, my daughter, who was two years old at the time, identified the beast immediately. 'That's a

'*What have you done with Dr. Millmoss?*'

'*Touché!*'

hippotomanus,' she said. *The New Yorker* was not so smart. They described the drawing for their files as follows: 'Woman with strange animal.' *The New Yorker* was nine years old at the time.

Category No. 4 is represented by perhaps the best known of some fifteen drawings belonging to this special grouping, which may be called the Contributed Idea Category. This drawing ('Touché!') was originally done for *The New Yorker* by Carl Rose, caption and all. Mr Rose is a realistic artist, and his gory scene distressed the editors, who hate violence. They asked Rose if he would let me have the idea, since there is obviously no blood to speak of in the

'Well, I'm disenchanted, too. We're all disenchanted.'

people I draw. Rose graciously consented. No one who looks at 'Touché!' believes that the man whose head is in the air is really dead. His opponent will hand it back to him with profuse apologies, and the discommoded fencer will replace it on his shoulders and say, 'No harm done, forget it.' Thus the old controversy as to whether death can be made funny is left just where it was before Carl Rose came along with his wonderful idea.

Category No. 5, our final one, can be called, believe it or not, the Intentional or Thought-Up Category. The idea for each of these two drawings just came to me and I sat down and made a sketch to fit the prepared caption. Perhaps, in the case of 'Well, I'm disenchanted, too. We're all disenchanted,' another one of those Outside Forces played a part. That is, I may have overheard a husband say to his wife, on the street or at a party, 'I'm disenchanted.' I do not think this is true, however, in the case of the rabbit-headed doctor and his woman patient. I believe that scene and its caption came to me one night in bed. I *may* have got the idea in a doctor's office or a rabbit hutch, but I don't think so.

As my eyesight grew dimmer, the paper I drew on grew larger, and even though I used a heavy black crayon, the fine Ohio clarity of my work diminished. In one of my last drawings I had to make the eyes of a young lady so large that it was easy to arrive at the caption: 'Where did you get those big brown eyes and that tiny mind?' Seven years ago I shifted to luminous white crayon on dead black paper, and then finally gave up drawing altogether for writing, meditation, and drinking.

'You said a moment ago that everybody you look at seems to be a rabbit. Now just what do you mean by that, Mrs Sprague?'

Most of my originals have disappeared, mysteriously or otherwise. Thirty were never heard of again after a show in Los Angeles. Several pretty girls with big brown eyes and minds of various sizes have swiped a dozen or so of the scrawls, and a man I loved, now dead, told me one day he had taken seven drawings from my office desk to give to some friends of his in California. That is what became of Dr Millmoss, among others. My favourite loss, however, occurred at the varnishing, or vanishing, of a show of my drawings in London in 1937. Seems that someone eased a portfolio of two dog drawings. I'm mighty proud of that, and I like to think that Scotland Yard was duly informed of the incident. Theft is an even higher form of praise than emulation, for it carries with it the risk of fine and imprisonment, or, in the case of my 'work,' at least a mild dressing down by the authorities.

If you should ever run across 'Home' or 'What have you done with Dr Millmoss?' write to me, not to J. Edgar Hoover. We are equally busy, but he would only be puzzled, and possibly irked. So much for my drawings, wherever they are.

The Ordeal of Mr Matthews

'THE PRACTICE of wit as a fine art is one with the carriage horse and the dulcimer,' I said to the businessman who got stuck with me at a party in the country one afternoon. The sounds of modern teatime – gabble and loud laughter – drifted into the small study where I had found him sitting down over a back copy of *Life*. 'For one thing,' I went on, 'the appointments, the accoutrements, the accessories have vanished like the snows of the famous ballade.'

'My name is Matthews,' he said, and shifted a glass of ale from his right hand to his left. We shook hands.

'Where now, Matthews,' I demanded, 'are the long draperies, the bright chandeliers, the shining floors, the high ceilings, the snuffbox, the handkerchief stuck in the sleeve with careless care, the perfect bow from the waist, the formal but agile idiom?'

'Setup is different today,' Matthews said.

'Gone,' I told him. 'Lost in the oblivious plangency of our darkening era, crumbled of their lustre, save for a sparkle here, a twinkle there, in the remembered dust of the stately centuries.'

Matthews put the copy of *Life* on the floor and got up. 'Think I'll have some more of this ale,' he said.

To my surprise, he came back a minute later, with an uncapped bottle and the dogged expression of a man determined to make out the meaning of voices heard dimly beyond a wall.

'The high tradition of wit in court and chancellery,' I resumed, 'died, I suppose, with Joseph Choate. His weapon was a sabre, not a rapier, but even the clangor of that bold steel did not linger in London Town to inspire with its faraway echoes Walter Page and Joseph Kennedy.'

'Lots of energy, Joe Kennedy,' Matthews said. 'Tackle anything, handle it well.'

'Choate lived to see the lights diminish, the magnificence dwindle, and the men decline,' I said. 'He saw the thrust lose its deftness until there was no longer need for skilful parry and riposte. The querulous and the irritable then had their day, giving way, in our land and time, to the wisecrack and the gag, the leg pull and the hotfoot, the gimmick and the switcheroo.'

Matthews grunted and sought sanctuary in the close examination of a cigar.

'For the exercise of wit in the grand manner,' I told him, 'for the slash supreme, the stab sublime, or, if you prefer Untermeyer, the devastating crusher, one has to go back to the golden age of John Wilkes and Benjamin Disraeli.'

Matthews lighted his cigar. 'What'd you say it was Sam Untermeyer said?' he asked.

'Not Sam,' I said. 'Louis.'

A woman appeared at the door of the study. 'Have you seen Nora?' Matthews asked her.

'She's in the dining room with Ed and Carl, having fun and laughs. Don't you want a drink, Mr Thurber?'

'I'm on the wagon,' I said. Matthews looked at me as if he didn't believe it. The woman went away. 'Who was that?' I asked.

'Our hostess,' he said simply. He tried a sudden tack. 'Ed's certainly brought that business of his up from nowhere.'

I quickly by-passed the looming discussion of Ed's acumen and went on talking. 'Both Wilkes and Disraeli enjoyed, of course, those unique advantages of décor and deportment which were so conducive and becoming to the brilliant verbal duel. Wilkes, for example, had that most superb of foils, that greatest straight man in the history of wit, Lord Sandwich, almost always at his side in resplendent assemblages. At one of these, with all the important ears in town cocked, Sandwich accosted Wilkes with "You will die of a pox, sir, or on the gallows," to which Wilkes replied, "That depends, sir, on whether I embrace your mistress or your principles." '

Matthews turned his glass in his hand. 'Had 'em more openly in those days, of course – mistresses,' he said.

'Disraeli also had the luck of the witty,' I said. 'A lady once asked him at a reception if he could tell her the difference between a misfortune and a calamity. While all London listened, the great man replied, 'If Mr Gladstone were to fall into the Thames it would be a misfortune. If someone pulled him out it would be a calamity.'

'Great deal of bickering among the English in those days,' Matthews said. 'Still is,' he added after a moment. I made an impatient gesture.

'The Disraeli woman,' I went on, 'with her eager interest in definition, is extinct. The curiosity of the American woman, cabined and confined, rarely takes provocative or stimulating shape. It is all but impossible, for instance, to conceive of a lady upping to Swope, say, at the bar in "21," with a question calculated to evoke an immortal reply. For one thing, the cramped and noisy setting is distinctly unpropitious, since it is far removed indeed from the resplendent assemblage with its gracious and convenient lulls in conversation. One would have to say to our hypothetical lady, "How's that?" or "I beg your pardon?", and the precise timing so essential to the great retort would be irreparably ruined.'

A woman came into the study with a cocktail in her hand.

'Don't you think we ought to be getting along, Nora?' Matthews asked.

'Nonsense,' she said. 'It's early.'

'This is Mr Thurber,' he told her. 'My wife.' I stood up. 'Mr Thurber has been telling a story about Gerard Swope.'

'Not Gerard,' I said. 'Herbert Bayard.'

'Oh,' said Matthews.

'That's nice,' said his wife, and she went away.

'Only yesterday,' I said, sitting down, 'my secretary straightened up the room I work in – and an imposing task it was, to be sure. She separated answered and unanswered mail, soiled handkerchiefs and telegrams, dog drawings and razor blades, and in the process she came up with a folder of news clippings marked "Things You Said." '

'Things you said yourself, eh?' Matthews' eyes narrowed a little.

'Well, so the record shows.' I sighed. 'It all supports our theory of the changing setup, the deterioration of the players and the scene, the passing of the ancient glories. I have the contents of the folder fairly well in mind. They're skimpy enough, God knows. The first item is a clipping from the Chicago *Sun*.'

'Field,' said Matthews. 'Big operator.'

'It seems that Freddy Wakeman, the millionaire novelist, told the *Sun's* Spectorsky an anecdote about me when I was in Bermuda. A dewy young thing came up to me in a bar in Somerset, the story goes, and asked me why I had sold a certain piece of mine to the movies. Quick as a flash, I answered, "M-o-n-e-y." '

'Government probably got most of it,' Matthews said.

The man was beginning to make me nervous. 'The point is not in the financial transaction itself,' I said testily. 'The point is in the payoff at the bar down there in Somerset. I spelled it out. There is no surer way to blunt the crusher and destroy the devastation.'

'You don't have any recollection of the incident, eh?' Matthews asked shrewdly.

'None,' I said. 'Of course, I was fifty-one at the time, and perhaps a little cockeyed. If I spelled out the payoff, it is an indictment of my slowing mind or a proof of my decrepitude.'

Matthews sat forward in his chair, as if poised for flight. 'How big a folder'd you say this was?' he asked.

'Sparse,' I snapped. 'It won't detain you long. Why don't you get some more ale?'

'I believe I will,' he said, and went away.

When Matthews came back, I began again. 'Well, it seems I came out of this movie theatre with a group of friends – I always attend the cinema in the bosom of my circle – and one of them said, "I think that picture stinks," to which I instantly replied, "I didn't think it was that good." ' I got out a cigarette and lighted it.

'My wife and daughter are crazy about this James Mason,' Matthews said.

'The anecdote limps so obviously that I feel myself, now and then, attempting to repair or recap it,' I went on. 'Like this, for example: "If a picture worse than stinks," put in Louis Sobol, who was also there, "metrofaction may be said to have set in." '

'What was that?' asked Matthews.

I exhaled slowly. 'Nothing,' I said. 'But if you have already been blinded by the brilliance, shade your mental eyes against what is still to come. In the summer of 1946, some months after the movie episode, a sensitive *Time* reporter got me on the long-distance phone to chat about the I.C.C. He said, "Do you know Jo Davidson?" '

'No,' said Matthews, 'I don't.'

'The reporter asked *me* that,' I snarled. 'The files of *Time*, forever antic and forever wrong, reveal that I shot back, "I met him once. He has a beard." '

Matthews shifted his glass to his left hand and adjusted his tie.

'The *Time* man omitted to report, for some obscure reason, that I thought Mr Davidson was head of the Interstate Commerce Commission. It's too bad, because Timen and Tiwomen – in fact, the whole Lucempire – would still be laughing.'

'Never miss an issue of *Time* if I can help it,' Matthews said.

'As keen as my famous Davidson quip was,' I said, 'I was to top it in that same remarkable year. A few months later, Earl Wilson, the sympathetic columnist of the New York *Post*, called on me at my office in the city. When he came in, I was drinking black coffee. My greeting was what I can only describe as a staggeroo. "I'm having some formaldehyde," I'm supposed to have said. "Will you join me?" '

Matthews took out another cigar and gave it a squirrelly inspection.

'Well, sir, to get on with the folder,' I began again, 'it seems that I came out of a movie theatre last July after seeing a picture based rather insecurely on a piece I wrote years ago. On this occasion, the story goes, I emerged in the company of a distinguished group of New York cognoscenti. "Did anybody catch the name of that picture?" I asked drolly. Bennett Cerf, a wit in his own right, and in several other persons', printed my comment in his column. The town is still chuckling.'

Matthews lighted his cigar and seemed to be trying to hide behind it.

'The most recent and, you will be glad to hear, the final item in the folder,' I said, 'appeared in an issue of the *Hollywood Reporter*. I think I can quote it exactly. "His" – mine, that is – "favourite line about Hollywood is 'Look what they did to Maurice Costello'." I take it that one repeats one's favourite line as one rereads one's favourite book. The appalling thought has occurred to me that at some party or other I may have repeated the line several times to the same person. I wonder that no one has shouted at me, "Will you, for the love of God, stop saying that!" '

'What's going on in here? Are you two fighting?' It was Nora back again, with a fresh cocktail.

'No,' I said. 'You overheard an inner quote.'

'Some woman yelled at him at a party,' Matthews explained.

'The wretch!' cried Nora.

'We must be charitable,' I said. 'After all, she had been through a lot.'

'Nora, don't you think –' Matthews began.

'It's the shank of the afternoon,' she said, and left the room. Matthews finished his ale and puffed at his cigar. He was getting fidgety.

'So endeth,' I sighed, 'the paltry, the pathetic folder.'

Matthews' elbows seemed about to lift him out of his chair, but he relaxed when I began again.

'One of my colleagues is reported to have watched, on a Long Island estate, the transplanting of a great elm. "This little job," his host told him, "is costing me two hundred thousand dollars." "Shows what God could do if he had money," my friend commented. He modestly disclaims the observation, but the point I want to make is this. If it had been hung on me, the story would go: " 'This little job is costing me two hundred thousand dollars.' 'That,' remarked Thurber, 'is a lot of money.' " 'I resent, Matthews,' I added angrily, 'what has all the appearance of a conspiracy to place on my shoulders the mantle of Calvin Coolidge.'

Matthews frowned for a long moment. 'Things you really said never got printed, eh?' he shrewdly inquired.

I laughed modestly and put on an expression of feigned embarrassment. 'Well, they don't exactly ripple off my tongue,' I said. 'I'm no Jack Warner. But as a matter of fact, since you ask, there *was* one. This happened – oh, fifteen years ago. I had completely forgotten about it until something reminded me of it about six months ago. A tall, thin, serious-looking man came into the reception room of the magazine I worked for and asked for me. He told me he represented a publisher of high-priced special editions. He said his firm had hit on the idea of having me do new illustrations for "Alice in Wonderland." I said, "Let's keep the Tenniel drawings and I'll rewrite the story." The chap bowed and went away.'

Matthews scowled. 'Fellow thought you were an artist instead of a writer, eh?' he brought out finally.

'Precisely,' I said. 'Well, as it happened, there was no one but this man and me in the reception room at the time. I never have any luck that way. However, I sauntered into the office of a colleague and told him what I had said. Weeks went by, then months, and years, but no one ever spoke to me about the incident. My colleague, absorbed with some problem of his own, had apparently not listened to what I told him. The tall, thin man obviously never repeated the bit of dialogue, either.'

'Turned down, probably disappointed,' said Matthews.

'When I was reminded of the incident six months ago,' I went on, 'I told it to a writer friend of mine. He put it in the first act of a play he was writing, giving me credit by name and retelling the story perfectly.'

'What play was that?' asked Matthews.

'It was never produced,' I said.

Matthews pushed himself up out of his chair, mumbled something about having to see Ed, and walked away – swiftly, I thought, for a man of his bulk. He had pretty well worn me out.

A middle-aged woman flounced into the room and sat down in the chair he had left. 'What do you know about Putney?' she yelped.

'Everything,' I lied, hastily, but it was no good. She told me about Putney until it was time to leave.

Another woman came up to me before I could find my hostess or my hat. 'John Matthews has been telling us a perfectly wonderful story, Mr Thurber,' she squealed, 'about how you absolutely refused to rewrite "Alice in Wonderland," in spite of all the money they offered you.'

'M-o-o-l-a,' I said, coldly.

'Well, I think it was perfectly wonderful of you, I really do!'

'It was nothing at all,' I said. 'Anybody would have done the same thing.'

She shrieked, 'You're much too modest, Mr Thurber, really!'

'I'm not modest, Madam!' I snarled. 'I'm simply too g-o-d-d-a-m-n unlucky for words.' I felt my wife's firm, familiar grip on my arm.

'Come on,' she said. 'It's time to go. I said good-bye to Harriet for you.' She found my hat and we went out and got in the car.

'What were you shouting at Ida Barlow for?' she asked, starting the engine.

'Madam,' I said, 'if a man shouts at Ida Barlow, he makes an ass of her, but if he does not shout at Ida Barlow, he makes an ass of himself. Ask me anything and I'll give you a comeback.'

'How did you manage not to fall off the wagon?' she asked. 'I was sure you were going to when I saw you were stuck with John Matthews.'

'Putney anything else would have been as bad,' I said. She glanced at me with a hint of concern. 'Ask me why I didn't fall off the wagon,' I demanded.

She sighed. 'All right, why didn't you fall off the wagon?'

'They didn't have any formaldehyde,' I chortled.

It didn't strike her as funny, for some reason, but I had to laugh. I laughed most of the way home.

A Guide to the Literary Pilgrimage

IN A CERTAIN restaurant on Third Avenue, whose proprietors are patrons of the arts, I was standing at the bar one evening, smiling in my beer, when a short, bald, middle-aged man appeared at my shoulder and said, 'What sets *you* off from the other temperaments in this ateleer, Mac?' I could have run the fellow through with that cold, steady stare of mine which has been called 'brown ice,' but I found, a little to my surprise, that I had an answer to his question. 'I am the only living writer,' I said, 'who has not called on George Bernard Shaw and who does not want to call on George Bernard Shaw.' The character at my shoulder, who had expected to call forth from me a foolish grin and a few stammered words, slunk sheepishly down the bar to insult a rather peaked etcher who was quietly cursing to himself. I was left to examine, the way a squirrel examines a nut, the sudden little definition of singularity which I had tossed off. I could find no flaws in it.

It is not that I have anything against George Bernard Shaw or fail to appreciate his genius. It is neither an emotional blockage nor a mental judgment which stands in the way of my wanting to call on him. It is, I think, a purely nervous apprehension. I am afraid, perhaps, that I would sit in the great man's study gaping like a badly carved jack-o'-lantern, squirming and stammering like the hobbledehoy I really am under my well-groomed exterior, behind my mask of cold indifference.

On top of this singularly personal attitude toward calling on Shaw, there has been superimposed a pattern of actual experience – not my own experience, to be sure, but that of two other writers, Ralph Waldo Emerson and a man whom I shall call Mitchell Morris. The adventures of these two gentlemen in the homes of the literary great have persuaded me of a basic and unfortunate fact about the literary pilgrimage: it almost never comes off very well.

Emerson may have founded the American cult of the literary pilgrimage; at any rate, he risked a tricky stomach on a sailing ship more than a hundred years ago to pay his respects to Wordsworth, Coleridge, Carlyle, and Landor. He found in Carlyle a man who was to become a lifelong friend (they even kind of romped together, a thing I would have gone a long way to see), but he didn't do so well with the others. Wordsworth, who had just broken a front tooth, recited two sonnets while he and his guest both stood looking at each other – surely one of the most uncomfortable moments in the annals of the literary pilgrimage. Coleridge wore green spectacles and argued querulously about Unitarianism. Landor disagreed about almost everything his visitor brought up, from military leaders through Southey to the Latin poets.

The case of my writer friend, Mitchell Morris, was more recent and quite different. Morris called on the late William Bolitho at his villa in southern France about fifteen years ago. After my friend had presented himself, Bolitho said, 'I will talk for an hour and you will talk for an hour.'

The Bolitho system of literary communion has never seemed sound to me. If I were the man told off to speak last, I would not be able to take in what the other man was saying because I would be trying to think of something to say when my own turn came. This would lead to the stiff posture, the horrible smile, the inattentive monosyllabic interjection, and the glazed expression of the eye. When my host's hour was up, I am afraid I would only be able to repeat over and over, 'This is a mighty nice place you've got here.'

If the adventures of Emerson and Morris in the living rooms of the great serve to prove that the literary communion of literary men is by no means a pleasurable and relaxing way to pass an afternoon, the experience of another writer I know who called on André Gide in North Africa recently establishes the rare and pleasant exception to the rule. The distinguished old Frenchman, it came out, was, at the moment, immersed in a profound study of the works of the American intellectual, Dashiell Hammett. Now, the works of Dashiell Hammett happen to constitute a field in which I can hold my own with anyone, a field in which, on one occasion, I even held my own with the celebrated author himself.

I should explain, at this point, that Mr Hammett and I did not meet by appointment. He did not call on me and I did not call on him. We ran into each other at Tony's, once the fashionable meeting place of the literati of two continents. In Tony's in the old days, literary communion was informal to the point of rough-and-tumble, and a writer did not sit at the feet of another writer unless he was knocked there.

Well (to get farther and farther away from my friend's call on Gide), Hammett was pleased to announce that the only author whose writing had influenced his own was the late Henry James. It chanced that the subtle but notable similarities between 'The Maltese Falcon' and 'The Wings of the Dove' had been apparent to me long before they were exposed by Henry Morton Robinson. My own monograph on this curious literary resemblance, 'Could Dashiell Hammett Have Created Sam Spade and Ned Beaumont if Henry James had Not Created Merton Densher and Lambert Strether?', had, unfortunately, been stored in a warehouse in Bridgeport which burned down in 1934.

Furthermore, it would be just my luck, if I called on Gide, to catch him during a period of Hammett-fag, so that he would be in no mood to listen to the brilliant and carefully prepared parallel I can draw between 'The Glass Key' and 'The Golden Bowl.' Monsieur Gide would probably open up on me by saying, 'You are familiar, of course, with the works of Aristide Luchon?' It is my embarrassed tendency in such cases to reply, 'Yes. Oh, yes, indeed.' Surely no one can imagine a more awful way to spend an afternoon than by attempting to discuss novels or plays one has never read, written by a man one has never heard of.

P

My fear about Shaw is that he might, to get back at me for some casual mention of the resemblance between 'The Thin Man' and 'The Sacred Fount,' *invent* out of thin air a writer named Aristide Luchon. In all the calendar of dirty tricks one writer can play on another, this is the dirtiest. I believe that Shaw would be capable of such black deviltry. In fact, I sometimes see him, in my dreams, leaning toward me and saying, 'Do you agree with me that the character of Mathilde in Luchon's *Dormer Avant le Coucher du Soleil* is badly thought out?' I ride into that with all the reckless courage of Senator Bricker, crying, 'I do, indeed!' and the fat is in the fire, the cat out of the bag, the jig up, and my audience with Shaw at an end. His satanic laughter, as I run full upon his rapier, rings through my nightmares and brings me, panting and terrified, awake.

These nightmares inspired me to work on a set of rules called 'The Young Writer's Guide to the Literary Pilgrimage.' The rules are by no means complete, but if they serve to lighten in any way the burden of the visiting – or of the visited – author, I shall be amply repaid for my pains.

RULE I. Bear in mind always that you are the minor artist and that the man you are calling on is the major artist. Otherwise, he would be calling on you. He is not going to write an article about your visit to him; hence, who you are and what you have written will serve only to embarrass him. Thus, it is extremely bad form to present yourself with a loud, proud 'I am George Benton Fields.' The great man might respond with a pseudo-hearty 'Well, I should say you are!'* and the interview would be off to an awkward start. It is equally unfortunate and dangerous to open up with a muttered 'My name is Fields, sir.' Your host might bellow irritably, 'Speak up, man!', or he might address you all afternoon as Mr Fieldser, which would be most uncomfortable.

Sedulously avoid any of the three principal forms of the General or Indefinite Introduction. These are as follows: 1. The Modest or Casual Presentation: 'I am a writer from Seattle, Washington.' 2. The Self-Derogatory Introduction: 'I am a broken-hearted bum from Warren, Ohio.' 3. The Flippant or Facetious Identification: 'I am a little stiff from Bowling Green, and my actuary gives me only thirty-five years to live.' In the first place, you will have made an appointment (if not, you might as well get back on your bicycle), so the Master will know who you are and what you want, in a general sort of way. Just say 'How do you do, sir?' and let him take the lead from there.

RULE II. Do not attempt to impress the great man with some observation or aphorism of your own which you have carefully polished up for the occasion, such as 'The noblest study of mankind is insects,' or 'The César Franck D Minor Symphony is a fraternity whistle,' or 'Clover leaves rarely strike four times in the same place,' or 'There are two ways to get a subject down – pat and mike.' The ice may never be broken if you start out like that.

RULE III. Do not come out with (and this is especially directed to the visiting female author) 'I have simply *devoured* every line you have ever written, and I

---

* A comeback made by the late Clare Briggs when a total stranger approached him with 'I am Henry Preston Barnes.'

adore them all!' If, by the end of the afternoon (or of the first five minutes), the great man comes to the conclusion that you are an indiscriminating ass, he may be moved to do some rash and deplorable violence to his novels or plays. Many a distinguished author in his advanced years has completely revised the entire body of his work, usually for the worse. The reason has long remained a mystery, but in the lady who devours and adores every line, I think we have the answer.

R ULE IV. Keep all critics' names out of the conversation. Do not say, 'As Van Wyck Brooks [or Bernard De Voto] so aptly put it . . .' It is more than likely that the mention of the name of any critic since Sainte-Beuve has been strictly forbidden in the shrine for more than forty years.

R ULE V. Be careful, if you mention any of the writer's works (and you better had), not to confuse him with some other writer. H. G. Wells once said that most of the people who visited him informed him that his best novel by far was 'The Old Wives' Tale.'

R ULE VI. For God's sake don't recite anything. What do you suppose Wordsworth would have thought if Emerson had recited a couple of his own poems to *him* (Wordsworth)?

R ULE VII. Don't bring the celebrated artist a letter of introduction from Herbert Bayard Swope, Clarence Budington Kelland, Robert Alphonso Taft, Gene Tunney, George Palmer Putnam, H. V. Kaltenborn, Dan Golenpaul, or some Scarsdale woman who claims she met the old boy on a ship during a frightful crossing to Pernambuco. It is better not even to mention this woman's name or the name of the ship (or Pernambuco or Scarsdale).

R ULE VIII. Do not come into the Presence bearing gifts. He has almost everything, doesn't need anything, and likes practically nothing. Furthermore, it is very hard for him to say 'Thank you.' In the case of a great many offerings, I don't blame him. Here is a list of gifts which should especially be excluded: a clipping of an article written by the eminent gentleman for a school paper when he was fifteen; a copy of one of his plays done on the head of a tenpenny nail; a copy of one of his plays translated into Shawnee by an employee of the Department of the Interior; a paragraph laboriously constructed by rearranging all the words in the titles of all his books and intended to supply a key to What He Has Been Trying to Say; any caricatures, effigies, or likenesses of the great man, particularly those made out of typewriter punctuation marks, embroidery floss, field-corn kernels, buckeyes, matches, toothpicks, pipe cleaners, paper clips, tiddlywinks, dice, pigeon feathers, spools, milk-bottle caps, cigar bands, BB shot, or potatoes. The value of these objects is not enhanced by the fact that they were made by a child under seven, a woman over ninety, a Camp Fire Girl, Mayor O'Dwyer, the seventh daughter of a seventh daughter, or a midget.

R ULE IX. Do not take with you your friends and neighbours, Mr and Mrs Howard M. Phillips, who happen to be travelling with you. If I know Mrs Phillips, and I think I do, she will tell about her niece who, though only nine, writes verse and composes music. She will try to read some of the poems, which she always carries in her handbag, and, if there is a piano, she may even play one of the child's sonatas.

RULE X. If, on your arrival, the door is opened by a member of the literary figure's household who says that the Master will not be able to see you for forty-eight hours, do not hang around the house or the neighbourhood. Go away.

RULE XI. If, in such a case, you do go away, do not leave behind, for the distinguished writer to read, a thousand-word note written in longhand and beginning, 'In 1908, when my brother-in-law was an oiler on a Danish cattle boat, he found one of your,' etc., etc., etc. Don't leave any note at all. Just go away.

RULE XII. And stay away.

If you are protesting that my Guide to the Literary Pilgrimage does not so much present my reasons for not wanting to call on Shaw as it does his probable reasons for not wanting me, or you (or your Aunt Clara, who once had a piece in *Harper's* 'Lion's Mouth'), to call on him, I can only point out that my reluctance to make the pilgrimage is implicit in the very nature of the rules. Beyond the suggestion that the visitor should begin with a simple 'How do you do, sir?' the rules do not offer any instructions as to what to say. This is because I have not been able to think of anything to say in the presence of George Bernard Shaw, and I do not believe that Shaw would be amused by anyone who just sat there and said nothing.

The only famous writer I have ever heard of who did not expect his companion to say anything at all was the late Hendrik Willem van Loon. A friend of mine, who used to ride with van Loon from Stamford to New York several times a week, determined one day on a test. He decided to greet van Loon on the Stamford platform on this particular morning simply with a smile and a handshake and to leave him in Grand Central station the same way, having said no word. He wondered if the great man would catch on to the fact that his companion had not once opened his mouth. The next morning, he again came up to van Loon on the Stamford platform and said, 'That was a fine discussion we had on the train yesterday.' 'It was, indeed,' said van Loon. 'I enjoyed it a great deal.'

That would surely be too much to expect of Mr Shaw. Or perhaps I should say too much for Mr Shaw to expect of me. In any event, I have written enough about what I do not intend to say on a literary pilgrimage I am never going to make.

Here Come the Tigers

IT WAS AFTER midnight and I had got up to turn off the radio and go to bed when a baritone began to sing 'Bye-Bye, Blackbird' with the rueful reverence the song deserves. I sat down again, and I was lost. If I had shut off the radio, turned out the lights, and locked the door, Jordan and Hayes would have driven up to a dark house and gone away, or if they had hammered on the door, I would have let them hammer till they got discouraged and drove off. The lights were on, though, and the door was unlocked. The tyres of a car swashed over the gravel of the driveway and came to a sudden, complaining stop. My door opened and they tumbled in without knocking, like a pair of comics taking an encore. I turned off the radio and reached for the light switch.

'Hold!' Jordan cried. 'Stay that naughty hand!'

I took my hand off the switch. 'I'm tired,' I said, 'and Alice is asleep.'

'Sleep! Sleep – on a night of wild discovery!' Jordan moaned. He went over to the bar in a corner of the living room and began mixing a bourbon-and-soda. Hayes took Jordan's place at the bar when his companion flopped into a chair and swung one leg over an arm. 'We have discovered a new dimension of meaning,' Jordan said. He took a great gulp of his drink. 'And a new plane of beauty.'

'You want a drink?' Hayes asked me.

'It's late,' I said, 'and I'm tired.'

Jordan snorted, choked on his whisky, and coughed for a full minute. 'The man wants torpor,' he spluttered finally. 'On a night like this, the man wants torpor.'

'Torpor is a good word,' Hayes said. He sat on the arm of a chair. 'Shall we take it apart for him?'

'You guys are stiff,' I said.

Jordan frowned, finished his drink, and went back to the bar. 'Stiff is better,' he said. 'I think stiff is probably perfect. Let me get at it.' He dropped into the chair again, with a new highball.

I stared at the ceiling. If I didn't humour them, they might go away.

'We're starting too high,' Jordan said. 'We're the hell too high. He won't get it. Look at him.'

'Nuts,' I said coldly.

'Let me unwrap stiff for you,' Jordan said. 'God knows that ought to be simple enough. Listen to this. It's perfect. Stiff, tiff, fists, fits.'

'He means that the mood and tone and colour of a word are echoed in its component parts,' Hayes said. 'Tiff is argument, fist is fight, fits – fits – '

435

'Don't make it glare,' Jordan said. 'You're making it glare. Let him feel it. You got to feel it.'

'Look–' I began wanly.

Jordan regarded me sorrowfully and shook his head. 'He's going to compare it to Joyce or Dada or Gertrude Stein,' he said. 'He is an enemy of the new dimension. Oh, no, he can't be,' he added. 'Not in *this* house, he can't be.' He had some trouble getting up, but he made the bar.

'It's *his* house,' Hayes said.

I was glad he was soberer than Jordan, who after a moment of deep thought said, 'Last place in the world a man should make an ass of himself. Host, you know, and all that.'

'Where have you guys been?' I asked.

Jordan looked at Hayes and shrugged, splashing a dollop of his new drink on the carpet. 'We have been in a new dimension of meaning and beauty,' he said, 'but I doubt if you could understand it.'

'Well, what the hell is it?' I demanded. I went to the bar and poured myself a short drink. 'Are you going to crawl around it all night, or are you coming out with it?'

'Tell him the quatrain,' Jordan said. 'I want him to hear the quatrain.'

Hayes studied the floor for a while. Then he recited the quatrain:

> 'There are lips in pistol
> And mist in times,
> Cats in crystal,
> and mice in chimes.'

I stared coldly at Jordan's transfigured face. 'Is this the spearhead of the New Beauty?' I asked.

Jordan globbered his drink down, ran his hand through his hair, and glared at me demoniacally. 'Shows what What's-his-name of "Christabel" and Keats of "Eve of St Agnes" could have done if the goddam fairy casements had opened on this lovely dimension!' he shouted.

'Coleridge,' Hayes said. He was nursing his drink along, and seemed to be getting sober.

Jordan went to the bar and sloshed out more bourbon. 'Well?' he demanded, but he didn't wait for me to answer. 'We were unlocking animals from almost every word you can think of when we got to cats in crystal and mice in chimes. Tell him some of 'em, Tom. You got 'em all written down.'

Hayes put his drink on the floor and pulled a piece of folded cardboard out of his pocket. I saw that it was a dinner menu with pencil scribblings on the back. 'There's the wolf in flower, the gander in danger, and the frog in forget,' he said. 'There's the emu in summer, the ant in autumn, the wren in winter, and the pig in spring.' He turned the cardboard upside down and scowled at it. 'There's the gnu in jungle,' he went on, 'the swan in answer, and the toad in toward.' He put the menu down, and I thought he looked a little unhappy, as if the whisky and the spell of the new dimension were wearing off at the same time.

Jordan kept snapping his fingers, trying to remember other beasts in other words.

'Try to find the tiger in a six-letter word,' Hayes said to me. 'It isn't easy. There are three six-letter words with tiger, but it isn't easy.'

'It's not a game, it's more than a game,' Jordan said severely. 'Let's not get back to the game.'

'It began as a game,' Hayes said to me. 'It's an old word game. You try to see how many words you can make out of another word.'

'We played it a million times before,' Jordan said, 'but tonight, for the first time, I see what we got, like Emily What's-her-name hearing the river in the trees. You might hear the wind in the trees all your life and never hear the river. Give me that thing, Tom.' He reached out and took the menu from Hayes, and began turning it slowly in his big hands. The writing on the back apparently ran in all directions. He sighed dolefully and handed it back to Hayes. 'There's practically a sentence in woman,' he said. 'It's perfect in mood and tone. In mood and tone it's practically perfect. See if you can find the sentence, Tom.'

Hayes patted away an incipient yawn. 'Woman: moan now won wan man,' he chanted, and then the yawn got the best of him.

'What'd I say it had in it, Tom?'

Hayes consulted the back of the menu. 'The thunder of Genesis,' he announced finally, 'it says here.'

'It's practically Biblical,' Jordan said, 'with only five letters.' He went to the bar again. 'Who wants a drink?' he asked. Neither of us said anything. Hayes had slumped a little in his chair. I leaned back, gazed at the ceiling, and hunted the tiger. For the next five minutes, I heard the sound of Jordan's voice but I didn't take in the sense. I found the roach in orchard, the horse in shore, the owl in wobble, the stag in ghastly, and the bear and zebra in brazen, but no glimmer of a tiger anywhere.

'It's like little boxes, one inside each other,' Jordan was saying when I came out of my own jungle of words. 'You lift out concentric meanings of practically identical mood and tone. Yet people have let the component parts of words go for a thousand years. They lose the depth and the roundness and the whole quality.' He turned to Hayes. 'Take pistol apart for Jim,' he begged. 'Take pistol apart.' I got up and went to the bar and poured out a stiff rye. 'Go ahead,' I said.

'It kind of rips and squirts and goes all to hell, the way pistol should,' Jordan said by way of foreword.

'Shoot,' I said.

'No gags,' Jordan implored me. 'For God's sake, no gags.'

'Pistol,' Hayes began. 'Slip, spit, split, spilt, spoil, spoilt, slop, slot, tips, tops, spot, pots, stop.'

'You see what I mean?' Jordan asked. I visualized the word and studied it for a while.

'He left out oils and soil,' I said finally, 'and what are Lois and silo doing in pistol?'

Jordan turned to Hayes, who had shut his eyes. 'Didn't I tell you we'd be up against that?' he demanded. 'What'd I say we'd be up against, Tom?'

'The obscurantism of the explicit,' Hayes brought out after frowning over it.

'That's it! That's what I said we'd be up against, like in chalice.'

Hayes decided to try another drink, and he went over and poured himself a short one. 'You get lace and hail and ice and Alice in chalice,' he said, 'but you got lice to account for.'

'So what?' said Jordan. 'So what the hell?' He spread his hands.

'What about the rats in crystal, with the cats?' I asked.

'Jordan hasn't got the technic and ethic worked out yet,' Hayes told me.

'I can handle the rats,' Jordan said.

'And the salt and the slat and the cyst and the cart?' I asked.

'Yeh, and the star and the cry and the satyr. They all mix into crystal.'

Hayes yawned openly. He was drinking slowly. 'It seems a little thin, somehow,' he said. 'I mean the whole thing, in times like these.'

'What does?' Jordan stared at him blankly.

I saved an argument by suddenly running across Roget in forget. 'If there were no forget,' I said to Jordan, 'it would not be necessary to create Roget.'

'I don't think you get the idea,' he said. 'I don't think he gets the idea, Tom. What was it I said earlier this evening? I said, "Tom, he'll never get it in a million years." I said, "Tom, the obscurantism of the explicit is what's going to louse up this lovely thing." Didn't I say that, Tom?'

'Yes,' Hayes said, tapping another yawn.

'Do hotels for him, Tom. Maybe that'll give him the idea.'

'Hotels,' Hayes read. 'Sot, lost, hose, stole, shoe. Hotel so hot she shot host. . . . I'm tired.' He sagged in his chair.

'A lost mood, see?' Jordan tried to express it with a gesture of his hands. 'You got to feel it like a child. Do you feel it?'

'I certainly do,' I said.

'What are you tired for, Tom?' Jordan gave his friend a worried glance.

'I don't know,' Hayes said. 'It just seems a little thin, somehow.'

'What does?'

'Mice in chimes. It seems a little thin.'

'What's he talking about?' Jordan asked me.

'I mean when you get to thinking of the hare twisting in the frozen grass and the mastiff bitch in the moonshine cold,' Hayes said.

'What the *hell*'s he talking about?' Jordan almost wailed.

'What's-his-name and Keats,' I said.

Jordan made a small, despairing gesture. 'Do phrase,' he pleaded.

'Oh, for God sake!' Hayes got up and went to the radio.

'Don't wake Alice,' I said.

'Do phrase and then we'll get the hell out,' Jordan said.

'Do phrase,' I insisted quickly.

'Explain about it first in its own words,' Jordan said. 'You know.'

'O.K., O.K.' Hayes sighed and sat down. 'You don't have to dwell on the parse phase, the sharp rasp, the rape shape,' he droned.

'Now show him where Tenniel and What's-his-name, the *douanier*, come in,' Jordan said eagerly.

'In the apes and the asp and the hares,' Hayes went on. 'In the peas and the pears and the tea, in the seraph and the harp.'

Jordan's eyes glowed, like a cat's in a barn. 'Tenniel and What's-his-name, the *douanier*,' he said in a throaty voice.

'Come on, let's go, I got to go,' Hayes said, getting up.

'You didn't have a hat,' I told him.

'Take the oranges and gibbons of What's-his-name,' Jordan went on, in a rapt croak.

'Rousseau, for God sake,' Hayes said. 'Come on.'

Jordan got to his feet. His eyes moved slowly around the room.

'You didn't have a hat,' Hayes said. 'Come on.'

He got Jordan just outside the living-room door. Four more steps would have taken them through the hall to the front door.

'Where do you get the tea in phrase?' I asked suddenly. 'There isn't any "t" in phrase.'

Jordan turned and loped back to his chair and sat down hard, like a tired setter. 'A posset for the highway!' he bawled.

'You asked for this,' Hayes told me wearily.

'Mix him a short one,' I said.

Hayes went slowly back into the living room and I closed the door behind him. I knew Alice was standing at the head of the stairs in the dark. 'What *is* it?' she whispered.

'A posset for the highway,' I told her.

'Jink Jordan? Oh, no!' She went back to her room.

I lingered in the hall, hoping they would come out, but Jordan's voice was loud and argumentative. 'Will you stop saying it's thin, for God sake?' he shouted.

'All right, all right, it's exiguous, then,' Hayes said.

'It's exiguous because it's undeveloped, that's why,' Jordan replied. 'You can't develop a thing like this in one night.'

I went back into the room and shut the door behind me. Jordan was sitting in the chair I had been in, pulling some papers out of his inside coat pocket.

'Put that stuff away,' Hayes commanded him sharply.

'Just a second,' Jordan said. 'I knew we'd left something out. How in the hell could you let me leave Blake out?' He began to pore over a pencilled scrawl on the back of a typewritten page. 'We proved Blake had it,' he said loudly. 'We proved Blake knew all about it, and here it is!'

Hayes grabbed the sheet of paper away from him. 'If I read it, will you get up and go home?' he asked. 'And don't drink that so fast.'

'Read it,' Jordan said, waving his glass. 'Wait a minute!' He pointed a finger at me. 'How many tigers are there in – what's the line, Tom?'

' "Tiger! Tiger! burning bright in the forests of the night",' Tom recited.

'One tiger,' I said. 'How many Toms are there in "Tom, Tom, the piper's son"?'

Jordan set his drink down and waved his arms despairingly. 'Journalist!' he said bleakly.

'This is kind of interesting,' Hayes said hurriedly. 'There are actually five tigers in the first two lines of the poem – that is, the necessary letters are repeated often enough to spell the word five times, three times in addition to "tiger, tiger," with a couple of "t"s and an "i" left over.'

Jordan finished his drink in a gulp. 'Nursery rhymes!' he said bitterly.

'In those two lines,' Hayes cut in, 'Blake used only twelve letters of the alphabet, so Jink thinks he was on to the new dimension.'

'Thinks!' Jordan cried.

'Wordsworth, who was not on to it,' Hayes continued, 'used nineteen letters in "She dwelt among the untrodden ways, beside the springs of Dove." '

Jordan shook his head at me slowly. 'It'll take me ten years to work this thing out,' he snarled, 'and you giggle at it like a girl. Tell him about Planters Peanuts, Tom.'

Hayes handed the sheet of paper back to Jordan and ran his hand over his forehead. 'There are nine letters in Planters Peanuts, or only three fewer than Blake used in those two lines. Come on, let's go.'

'One more, maybe?' Jordan said, holding out his glass.

'I'm going,' Hayes snapped. 'I'll wait just two minutes for you in the car.' He walked over and opened the door, closed it behind him, went out the front door, got in the car, and slammed the car door shut.

'There goes one of the sweetest characters in the whole world,' Jordan said.

I started turning out the table lamps, and Jordan got to his feet. 'So long, Jink,' I said. He walked slowly to the door, opened it, and said over his shoulder, 'Not in a million years.' The only light left on now was the one in the hall. Jordan closed the front door after him with great care. After a moment, the engine started and the car drove off.

Half an hour later, in bed, I had almost dropped off when, in the narrow strip of lucidity between the bright compound of consciousness and the dark jungle of sleep, I remembered, with a start like a gunshot, the tiger in the three six-letter words. I tried all the permutations I could think of, using one consonant after another, from 'b' to 'z'. I couldn't fit the tiger into any six-letter word except tigers, and that obviously didn't count. I began all over again: tibger, bitger, grebit, trebig, briget, ticger, grecit, gercit, tidger, gertid, dregit.

The dawn was fluttering at the window when I finally found the three words, one after another, with tiger in them.

Alice woke up. 'Haven't you been to sleep *yet*?' she asked.

'Gaiter, goitre, aigret,' I said. 'Avoid the consonants. It's as simple as that.'

'Go to sleep,' she said.

I managed it finally. It wasn't easy.

(AUTHOR'S NOTE: Shortly after the foregoing story appeared in *The New*

Yorker the editors received and passed on to me a letter written by Mr George Rose Smith, an eminent tiger hunter of Little Rock, Arkansas. Mr Smith's letter went in part as follows: 'In James Thurber's recent story, Here Come the Tigers, his friends assured him that there are three six-letter words containing the letters t-i-g-e-r. Thurber spent a sleepless night in tracking down the tigers in gaitre, goitre and aigret, and apparently concluded that he had exhausted the possibilities...Disturbed by the thought that the tiger is as near to extinction as Thurber intimates, I sent two native beaters through the Websterian veldts and quickly bagged the limit of ten.

'The girt group of words is infested with the beasts, both girted and begirt being perfectly good usage. For some reason engirt is branded as obsolete, though it happens that we in the South have occasion to use it almost daily. The prefix re-conceals two fine tigers, in regilt and regift. In the latter the prefix is used in the sense of "back to an original or former position," so that regift is closely allied to the familiar concept of an Indian giver...

'The suffix -er is also good for two tigers. Tigger is an attractive word, which the lexicographer (probably late for a date) hurriedly defined as "one who tigs." Tig itself means to run about, as cattle pestered by flies. Pestered by tigers is doubtless historically correct, but such tigging doesn't become habitual. Our lexicographer spent more time on tinger, defining it as "one who or that which tinges." We do not seem to have any word for one who, or even that which, tings. Perhaps the best choice would be ting-er, the hyphen giving a subtle indication of the tiger's stripes. The definition of gitter, a foreign word for a kind of grating, already carries this connotation of straight lines.

'A rare tiger is preserved in the Scotch word erting, which means urging on – a derivation from a root meaning to tease or provoke. This ancient custom of teasing or provoking tigers, while not mentioned in modern histories of Scotland, was probably a tribal method of demonstrating bravery.

'Thurber and his companions were interested in finding animals in odd places, as the mice in chimes and the cats in crystal, but they completely overlooked the tiger in a six-letter animal, the common or garden variety of grivet. As every schoolboy knows, the grivet is an intelligent and docile monkey, having a dull olive-green back....')

A Call on Mrs Forrester

(After re-reading, in my middle years, Willa Cather's *A Lost Lady*
and Henry James's *The Ambassadors*.)

I DROPPED off a Burlington train at Sweet Water one afternoon last fall to call
on Marian Forrester. It was a lovely day. October stained the hills with
quiet gold and russet, and scarlet as violent as the blood spilled not far away
so many years ago along the banks of the Little Big Horn. It had been just such
a day as this when I was last in Sweet Water, fifteen years before, but the glory
of the earth affected me more sharply now than it had when I was midway
through my confident thirties. October weather, once a plentiful wine, had
become a rare and precious brandy and I took my time savouring it as I walked
out of the town toward the Forrester house. Sweet Water has changed greatly
since the days when Frank Ellinger stepped down from the Burlington and
everybody in the place knew about it. The town is large and wealthy now and,
it seemed to me, vulgar and preoccupied. I was afflicted with the sense of having come into the presence of an old uncle, declining in the increase of his
fortune, who no longer bothered to identify his visitors. It was a relief to leave
the town behind, but as I approached the Forrester house I felt that the lines
of my face were set in brave resolution rather than in high anticipation. It was
all so different from the free, lost time of the lovely lady's 'bright occasions'
that I found myself making a little involuntary gesture with my hand, like one
who wipes the tarnish from a silver spoon, searching for a fine forgotten mono-
gram.

I first met Marian Forrester when I was twenty-seven, and then again when
I was thirty-six. It is my vanity to believe that Mrs Forrester had no stauncher
admirer, no more studious appreciator. I took not only her smallest foible but
her largest sin in my stride; I was as fascinated by the glitter of her flaws as by
the glow of her perfections, if indeed I could tell one radiance from the other.
There was never anything reprehensible to me in the lady's ardent adventures,
and even in her awfullest attachment I persisted in seeing only the further
flowering of a unique and privileged spirit. As I neared her home, I remembered a dozen florid charities I had invented to cover her multitude of frailties:
her dependence on money and position, her admiration of an aristocracy, half
false and half imaginary, her lack of any security inside herself, her easy loneli-
ness. It was no use, I was fond of telling myself, to look for the qualities of the
common and wholesome morning glory in the rare and wanton Nicotiana.
From the darkest earth, I would add, springs ever the sweetest rose. A green
isle in the sea, if it has the sparkling fountain, needs not the solemn shrine, and
so forth and so on.

I had built the lady up very high, as you see. I had commanded myself to believe that emotional literacy, a lively spirit, and personal grace, so rarely joined in American females, particularly those who live between Omaha and Denver, were all the raiment a lady needed. As I crossed the bridge, with the Forrester house now in full view, I had, all of a sudden, a disturbing fancy. There flashed into my consciousness a vivid vision of the pretty lady, seated at her dressing table, practising in secrecy her little arts, making her famous earrings gleam with small studied turnings of her head, revealing her teeth for a moment in a brief mocking smile, and, unhappiest picture of all, rehearsing her wonderful laughter.

I stopped on the bridge and leaned against the rail and felt old and tired. Black clouds had come up, obscuring the sun, and they seemed to take the mushroom shape of atomic dust, threatening all frail and ancient satisfactions. It began to rain.

I wondered what I would say to Marian Forrester if she appeared at the door in one of her famous, familiar postures, *en déshabillé*, her hair down her back, a brush in her hand, her face raised in warm, anachronistic gaiety. I tried to remember what we had ever talked about, and could think only of the dreadful topic of grasping women and eligible men. We had never discussed any book that I could recall, and she had never mentioned music. I had another of my ungallant fancies, a vision of the lovely lady at a concert in the town, sitting with bright eye and deaf ear, displaying a new bonnet and gown, striving, less subtly than of old, to capture the attention of worried and oblivious gentlemen. I recalled with sharp clarity a gown and bonnet she had once worn, but for the life of me I could not put a face between them. I caught the twinkle of earrings, and that was all.

The latest newspaper lying open on a chair, a note stuck in a milk bottle on the back porch, are enough to indicate the pulse of a living house, but there would not even be these faint signs of today and tomorrow in Marian Forrester's house, only the fibrillation of a yesterday that had died but would not stay dead. There would be an old copy of *Ainslee's* on the floor somewhere, a glitter of glass under a broken windowpane, springs leaking from a ruptured sofa, a cobweb in a chandelier, a dusty etching of Notre Dame unevenly hung on the wall, and a stopped clock on the marble mantel above a cold fireplace. I could see the brandy bottle, too, on a stained table, wearing its cork drunkenly.

Just to the left of the front door, the big hall closet would be filled with relics of the turn of the century, the canes and guns of Captain Forrester, a crokinole board, a diavolo, a frivolous parasol, a collection of McKinley campaign buttons, a broken stereopticon, a table tennis net, a toppled stack of blue poker chips and a scatter of playing cards, a woodburning set, and one of those large white artificial Easter eggs you put to your eye and, squinting into it, behold the light that never was, in a frosty fairyland. There would be a crack in the crusty shell, and common daylight would violate the sanctuary of the yellowed and tottery angels. You could find, in all the litter, as measuring sticks of calamity, nothing longer than an envelope firmly addressed in a gentleman's hand, a cancelled cheque, a stern notice from the bank.

The shade of one upstairs window was pulled all the way down, and it suddenly had the effect of making the house appear to wink, as if it were about to whisper, out of the corner of its door, some piece of scandal. If I went in, I might be embarrassed by the ungainly sounds of someone moving about upstairs, after the lady had descended, sounds which she would cover by riffling nervously through a dozen frilly seasons of her faded past, trying a little shrilly to place me among the beaux in some half-remembered ballroom. I was afraid, too, that I might encounter in some dim and dusty mirror a young man frowning disapproval of an older self come to make a judgment on a poor lady not for her sake and salvation but, in some strange way, for his own. And what if she brought out, in the ruins of her famous laughter, what was left of the old disdain, and fixed me shrewdly for what I was, a frightened penitent, come to claim and take away and burn the old praises he had given her? I wouldn't succeed, of course, standing there in my unbecoming middle years, foolishly clutching reasons and arguments like a shopper's husband loaded down with bundles. She would gaily accuse me of being in love with another and, with the ghost of one of her poses of charming bewilderment, would claim a forfeit for my cruelty and insist that I sit down and have a brandy. I would have one – oh, several – and in the face of my suspicions of the presence of a man upstairs, my surrender would compromise the delicacy of my original cool intentions, and the lost individual would be, once again as always in this house, myself. I wondered, standing there in the rain, how it would all come out.

She would get the other lady's name out of me easily enough, when the brandy began to ebb in the bottle, and being Marian Forrester, for whom jealousy was as simple as a reflex, she would be jealous of the imaginary relations of a man she could not place, with a woman she had never heard of. I would then confess my love for Madame de Vionnet, the lady of the lilacs, of Gloriani's bright Sunday garden, of the stately house in the Boulevard Malesherbes, with its cool parlour and dark medallions. I would rise no doubt to the seedy grandiloquence of which I am capable when the cognac is flowing, and I could hear her pitiless comment. 'One of those women who have something to *give*, for heaven's sake!' she would say. 'One of those women who save men, a female whose abandon might possibly tiptoe to the point of tousling her lover's hair, a woman who at the first alarm of a true embrace would telephone the gendarmes.' 'Stop it!' I heard myself shout there in the rain. 'I beg you to remember it was once said of Madame de Vionnet that when she touched a thing the ugliness, God knows how, went out of it.' 'How sweet!' I could hear Mrs Forrester go on. 'And yet, according to you, she lost her lover, for all her charm, and to a snippet of an applecheek from New England. Did the ugliness go out of *that*? And if it did, what did the poor lady do with all the prettiness?'

As I stood there in the darkening afternoon, getting soaked, I realized sharply that in my phantasy I had actually been handing Marian Forrester stones to throw at the house in Paris, and the confusion in my viewpoint of the two ladies, if up to that moment I had had a viewpoint, overwhelmed me. I figured what would happen as the shadows deepened in the Forrester house, and we drank what was left of the brandy out of ordinary tumblers – the *ballons* of the great days would long since have been shattered. Banter would take on the sharp edge of wrangling, and in the end she would stand above me, maintaining a reedy balance, and denounce the lady of the lilacs in the flat terms she had overheard gentlemen use so long ago over their cigars and coffee in the library. I would set my glass down on the sticky arm of the chair and get up and stalk out into the hall. But though she had the last word, she would not let me have the last silence, the gesture in conclusion. She would follow me to the door. In her house, by an ancient rule, Marian Forrester always had the final moment – standing on the threshold, her face lifted, her eyes shining, her hand raised to wave good-bye. Yes, she would follow me to the door, and in the hall – I could see it so clearly I shivered there on the bridge – something wonderful would happen. With the faintest of smiles and the slightest of murmurs I would bow to my hostess, open the door and walk, not out into the rain, but into that damn closet, with its junk and clutter, smashing the Easter egg with my shoe, becoming tangled in the table tennis net, and holding in my hand, when I regained my balance, that comic parasol. Madame de Vionnet would ignore such a calamity, she would pretend not to see it, on the ground that a hostess is blind – a convention that can leave a man sitting at table with an omelet in his lap, unable to mention it, forced to go on with the conversation. But Marian would laugh, the lost laugh of the bright occasions, of the day of her shameless passion in the snow, and it would light the house like candles, reducing the sounds upstairs, in some miraculous way, to what they really were, the innocent creaking of the old floor boards. 'What's all this about saving men?' I would cry. 'Look who's talking!' And, still holding the parasol, I would kiss her on the cheek, mumble something about coming back some day, and leave, this time by the right door, finding, as I went to rejoin myself at the bridge, a poker chip in the cuff of my trousers.

It seems like a long time ago, my call on Mrs Forrester. I have never been back. I didn't even send her a Valentine last February. But I did send a pretty book of impeccable verses to Madame de Vionnet, writing in the inscription something polite and nostalgic about *ta voix dans le Bois de Boulogne*. I did this, I suppose, out of some obscure guilt sense – these things are never very clear to any man, if the truth were told. I think the mental process goes like this, though. Drinking brandy out of a water glass in the amiable company of a lady who uses spirits for anodyne and not amenity, a timid gentleman promises his subconscious to make up for it later on by taking a single malaga before *déjeuner à midi* with a fastidious lady, toying with aspic, discussing Thornton Wilder, praising the silver point in the hall on the way out, and going home to lie down, exhausted but somehow purified.

I will carry lilacs, one of these summers, to the house in the Boulevard Malesherbes, and take Madame de Vionnet to a matinee of 'Louise,' have a white port with her at one of the little terraces at the quietest corner of the Parc Monceau, and drop her at her door well before the bold moon has begun to wink at the modest twilight. Since, in the best Henry James tradition, I will get nothing out of this for myself, it ought to make up for something. I could do worse than spend my last summers serenely, sipping wine, clop-clopping around town, listening to good music, kissing a lady's hand at her door, going to bed early and getting a good night's sleep. A man's a fool who walks in the rain, drinks too much brandy, risks his neck floundering around in an untidy closet. Besides, if you miss the 6.15, the east-bound Burlington that has a rendezvous with dusk in Sweet Water every day except Sundays and holidays, you have to wait till midnight for the next train east. A man could catch his death, dozing there in that cold and lonesome station.

A New Natural History

A Trochee (left) encountering a Spondee.

The Hopeless Quandary.

CREATURES OF THE MEADOW

Left, the Aspic on a stalk of Visiting Fireman. Centre, the Throttle. Right, a Ticket in a patch of Marry-in-Haste. Below, a 99-year lease working slowly toward the surface through the years.

A pair of Martinets.

The Hoodwink on a spray of Ragamuffin.

The Bodkin (left) and the Chintz.

449

Flowers (left to right): Baker's Dozen, Shepherd's Pie, Sailor's Hornpipe, Stepmother's Kiss.
Butterflies (left to right): The Admirable Crichton, the Great Gatsby, The Magnificent Ambersons (male and female), the Beloved Vagabond.

The White-faced Rage (left) and the Blind Rage.

A GROUP OF MORE OR LESS PLEASANT BIRDS

Left to right: the Apothecary, the Night Watchman, the Scoutmaster,
and the Barred Barrister.

The Goad.

The male Wedlock (left) cautiously approaching a clump of Devil-May-Care; at right, the female.

A female Shriek (right) rising out of the Verbiage to attack a female Swoon.

The Lapidary in a clump of Merry-Go-Round.

A Garble with an Utter in its claws.

The Dudgeon.

*Two widely distributed rodents: the Barefaced Lie (left) and the
White Lie.*

The female Snarl (left) and the male Sulk.

An Upstart rising from a clump of Johnny-Come-Lately. The small rodent (right) is a Spouse.

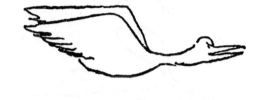

(Left to right) The Whited Sepulchre; the Misfit; the American Playboy, or Spendthrift, also sometimes called (southern U.S.A.) the Common Blackguard; a Stuffed Shirt; and (above) a Termagant.

The Femur (left) and the Metatarsal.

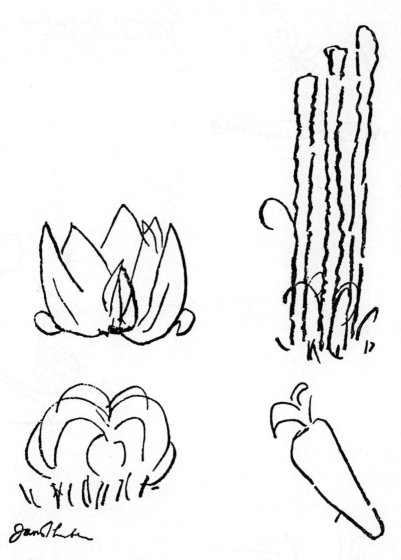

Top: Quench (left) and Arpeggio. Bottom: Therapy (left) and Scabbard.

The Living, or Spitting, Image (left) and a Dead Ringer.

A female Volt with all her Ergs in one Gasket.

The male and female Tryst.

The Early and the Late Riser.

A TRIO OF PREHISTORIC CREATURES

Left to right: the Thesaurus, the Stereopticon, and the Hexameter.
The tree is a Sacroiliac.

A Scone (left) and a Crumpet, peering out of the Tiffin.

The Tantamount.

A Serenade (left) about to engage in combat with a Victual.

THREE FRESH–WATER CREATURES

The Qualm   *The Glib*   *The Moot*

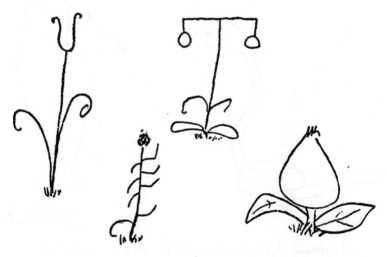

Left to right: Single Standard, False Witness, Double Jeopardy, Heartburn.

The Huff.

A Gloat near a patch of I-Told-You-So.

A Grope approaching, unaware, a Clinch in hiding.

The Peeve (or Pet Peeve).

The Troth, Plighted (right) and Unplighted.

The Common Carrier.

A GROUP OF DESTRUCTIVE INSECTS

The Coal Bin

The Door Latch

The Clock Tick (or Stop Watch)

The Tyre Tool

The Window Ledge

The Ball Bat

A Miscellany

'*I'm getting tired of you throwing your weight around.*'

'*Mush!*'

'*Let me take your hat, Mr Williams.*'

'I wear it for luck.'

'The eternal feminine, Mr. Blake, the eternal feminine!'

469

'No, I won't apologise—and neither will your father.'

'I can't find any serenity in contemplation because I keep thinking of this one girl.'

'Well, sir, he was the most astonished magician you ever saw in your life.'

'I wouldn't even let Cary Grant lounge around my house in the afternoon'.

'Sometimes the news from Washington forces me to the conclusion
that your mother and brother Ed are in charge.'

American Folk Dance.

'Don't you want to greet the rosy-fingered dawn?'

'Where did you get those big brown eyes and that tiny mind?'

'Comb the woods!'

'I couldn't make any man happy. I'm a femme fatale.'

Thurber Country

A COLLECTION OF PIECES ABOUT
MALES AND FEMALES MAINLY
OF OUR OWN SPECIES

FOR

ROSIE AND FRED

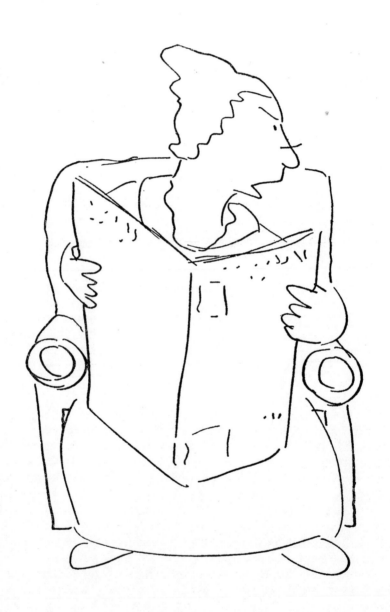

The Figgerin' of Aunt Wilma

WHEN I WAS a boy, John Hance's grocery stood on the south side of
Town Street, just east of Fourth, in the Central Market region of
Columbus, Ohio. It was an old store even then, forty-five years ago,
and its wide oak floor boards had been worn pleasantly smooth by the shoe
soles of three generations of customers. The place smelt of coffee, pepper-
mint, vinegar, and spices. Just inside the door on the left, a counter with a
rounded glass front held all the old-fashioned penny candies – gumdrops,
liquorice whips, horehound, and the rest – some of them a little pale with age.
On the rear wall, between a barrel of dill pickles and a keg of salt mackerel in
brine, there was an iron coffee grinder, whose handle I was sometimes allowed
to turn.

Once, Mr Hance gave me a stick of Yucatan gum, an astonishing act of
generosity, since he had a sharp sense of the value of a penny. Thrift was John
Hance's religion. His store was run on a strictly cash basis. He shared the cost
of his telephone with the Hays Carriage Shop, next door. The instrument was
set in a movable wooden cubicle that could be whirled through an opening in
the west wall of the store. When I was ten, I used to hang around the grocery
on Saturday afternoons, waiting for the telephone to disappear into the wall.
Then I would wait for it to swing back again. It was a kind of magic, and I was
disappointed to learn of its mundane purpose – the saving of a few dollars a
month.

Mr Hance was nearly seventy, a short man with white hair and a white
moustache and the most alert eyes that I can remember, except perhaps Aunt
Wilma Hudson's. Aunt Wilma lived on South Sixth Street and always
shopped at Mr Hance's store. Mr Hance's eyes were blue and capable of a
keen concentration that could make you squirm. Aunt Wilma had black agate
eyes that moved restlessly and scrutinized everybody with bright suspicion. In
church, her glance would dart around the congregation seeking out irreverent
men and women whose expressions showed that they were occupied with
worldly concerns, or even carnal thoughts, in the holy place. If she lighted on a
culprit, her heavy, dark brows would lower, and her mouth would tighten in
righteous disapproval. Aunt Wilma was as honest as the day is long and as
easily confused, when it came to what she called figgerin', as the night is dark.
Her clashes with Mr Hance had become a family legend. He was a swift and
competent calculator, and nearly fifty years of constant practice had enabled
him to add up a column of figures almost at a glance. He set down his columns
swiftly on an empty paper sack with a stubby black pencil. Aunt Wilma, on the

479

other hand, was slow and painstaking when it came to figgerin'. She would go over and over a column of numbers, her glasses far down on her nose, her lips moving soundlessly. To her, rapid calculation, like all the other reckless and impulsive habits of men, was tainted with a kind of godlessness. Mr Hance always sighed when he looked up and saw her coming into his store. He knew that she could lift a simple dollar transaction into a dim and mystic realm of confusion all her own.

I was fortunate enough to be present one day in 1905 when Mr Hance's calculating and Aunt Wilma's figgerin' came together in memorable single combat. She had wheedled me into carrying her market basket, on the ground that it was going to be too heavy for her to manage. Her two grandsons, boys around my own age, had skipped out when I came to call at their house, and Aunt Wilma promptly seized on me. A young'un, as she called everybody under seventeen, was not worth his salt if he couldn't help a body about the house. I had shopped with her before, under duress, and I knew her accustomed and invariable route on Saturday mornings, when Fourth Street, from Main to State, was lined with the stands of truck gardeners. Prices were incredibly low in those days, but Aunt Wilma questioned the cost, the quality, and the measure of everything. By the time she had finished her long and tedious purchases of fresh produce from the country, and we had turned east into Town Street and headed for Mr Hance's store, the weight of the market basket was beginning to pain my arm. 'Come along, child, come along,' Aunt Wilma snapped, her eyes shining with the look of the Middle Western housewife engaged in hard but virtuous battle with the wicked forces of the merchandising world.

I saw Mr Hance make a small involuntary gesture with his right hand as he spied Aunt Wilma coming through the door. He had just finished with a customer, and since his assistant was busy, he knew he was in for it. It took a good half hour for Aunt Wilma to complete her shopping for groceries, but at length everything she wanted was stacked on the counter in sacks and cans and boxes. Mr Hance set deftly to work with his paper sack and pencil, jotting down the price of each article as he fitted it into the basket. Aunt Wilma watched his expert movements closely, like a hostile baseball fan waiting for an error in the infield. She regarded adroitness in a man as 'slick' rather than skilful.

Aunt Wilma's purchases amounted to ninety-eight cents. After writing down this sum, Mr Hance, knowing my aunt, whisked the paper bag around on the counter so that she could examine his addition. It took her some time, bending over and peering through her glasses, to arrive at a faintly reluctant corroboration of his figgerin'. Even when she was satisfied that all was in order, she had another go at the column of numbers, her lips moving silently as she added them up for the third time. Mr Hance waited patiently, the flat of his hands on the counter. He seemed to be fascinated by the movement of her lips. 'Well, I guess it's all right,' said Aunt Wilma, at last, 'but everything *is* so dear.' What she had bought for less than a dollar made the market basket bulge.

Aunt Wilma took her purse out of her bag and drew out a dollar bill slowly and handed it over, as if it were a hundred dollars she would never see again.

Mr Hance deftly pushed the proper keys of the cash register, and the red hand on the indicator pointed to $.98. He studied the cash drawer, which had shot out at him. 'Well, well,' he said, and then, 'Hmm. Looks like I haven't got any pennies.' He turned back to Aunt Wilma. 'Have you got three cents, Mrs Hudson?' he asked.

That started it.

Aunt Wilma gave him a quick look of distrust. Her Sunday suspicion gleamed in her eyes. '*You* owe *me two* cents,' she said sharply.

'I know that, Mrs Hudson,' he sighed, 'but I'm out of pennies. Now if you'll give me three cents, I'll give you a nickel.'

Aunt Wilma stared at him cautiously.

'It's all right if you give him three cents and he gives you a nickel,' I said.

'Hush up,' said Aunt Wilma. 'I'm figgerin'.' She figgered for several moments, her mouth working again.

Mr Hance slipped a nickel out of the drawer and placed it on the counter. 'There is your nickel,' he said firmly. 'Now you just have to give me three cents.'

Aunt Wilma pecked about in her purse and located three pennies, which she brought out carefully, one at a time. She laid them on the counter beside the nickel, and Mr Hance reached for them. Aunt Wilma was too quick for him. She covered the eight cents with a lean hand. 'Wait, now!' she said, and she took her hand away slowly. She frowned over the four coins as if they were a difficult hand in bridge whist. She ran her lower lip against her upper teeth. 'Maybe if I give you a dime,' she said, 'and take the eight cents . . . It is *two* cents you're short, ain't it?'

Mr Hance began to show signs of agitation. One or two amused customers were now taking in the scene out of the corners of their eyes. 'No, no,' said Mr Hance. 'That way, you would be making me a present of seven cents!' This was too much for Aunt Wilma. She couldn't understand the new and preposterous sum of seven cents that had suddenly leaped at her from nowhere. The notion that she was about to do herself out of some money staggered her, and her eyes glazed for a moment like a groggy prizefighter's. Neither Mr Hance nor I said anything, out of fear of deepening the tangle. She made an uncertain move of her right hand and I had the wild thought that she was going to give Mr Hance one of the pennies and scoop up the seven cents, but she didn't. She fell into a silent clinch with the situation and then her eyes cleared. 'Why, of *course*!' she cried brightly. 'I don't know what got into me! You take the eight cents and give me a dime. Then I'll have the two cents that's coming to me.' One of the customers laughed, and Aunt Wilma cut him down with a swift glare. The diversion gave me time to figure out that whereas Mr Hance had been about to gain seven cents, he was now going to lose a nickel. 'That way, *I* would be making *you* a present of *five* cents, Mrs Hudson,' he said stiffly. They stood motionless for several seconds, each trying to stare the other down.

'Now, here,' said Mr Hance, turning and taking her dollar out of the still open cash drawer. He laid it beside the nickel and the pennies. 'Now, here,' he said again. 'You gave me a dollar three, but you don't owe me a dollar three – you owe me five cents less than that. Here is the five cents.' He snatched it up and handed it to her. She held the nickel between thumb and forefinger, and her eyes gleamed briefly, as if she at last comprehended the peculiar deal, but the gleam faded. Suddenly she handed him his nickel and picked up her dollar and her three cents. She put the pennies back in her purse. 'I've rung up the ninety-eight cents, Mrs Hudson,' said Mr Hance quickly. 'I must put the dollar back in the till.' He turned and pointed at the $.98 on the indicator. 'I tell you what. If you'll give me the dollar, I'll give you the nickel and we'll call it square.' She obviously didn't want to take the nickel or give up the dollar, but she did, finally. I was astounded at first, for here was the penny-careful Mr Hance knocking three cents off a bill, but then I realized he was afraid of losing the dollar and was willing to settle for the lesser of two evils.

'Well,' said Aunt Wilma irritably, 'I'm sure I don't know what you're trying to do.'

I was a timid boy, but I had to plunge into the snarl, if only on behalf of the family honour. 'Gee, Aunt Wilma,' I told her, 'if you keep the nickel, he's giving you everything for ninety-five cents.'

Mr Hance scowled hard at me. He was afraid I was going to get him in deeper than he already was. 'It's all right, son,' he said. 'It's all right.' He put the dollar in the till and shoved the drawer shut with a decisive bang, but I wasn't going to give up.

'Gee whizz, Aunt Wilma,' I complained, 'you still owe him three cents. Don't you see that?'

She gave me the pitying glance of a superior and tired intelligence. 'I never owed him three cents in my life,' she said tartly. 'He owes me two cents. You stay out of things you don't understand.'

'It's all right,' said Mr Hance again, in a weary voice. He was sure that if she scrabbled in her purse again for the three pennies, she would want her dollar back, and they would be right where they had started. I gave my aunt a look of disenchantment.

'Now, wait!' she cried suddenly. 'Maybe I have the exact change! I don't know what's got into me I didn't think of that! I think I have the right change after all.' She put back on the counter the nickel she had been clutching in her left hand, and then she began to peck at the coins in her purse and, after a good minute, arranged two quarters, four dimes, Mr Hance's nickel, and three pennies on the counter. 'There,' she said, her eyes flashing triumph. 'Now you give me my dollar back.'

Mr Hance sighed deeply, rang out the cash drawer by pushing 'No Sale,' and handed her the dollar. Then he hastily scraped up the change, deposited each coin in its proper place in the till, and slammed the drawer shut again. I was only ten, and mathematics was not my best study, but it wasn't hard to figure that Mr Hance, who in the previous arrangement had been out three cents, was now out five cents. 'Good day, Mrs Hudson,' he said grimly. He felt my sympathetic eyes on him, and we exchanged a brief, knowing masculine glance of private understanding.

'Good day, Mr Hance,' said Aunt Wilma, and her tone was as grim as the grocer's.

I took the basket from the counter, and Mr Hance sighed again, this time with relief. 'Goodbye, goodbye,' he said with false heartiness, glad to see us on our way. I felt I should slip him the parsley, or whatever sack in the basket had cost a nickel.

'Come on, child,' said Aunt Wilma. 'It's dreadfully late. I declare it's taken hours to shop today.' She muttered plaintively all the way out of the store.

I noticed as I closed the door behind us that Mr Hance was waiting on a man customer. The man was laughing. Mr Hance frowned and shrugged.

As we walked east on Town Street, Aunt Wilma let herself go. 'I never heard of such a thing in all the born days of my life,' she said. 'I don't know where John Hance got his schooling, if he got any. The very idea – a grown man like that getting so mixed up. Why, I could have spent the whole day in that store and he'd never of figgered it out. Let him keep the two cents, then. It was worth it to get out of that store.'

'*What* two cents, Aunt Wilma?' I almost squealed.

'Why, the two cents he still owes me!' she said. 'I don't know what they teach you young'uns nowadays. Of course he owes me two cents. It comes to ninety-eight cents and I give him a dollar. He owed me two cents in the beginning and he still owes me two cents. Your Uncle Herbert will explain it to you. Any man in the world could figger it out except John Hance.'

I walked on beside her in silence, thinking of Uncle Herbert, a balding, choleric man of high impatience and quick temper.

'Now, you let *me* explain it to your Uncle Herbert, child,' she said. 'I declare you were as mixed up as John Hance was. If I'd of listened to you and given him the three cents, like you said, I'd never of got my dollar back. He'd owe me five cents instead of two. Why, it's as plain as day.'

I thought I had the solution for her now, and I leaped at it. 'That's right, Aunt Wilma,' I almost yelled. 'He owed you a nickel and he gave you the nickel.'

Aunt Wilma stabbed me with her indignation. 'I gave *him* the nickel,' she said. 'I put it on the counter right there under your very eyes, and you saw him scoop it up.'

I shifted the market basket to my left arm. 'I know, Aunt Wilma,' I said, 'but it was *his* nickel all the time.'

She snorted. 'Well, he's got his precious nickel, ain't he?' she demanded. I shifted the basket again. I thought I detected a faint trace of uneasiness in her tone. She fell silent and quickened her cadence, and it was hard for me to keep up with her. As we turned south into Sixth Street, I glanced up and saw that she was frowning and that her lips were moving again. She was rehearsing the story of the strange transaction for Uncle Herbert. I began to whistle. 'Hush up, child,' she said. 'I'm figgerin'. '

Uncle Herbert was sitting in the living room, eating an apple. I could tell from his expression that he was in one of his rare amiable moods. Aunt Wilma grabbed the basket away from me. 'Now, you let me explain it to your uncle,' she said. 'You wait till I get back.' She sailed out of the room on her way to the kitchen.

A little breathlessly, I told Uncle Herbert the saga of Aunt Wilma's complicated financial quandary. He was chuckling when she came back into the room.

Uncle Herbert's amusement nettled her. 'The boy got it wrong,' she said accusingly. 'He didn't tell it right. He was ever' bit as mixed up as John Hance.' Uncle Herbert's chuckle increased to full and open laughter. Aunt Wilma glared at him until he subsided. 'Now, Herbert, you listen to me,' she began, but he cut in on her.

'If Hance ever gives you that two cents he owes you, Wilma,' he said, 'I tell you what you have to do to square accounts. Someday you're going to have to give him a dime for three cents.' He began to laugh again.

Aunt Wilma Hudson stared at each of us in turn, with a look of fine, cold scorn, and then she raised both her hands and let them fall helplessly. 'I declare,' she said, 'I don't know how the world gets along with the men runnin' it.'

The White Rabbit Caper

(As the boys who turn out the mystery programmes on the air
might write a story for children.)

FRED FOX was pouring himself a slug of rye when the door of his office
opened and in hopped old Mrs Rabbit. She was a white rabbit with pink
eyes, and she wore a shawl on her head, and gold-rimmed spectacles.

'I want you to find Daphne,' she said tearfully, and she handed Fred Fox a
snapshot of a white rabbit with pink eyes that looked to him like a picture of
every other white rabbit with pink eyes.

'When did she hop the hutch?' asked Fred Fox.

'Yesterday,' said old Mrs Rabbit. 'She is only eighteen months old, and I am
afraid that some superstitious creature has killed her for one of her feet.'

Fred Fox turned the snapshot over and put it in his pocket. 'Has this bunny
got a throb?' he asked.

'Yes,' said old Mrs Rabbit. 'Franz Frog, repulsive owner of the notorious
Lily Pad Night Club.'

Fred Fox leaped to his feet. 'Come on, Grandma,' he said, 'and don't step
on your ears. We got to move fast.'

On the way to the Lily Pad Night Club, old Mrs Rabbit scampered so fast
that Fred Fox had all he could do to keep up with her. 'Daphne is my great-
great-great-great-great-granddaughter, if my memory serves,' said old Mrs
Rabbit. 'I have thirty-nine thousand descendants.'

'This isn't going to be easy,' said Fred Fox. 'Maybe you should have gone to
a magician with a hat.'

'But she is the only one named Daphne,' said old Mrs Rabbit, 'and she lived
alone with me on my great carrot farm.'

They came to a broad brook. 'Skip it!' said Fred Fox.

'Keep a civil tongue in your head, young man,' snapped old Mrs Rabbit.

Just as they got to the Lily Pad, a dandelion clock struck twelve noon. Fred
Fox pushed the button on the great green door, on which was painted a white
water lily. The door opened an eighth of an inch, and Ben Rat peered out.
'Beat it,' he said, but Fred Fox shoved the door open, and old Mrs Rabbit
followed him into a cool green hallway, softly but restlessly lighted by thousands of fireflies imprisoned in the hollow crystal pendants of an enormous
chandelier. At the right there was a flight of green-carpeted stairs, and at the
bottom of the steps the door to the cloakroom. Straight ahead, at the end of the
long hallway, was the cool green door to Franz Frog's office.

'Beat it,' said Ben Rat again.

'Talk nice,' said Fred Fox, 'or I'll seal your house up with tin. Where's the
Croaker?'

'Once a gumpaw, always a gumpaw,' grumbled Ben Rat. 'He's in his office.'

'With Daphne?'

'Who's Daphne?' asked Ben Rat.

'My great-great-great-great-great-granddaughter,' said old Mrs Rabbit.

'Nobody's that great,' snarled Ben Rat.

Fred Fox opened the cool green door and went into Franz Frog's office, followed by old Mrs Rabbit and Ben Rat. The owner of the Lily Pad sat behind his desk, wearing a green suit, green shirt, green tie, green socks, and green shoes. He had an emerald tiepin and seven emerald rings. 'Whong you wong, Fonnxx?' he rumbled in a cold, green, cavernous voice. His eyes bulged and his throat began to swell ominously.

'He's going to croak,' explained Ben Rat.

'Nuts,' said Fred Fox. 'He'll outlive all of us.'

'Glunk,' croaked Franz Frog.

Ben Rat glared at Fred Fox. 'You oughta go on the stage,' he snarled.

'Where's Daphne?' demanded Fred Fox.

'Hoong Dangneng?' asked Franz Frog.

'Your bunny friend,' said Fred Fox.

'Nawng,' said Franz Frog.

Fred Fox picked up a cello in a corner and put it down. It was too light to contain a rabbit. The front-door bell rang. 'I'll get it,' said Fred Fox. It was Oliver (Hoot) Owl, a notorious fly-by-night. 'What're you doing up at this hour, Hoot?' asked Fred Fox.

'I'm trying to blind myself, so I'll confess,' said Hoot Owl testily.

'Confess to what?' snapped Fred Fox.

'What can't you solve?' asked Hoot Owl.

'The disappearance of Daphne,' said Fred Fox.

'Who's Daphne?' asked Hoot Owl.

Franz Frog hopped out of his office into the hall. Ben Rat and old Mrs Rabbit followed him.

Down the steps from the second floor came Sherman Stork, carrying a white muffler or something and grinning foolishly.

'Well, bless my soul!' said Fred Fox. 'If it isn't old mid-husband himself! What did you do with Daphne?'

'Who's Daphne?' asked Sherman Stork.

'Fox thinks somebody killed Daphne Rabbit,' said Ben Rat.

'Fonnxx cung brong,' rumbled Franz Frog.

'I *could* be wrong,' said Fred Fox, 'but I'm not.' He pulled open the cloakroom door at the bottom of the steps, and the dead body of a female white rabbit toppled furrily on to the cool green carpet. Her head had been bashed in by a heavy blunt instrument.

'Daphne!' screamed old Mrs Rabbit, bursting into tears.

'I can't see a thing,' said Hoot Owl.

'It's a dead white rabbit,' said Ben Rat. 'Anybody can see that. You're dumb.'

'I'm wise!' said Hoot Owl indignantly. 'I know everything.'

'Jeeng Crine,' moaned Franz Frog. He stared up at the chandelier, his eyes bulging and his mammoth mouth gaping open. All the fireflies were frightened and went out.

The cool green hallway became pitch dark. There was a shriek in the black and a feathery 'plump.' The fireflies lighted up to see what had happened. Hoot Owl lay dead on the cool green carpet, his head bashed in by a heavy blunt instrument. Ben Rat, Franz Frog, Sherman Stork, old Mrs Rabbit, and Fred Fox stared at Hoot Owl. Over the cool green carpet crawled a warm red stain, whose source was the body of Hoot Owl. He lay like a feather duster.

'Murder!' squealed old Mrs Rabbit.

'Nobody leaves this hallway!' snapped Fred Fox. 'There's a killer loose in this club!'

'I am not used to death,' said Sherman Stork.

'Roong!' groaned Franz Frog.

'He says he's ruined,' said Ben Rat, but Fred Fox wasn't listening. He was looking for a heavy blunt instrument. There wasn't any.

'Search them!' cried old Mrs Rabbit. 'Somebody has a sap, or a sock full of sand, or something!'

'Yeh,' said Fred Fox. 'Ben Rat is a sap – maybe someone swung him by his tail.'

'You oughta go on the stage,' snarled Ben Rat.

Fred Fox searched the suspects, but he found no concealed weapon. 'You could have strangled them with that muffler,' Fred Fox told Sherman Stork.

'But they were not strangled,' said Sherman Stork.

Fred Fox turned to Ben Rat. 'You could have bitten them to death with your ugly teeth,' he said.

'But they weren't bitten to death,' said Ben Rat.

Fred Fox stared at Franz Frog. 'You could have scared them to death with your ugly face,' he said.

'Bung wung screng ta deng,' said Franz Frog.

'You're right,' admitted Fred Fox. 'They weren't. Where's old Mrs Rabbit?' he asked suddenly.

'I'm hiding in here,' called old Mrs Rabbit from the cloakroom. 'I'm frightened.'

Fred Fox got her out of the cool green sanctuary and went in himself. It was dark. He groped around on the cool green carpet. He didn't know what he was looking for, but he found it, a small object lying in a far corner. He put it in his pocket and came out of the cloakroom.

'What'd you find, shamus?' asked Ben Rat apprehensively.

'Exhibit A,' said Fred Fox casually.

'Sahng plang keeng,' moaned Franz Frog.

'He says somebody's playing for keeps,' said Ben Rat.

'He can say that again,' said Fred Fox as the front door was flung open and Inspector Mastiff trotted in, followed by Sergeant Dachshund.

'Well, well, look who's muzzling in,' said Fred Fox.

'What have we got here?' barked Inspector Mastiff.

'I hate a private nose,' said Sergeant Dachshund.

Fred Fox grinned at him. 'What happened to your legs from the knees down, sport?' he asked.

'Drop dead,' snarled Sergeant Dachshund.

'Quiet, both of you!' snapped Inspector Mastiff. 'I know Ollie Owl, but who's the twenty-dollar Easter present from Schrafft's?' He turned on Fred Fox. 'If this bunny's head comes off and she's filled with candy, I'll have your badge, Fox,' he growled.

'She's real, Inspector,' said Fred Fox. 'Real dead, too. How did you pick up the scent?'

Inspector Mastiff howled. 'The Sergeant thought he smelt a rat at the Lily Club,' he said. 'Wrong again, as usual. Who's this dead rabbit?'

'She's my great-great-great-great-great-granddaughter,' sobbed old Mrs Rabbit.

Fred Fox lighted a cigarette. 'Oh, no, she isn't, sweetheart,' he said coolly. 'You are *her* great-great-great-great-great-granddaughter.' Pink lightning flared in the live white rabbit's eyes. 'You killed the old lady, so you could take over her carrot farm,' continued Fred Fox, 'and then you killed Hoot Owl.'

'I'll kill you, too, shamus!' shrieked Daphne Rabbit.

'Put the cuffs on her, Sergeant,' barked Inspector Mastiff. Sergeant Dachshund put a pair of handcuffs on the front legs of the dead rabbit. 'Not *her*, you dumb kraut!' yelped Inspector Mastiff. It was too late. Daphne Rabbit had jumped through a window-pane and run away, with the Sergeant in hot pursuit.

'All white rabbits look alike to me,' growled Inspector Mastiff. 'How could you tell them apart – from their ears?'

'No,' said Fred Fox. 'From their years. The white rabbit that called on me darn near beat me to the Lily Pad, and no old woman can do that.'

'Don't brag,' said Inspector Mastiff. 'Spryness isn't enough. What else?'

'She understood expressions an old rabbit doesn't know,' said Fred Fox, 'like "hop the hutch" and "throb" and "skip it" and "sap."'

'You can't hang a rabbit for her vocabulary,' said Inspector Mastiff. 'Come again.'

Fred Fox pulled the snapshot out of his pocket. 'The white rabbit who called on me told me Daphne was eighteen months old,' he said, 'but read what it says on the back of this picture.'

Inspector Mastiff took the snapshot, turned it over, and read, ' "Daphne on her second birthday." '

'Yes,' said Fred Fox. 'Daphne knocked six months off her age. You see,

Inspector, she couldn't read the writing on the snapshot, because those weren't her spectacles she was wearing.'

'Now wait a minute,' growled Inspector Mastiff. 'Why did she kill Hoot Owl?'

'Elementary, my dear Mastiff,' said Fred Fox. 'Hoot Owl lived in an oak tree, and she was afraid he saw her burrowing into the club last night, dragging Grandma. She heard Hoot Owl say, "I'm wise. I know everything," and so she killed him.'

'What with?' demanded the Inspector.

'Her right hind foot,' said Fred Fox. 'I was looking for a concealed weapon, and all the time she was carrying her heavy blunt instrument openly.'

'Well, what do you know!' exclaimed Inspector Mastiff. 'Do you think Hoot Owl really saw her?'

'Could be,' said Fred Fox. 'I happen to think he was bragging about his wisdom in general and not about a particular piece of information, but your guess is as good as mine.'

'What did you pick up in the cloakroom?' squeaked Ben Rat.

'The final strand in the rope that will hang Daphne,' said Fred Fox. 'I knew she didn't go in there to hide. She went in there to look for something she lost last night. If she'd been frightened, she would have hidden when the flies went out, but she went in there after the flies lighted up again.'

'That adds up,' said Inspector Mastiff grudgingly. 'What was it she was looking for?'

'Well,' said Fred Fox, 'she heard something drop in the dark when she dragged Grandma in there last night and she thought it was a button, or a buckle, or a bead, or a bangle, or a brooch that would incriminate her. That's why she rang me in on the case. She couldn't come here alone to look for it.'

'Well, what was it, Fox?' snapped Inspector Mastiff.

'A carrot,' said Fred Fox, and he took it out of his pocket, 'probably fell out of old Mrs Rabbit's reticule, if you like irony.'

'One more question,' said Inspector Mastiff. 'Why plant the body in the Lily Pad?'

'Easy,' said Fred Fox. 'She wanted to throw suspicion on the Croaker, a well-known lady-killer.'

'Nawng,' rumbled Franz Frog.

'Well, there it is, Inspector,' said Fred Fox, 'all wrapped up for you and tied with ribbons.'

Ben Rat disappeared into a wall. Franz Frog hopped back to his office.

'Mercy!' cried Sherman Stork. 'I'm late for an appointment!' He flew to the front door and opened it.

There stood Daphne Rabbit, holding the unconscious form of Sergeant Dachshund. 'I give up,' she said. 'I surrender.'

'Is he dead?' asked Inspector Mastiff hopefully.

'No,' said Daphne Rabbit. 'He fainted.'

'I never have any luck,' growled Inspector Mastiff.

Fred Fox leaned over and pointed to Daphne's right hind foot. 'Owl feathers,' he said. 'She's all yours, Inspector.'

'Thanks, Fox,' said Inspector Mastiff. 'I'll throw something your way someday.'

'Make it a nice, plump Plymouth Rock pullet,' said Fred Fox, and he sauntered out of the Lily Pad.

Back in his office, Fred Fox dictated his report on the White Rabbit Caper to his secretary, Lura Fox. 'Period. End of report,' he said finally, toying with the emerald stickpin he had taken from Franz Frog's green necktie when the fire-flies went out.

'Is she pretty?' asked Lura Fox.

'Daphne? Quite a dish,' said Fred Fox, 'but I like my rabbits stewed, and I'm afraid little Daphne is going to fry.'

'But she's so young, Fred!' cried Lura Fox. 'Only eighteen months!'

'You weren't listening,' said Fred Fox.

'How did you know she wasn't interested in Franz Frog?' asked Lura Fox.

'Simple,' said Fred Fox. 'Wrong species.'

'What became of the candy, Fred?' asked Lura Fox.

Fred Fox stared at her. 'What candy?' he asked blankly.

Lura Fox suddenly burst into tears. 'She was so soft, and warm, and cuddly, Fred,' she wailed.

Fred Fox filled a glass with rye, drank it slowly, set down the glass, and sighed grimly. 'Sour racket,' he said.

My Own Ten Rules for a Happy Marriage

NOBODY, I HASTEN to announce, has asked me to formulate a set of rules for the perpetuation of marital bliss and the preservation of the tranquil American boudoir and inglenook. The idea just came to me one day, when I watched a couple in an apartment across the court from mine gesturing and banging tables and throwing *objets d'art* at each other. I couldn't hear what they were saying, but it was obvious, as the shot-put followed the hammer throw, that he and/or she (as the lawyers would put it) had deeply offended her and/or him.

Their apartment, before they began to take it apart, had been quietly and tastefully arranged, but it was a little hard to believe this now, as he stood there by the fireplace, using an andiron to bat back the Royal Doulton figurines she was curving at him from her strongly entrenched position behind the davenport. I wondered what had started the exciting but costly battle, and, brooding on the general subject of Husbands and Wives, I found myself compiling my own Ten Rules for a Happy Marriage.

I have avoided the timeworn admonitions, such as 'Praise her new hat,' 'Share his hobbies,' 'Be a sweetheart as well as a wife,' and 'Don't keep a blonde in the guest room,' not only because they are threadbare from repetition, but also because they don't seem to have accomplished their purpose. Maybe what we need is a brand-new set of rules. Anyway, ready or not, here they come, the result of fifty years (I began as a little boy) spent in studying the nature and behaviour, mistakes and misunderstandings, of the American Male (*homo Americansis*) and his Mate.

RULE ONE: Neither party to a sacred union should run down, disparage or badmouth the other's former girls or beaux, as the case may be. The tendency to attack the character, looks, intelligence, capability, and achievements of one's mate's former friends of the opposite sex is a common cause of domestic discontent. Sweetheart-slurring, as we will call this deplorable practice, is encouraged by a long spell of gloomy weather, too many highballs, hang-overs, and the suspicion that one's spouse is hiding, and finding, letters in a hollow tree, or is intercepting the postman, or putting in secret phone calls from the corner drugstore. These fears almost always turn out to be unfounded, but the unfounded fear, as we all know, is worse than the founded.

Aspersions, insinuations, reflections or just plain cracks about old boy friends and girl friends should be avoided at all times. Here are some of the expressions that should be especially eschewed: 'That waffle-fingered, minor-league third baseman you latched on to at Cornell'; 'You know the girl I mean – the one with the hips who couldn't read'; 'That old flame of yours with the vocabulary of a hoot owl'; and 'You remember her – that old bat who chewed gum and dressed like Daniel Boone.'

This kind of derogatory remark, if persisted in by one or both parties to a marriage, will surely lead to divorce or, at best, a blow on the head with a glass ash tray.

RULE TWO: A man should make an honest effort to get the names of his wife's friends right. This is not easy. The average wife who was graduated from college at any time during the past thirty years keeps in close touch with at least seven old classmates. These ladies, known as 'the girls,' are named, respectively: Mary, Marian, Melissa, Marjorie, Maribel, Madeleine, and Miriam; and all of them are called Myrtle by the careless husband we are talking about. Furthermore, he gets their nicknames wrong. This, to be sure, is understandable, since their nicknames are, respectively: Molly, Muffy, Missy, Midge, Mabby, Maddy, and Mims. The careless husband, out of thoughtlessness or pure cussedness, calls them all Mugs, or, when he is feeling particularly brutal, Mucky.

All the girls are married, one of them to a Ben Tompkins, and as this is the only one he can remember, our hero calls all the husbands Ben, or Tompkins, adding to the general annoyance and confusion.

If you are married to a college graduate, then, try to get the names of her girl friends and their husbands straight. This will prevent some of those interminable arguments that begin after Midge and Harry (not Mucky and Ben) have said a stiff goodnight and gone home.

RULE THREE: A husband should not insult his wife publicly, at parties. He should insult her in the privacy of the home. Thus, if a man thinks the soufflés his wife makes are as tough as an outfielder's glove, he should tell her so when they are at home, not when they are out at a formal dinner party where a perfect soufflé has just been served. The same rule applies to the wife. She should not regale his men friends, or women friends, with hilarious accounts of her husband's clumsiness, remarking that he dances like a 1907 Pope Hartford, or that he locked himself in the children's rabbit pen and couldn't get out. All parties must end finally, and the husband or wife who has revealed all may find that there is hell to pay in the taxi going home.

RULE FOUR: The wife who keeps saying, 'Isn't that just like a man?' and the husband who keeps saying, 'Oh, well, you know how women are,' are likely to grow farther and farther apart through the years. These famous generalizations have the effect of reducing an individual to the anonymous status of a mere unit in a mass. The wife who, just in time, comes upon her husband about to fry an egg in a dry skillet should not classify him with all other males but should give him the accolade of a special distinction. She might say, for example, 'George, no other man in the world would try to do a thing like that.' Similarly, a husband watching his wife labouring to start the car without turning on the ignition should not say to the gardener or a passer-by, 'Oh, well, you know, etc.' Instead, he should remark to his wife, 'I've seen a lot of women in my life, Nellie, but I've never seen one who could touch you.'

Certain critics of this rule will point out that the specific comments I would substitute for the old familiar generalities do not solve the problem. They will maintain that the husband and wife will be sore and sulky for several days, no matter what is said. One wife, reading Rule Four over my shoulder, exclaimed, 'Isn't that just like a man?' This brings us right back where we started. Oh, well, you know how women are!

RULE FIVE: When a husband is reading aloud, a wife should sit quietly in her chair, relaxed but attentive. If he has decided to read the Republican platform, an article on elm blight, or a blow-by-blow account of a prize fight, it is not going to be easy, but she should at least pretend to be interested. She should not keep swinging one foot, start to wind her wrist watch, file her fingernails, or clap her hands in an effort to catch a mosquito. The good wife allows the mosquito to bite her when her husband is reading aloud.

She should not break in to correct her husband's pronunciation, or to tell him one of his socks is wrong side out. When the husband has finished, the wife should not lunge instantly into some irrelevant subject. It's wiser to exclaim, 'How interesting!' or, at the very least, 'Well, well!' She might even compliment him on his diction and his grasp of politics, elm blight or boxing. If he should ask some shrewd question to test her attention, she can cry, 'Good heavens!' leap up, and rush out to the kitchen on some urgent fictitious errand. This may fool him, or it may not. I hope, for her sake – and his – that it does.

RULE SIX: A husband should try to remember where things are around the house so that he does not have to wait for his wife to get home from the hair-dresser's before he can put his hands on what he wants. Among the things a husband is usually unable to locate are the iodine, the aspirin, the nail file, the French vermouth, his cuff links, studs, black silk socks and evening shirts, the snapshots taken at Nantucket last summer, his favourite record of 'Kentucky Babe,' the borrowed copy of *The Road to Miltown*, the garage key, his own towel, the last bill from Brooks Brothers, his pipe cleaners, the poker chips, crackers, cheese, the whetstone, his new raincoat, and the screens for the upstairs windows.

I don't really know the solution to this problem, but one should be found. Perhaps every wife should draw for her husband a detailed map of the house, showing clearly the location of everything he might need. Trouble is, I suppose, he would lay the map down somewhere and not be able to find it until his wife got home.

*

RULE SEVEN: If a husband is not listening to what his wife is saying, he should not grunt, 'Okay' or 'Yeah, sure,' or make little affirmative noises. A husband lost in thought or worry is likely not to take in the sense of such a statement as this: 'We're going to the Gordons for dinner tonight, John, so I'm letting the servants off. Don't come home from the office first. Remember, we both have to be at the dentist's at five, and I'll pick you up there with the car.' Now, an 'Okay' or a 'Yeah, sure' at this point can raise havoc if the husband hasn't really been listening. As usual, he goes all the way out to his home in Glenville – thirteen miles from the dentist's office and seventeen miles from the Gordons' house – and he can't find his wife. He can't find the servants. His wife can't get him on the phone because all she gets is the busy buzz. John is calling everybody he can think of except, of course, the dentist and the Gordons. At last he hangs up, exhausted and enraged. Then the phone rings. It is his wife. And here let us leave them.

RULE EIGHT: If your husband ceases to call you 'Sugarfoot' or 'Candy Eyes' or 'Cutie Fudge Pie' during the first year of your marriage, it is not necessarily a sign that he has come to take you for granted or that he no longer cares. It is probably an indication that he has recovered his normal perspective. Many a young husband who once called his wife 'Tender Mittens' or 'Taffy Ears' or 'Rose Lips' has become austere or important, like a common pleas Judge, and he wouldn't want reports of his youthful frivolity to get around. If he doesn't call you Dagmar when your name is Daisy, you are sitting pretty.

RULE NINE: For those whose husbands insist on pitching for the Married Men against the Single Men at the Fourth-of-July picnic of the First M. E. Church, I have the following suggestion: don't sit on the sidelines and watch him. Get lost. George is sure to be struck out by a fourteen-year-old boy, pull up with a charley horse running to first, and get his teeth knocked out by an easy grounder to the mound. When you see him after the game, tell him everybody knew the little boy was throwing illegal spitballs, everybody saw the first baseman spike George, and everybody said that grounder took such a nasty bounce even Phil Rizzuto couldn't have fielded it. Remember, most middle-aged husbands get to sleep at night by imagining they are striking out the entire batting order of the Yankees.

RULE TEN: A wife's dressing table should be inviolable. It is the one place in the house a husband should get away from and stay away from. And yet, the average husband is drawn to it as by a magnet, especially when he is carrying something wet, oily, greasy or sticky, such as a universal joint, a hub cap, or the blades of a lawn mower. His excuse for bringing these alien objects into his wife's bedroom in the first place is that he is looking for 'an old rag' with which to wipe them off. There are no old rags in a lady's boudoir, but husbands never seem to learn this. They search hampers, closets, and bureau drawers, expecting to find a suitable piece of cloth, but first they set the greasy object on the dressing table. The aggrieved wife may be tempted, following this kind of vandalism, to lock her bedroom door and kick her husband out for good. I suggest, however, a less stringent punishment. Put a turtle in his bed. The wife who is afraid to pick up a turtle should ask Junior to help her. Junior will love it.

Now I realize, in glancing back over these rules, that some of my solutions to marital problems may seem a little untidy; that I have, indeed, left a number of loose ends here and there. For example, if the husbands are going to mislay their detailed maps of household objects, I have accomplished nothing except to add one item for the distraught gentleman to lose.

Then, there is that turtle. Captious critics will point out that a turtle in a husband's bed is not a valid solution to anything, but merely a further provocation. The outraged husband will deliberately trip his wife during their next mixed-doubles match. She will thereupon retaliate by putting salt in his breakfast coffee. . . .

Two persons living in holy matrimony, I should have said long before this, must avoid slipping into blasphemy, despond, apathy, and the subjunctive mood. A husband is always set on edge by his mate's 'Far be it from me' or 'Be that as it may.' This can lead to other ominous openings: 'Would God that' and 'Had I only had the good sense to,' and the couple is then in the gloomy sub-cellar of the pluperfect subjunctive, a place in which no marriage can thrive. The safest place for a happily wedded pair is the indicative mood, and of its tenses the present is the most secure. The future is a domain of threats and worries, and the past is a wasteland of sorrows and regrets.

I can only hope, in conclusion, that this treatise itself will not start, in any household, a widening gap that can never be closed.

The Interview

'WONDERFUL PLACE you have here,' said the man from the newspaper. He stood with his host on a rise of ground from where, down a slope to the right, they could see a dead garden, killed by winter, and, off to the left, spare, grim trees stalking the ghost of a brook.

'Everybody says that,' said George Lockhorn. 'Everybody says it's a wonderful place, to which I used to reply "Thank you," or "I'm glad you think so," or "Yes, it is, isn't it?" At fifty-eight, Price, I say what I know. I say that you and the others are, by God, debasing the word wonderful. This bleak prospect is no more wonderful than a frozen shirt. Even in full summer it's no more wonderful than an unfrozen shirt. I will give you the synonyms for wonderful – wondrous, miraculous, prodigious, astonishing, amazing, phenomenal, unique, curious, strange. I looked them up an hour ago, because I knew you would say this is a wonderful place. Apply any of those words to that dahlia stalk down there.'

'I see what you mean,' said Price, who was embarrassed, and began looking in his pockets for something that wasn't there.

'I have known only a few wonderful things in my fifty-eight years,' said Lockhorn. 'They are easy to enumerate, since I have been practising up to toss them off to you casually: the body of a woman, the works of a watch, the verses of Keats, the structure of the hyacinth, the devotion of the dog. Trouble is, I tossed those off casually for the St. Louis *Post-Dispatch* man, or the Rochester *Times-Union* man. It's cold out here. Shall we go inside?'

'Just as you say,' said the interviewer, who had reached for the copy paper and the pencil in his pocket, but didn't bring them out. 'It's bracing out here, though.'

'You're freezing to death, without your hat and overcoat, and you know it,' said Lockhorn. 'It's late enough for a highball – do you drink cocktails?'

'No, sir. That is, not often,' said Price.

'You're probably a liar,' Lockhorn said. 'Everybody replies to my questions the way they think I want them to reply. You can say that I say "everybody-they"; I hate "everybody-he." "Has everybody brought his or her slate?" a teacher of mine, a great goat of a woman, used to ask us. There is no other tongue in the world as clumsy as ours is – with its back to certain corners. That's been used, too – and don't make notes, or don't let me see you make notes. Never made a note in my life, except after a novel was finished. Plot the chapters out, outline the characters, after the book has been published.'

'That is extremely interesting,' said Price. 'What do you do with the notes?'

They had reached the rear of the house now. 'We'll go in the back way,' said Lockhorn. 'I keep them around, tuck them away where my executor can find them if he's on his toes. This is the woodshed. We'll go through the kitchen. Some of my best character touches, some of the best devices, too, are in the notes. Anybody can write a novel, but it takes talent to do notes. We'll go through this door.'

'This is wonderful,' said Price. 'I'm sorry. I mean – '

'Let it stand,' said Lockhorn. 'Wonderful in the sense of being astonishing, curious, and strange. Don't take the chair by the fire,' he added as they reached the living room. 'That's mine.'

Lockhorn dropped into the chair by the fireplace and motioned his guest into another. 'Can I use that about the notes?' asked Price. 'Mr Hammer wants something new.'

'Make us both a drink,' Lockhorn said. 'That's a bar over there. I drink bourbon, but there's Scotch and rye, too.'

'I'll have bourbon,' said Price.

'Everybody has what I have,' Lockhorn growled. 'I said Scotch, and the *Times-Union* man had Scotch; I said rye, and the *Post-Dispatch* man had rye. No, you can't use that about the notes. Tell it to everybody. Beginning to believe it myself. Have you gained the idea in your half-hour here that I am a maniac?'

Price, noisily busy with bottles and glasses, laughed uncomfortably. 'Everybody knows that your methods of work are unusual,' he said. 'May I ask what you are working on now?'

'Easy on the soda,' said Lockhorn. 'Martha will raise hell when she finds me drinking. Just bow at her and grin.'

Price put two frightened squirts of soda in one glass and filled up the other. 'Mrs Lockhorn?' he asked, handing the strong highball to his host.

'What is this man Hammer like?' Lockhorn demanded. 'No, let me tell you.

He says "remotely resembles," he says "flashes of insight." He begins, by God, sentences with "moreover." I had an English teacher who began sentences with "too." "Too, there are other factors to be considered." The man says he's read Macaulay, but he never got past page six – Hammer, that is. Should have gone into real estate – subdivisions, opening up suburbs, and so on. This English teacher started every class by saying, "None of us can write." Hadn't been for that man, I would have gone into real estate – subdivisions, opening up suburbs, and so on. But he was a challenge. You can say my memoirs will be called "I Didn't Want to Write." ' Lockhorn had almost finished his drink. 'I'll have to see a proof,' he said. 'I'll have to see a proof of your article. Have you noticed that everybody says everything twice? They say everything twice. "Yes, they do," you'll say. "Yes, they do." Only contribution I've made to literature is the discovery of the duplicate statement. "How the hell are you, Bill?" a guy will say. "How the hell are you, anyway?" "Fine," Bill will say. "Just fine." '

'That's very interesting,' said Price, and, feeling that his host expected it, he added, 'That's very interesting.'

Lockhorn held out his glass and Price carried it back to the bar. 'The *Times* man, or whoever it was,' Lockhorn went on, 'put down that one of the things I regard as wonderful is the feminine anatomy. You can't get "body of a woman" in the papers. The feminine anatomy is something that can be touched only with the mind, and you'll notice that in my list everything can be touched by the hand. A watch a man never held would not be wonderful.'

'That's true,' said Price, speculating on the tactile aspect of devotion.

'There is only one thing I've never told an interviewer,' Lockhorn said, after a pause. 'I've never told any interviewer about the game. "Don't tell the man about the game," Mrs Lockhorn always says. "Promise me you won't tell the man about the game." Let me ask you one thing – why would Martha ask me not to tell you about the game if there were no game?'

'She wouldn't, of course,' said Price, taking a long slow sip of his drink to cover his embarrassment. The two men drank in silence for a while. 'My second wife left me because of the game,' Lockhorn said, 'but you can't print that, because she would deny it, and I would deny it.' Lockhorn took a great gulp of his drink and stared into the fire again. Two minutes of silence went by, during which Price found himself counting the ticks of the clock on the mantelpiece. 'My memory is beginning to slip,' Lockhorn said, 'but if you print that, I'll sue Hammer's pants off. Maybe I'll sue his pants off anyway. Sunday editors are the worst vermin in the world. If you use that, credit it to Mencken. I don't know why the hell you boys want to interview me. I've said a great many sharp things in my life, but I can't remember which ones are mine and which ones were said by Santayana, or John Jay Chapman, or Bernard De Voto. You can say my memory is slipping – maybe it will arouse pity. I'm the loneliest man in the United States.' Lockhorn had finished his drink very fast, and he got up and walked to the bar. Price's eyebrows went up as he heard the heavy slug of bourbon chortle into the glass. 'Martha'll be sore as a pup,' Lockhorn said with an owlish grin. 'Just touch your forelock to her. You can't argue with her. She's my fourth wife, you know. The others were Dorothy, Nettie, and Pauline, not necessarily in that order.' He came back to his chair and flopped into it. Price began to listen to the clock again. Lockhorn's head jerked up suddenly. 'Going to call my memoirs "I Had to Write," ' he said. 'You can put that in your piece if you want to.'

When Mrs Lockhorn came into the room, smiling her small, apprehensive smile, Price had just handed his host a seventh highball. 'This is Pricey,' said Lockhorn. Price, who had jumped to his feet, stood bowing and grinning at his hostess. She barely touched him with her smile. 'One for the house,' said Lockhorn, holding up his drink.

'It's early,' said Mrs Lockhorn. 'It isn't five yet.'

'I must be going,' Price said. 'May I make you a drink, Mrs Lockhorn?'

'No, thank you,' she said, in a tone that corked the bottles.

'Nonsense,' said Lockhorn. 'Sit down, Pricey. I've never, by God, known anything like the female timetable. They live by the clock. The purpose of 6 p.m. is to unlock their inhibitions about liquor. Sexual intercourse is for holidays – '

'George!' said Mrs Lockhorn sharply.

Price began to babble. 'Well, I guess it was us men – we men – who actually set a schedule for drinking, with that business about the sun over the yardarm, wasn't it, Mr Lockhorn?'

'Sun over your grandma's thigh,' said Lockhorn irritably, looking at Price but aiming the phrase at his wife. 'Who called tea "the five o'clock"? Women, French women. They don't even believe a man should smoke until he puts on his tuxedo. We are a prisoner of the hours, Pricey, and you know it.' Price flushed and became vastly conscious of his hands.

'Finish your drink,' said Martha Lockhorn to Price. 'My husband is going to finish his, and then I'm afraid he must rest. The new book has taken a great deal out of him.'

'You're goddam tootin' he's going to finish his,' said Lockhorn, his fingers whitening on his glass, 'and don't third-person me. Sit down, Pricey. We're just getting started.' Price sat stiffly on the edge of his chair. He saw that Mrs Lockhorn, who had moved behind her husband's chair, was trying to communicate with him by a shake of her head and a glance at the bar. 'Don't let 'em third-person you, Pricey,' said Lockburn sternly. 'Next comes the first person plural – they first-person-plural you to death. Then you might just as well go to bed and die. You might just as well go to bed and die.'

'I hope he hasn't been entertaining you with imprecations all afternoon,' said Mrs Lockhorn.

'Oh, no indeed,' exclaimed Price, picking up his glass and setting it down.

'She loves the happy phrase,' said Lockhorn. 'She spends more time on phrases than most women do on their hips.'

'Don't be tiresome, George,' said Mrs Lockhorn. She turned to Price. 'You

see, he has been interviewed constantly,' she told him. 'It seems as if there has
been an interviewer here every day since his novel came out. You all want
something different, and then it never comes out the way he says it. It's all
twisted and ridiculous.'

'I hope to avoid that sin,' said Price, noting that the famous author had
closed his eyes but still kept his tight grip on his glass.

'He's terribly tired.' Mrs Lockhorn's voice was lowered to a whisper, as if
they were in a sickroom. 'He worked four years on "The Flaw in the Crystal."
Some of the reviews have hurt him deeply.'

'It's selling wonderfully,' whispered Price.

Mrs Lockhorn made a gesture with her hands, but its meaning was lost on
him.

The novelist opened his eyes and quickly finished his drink. 'I'll tell you
some other wonderful things,' he said. 'A woman crying, children calling over
the snow – across the snow – dogs barking at a distance, dogs barking far off at
night.' He put his empty glass on the floor and groped in the air for more
wonders with his right hand. 'Things I've wanted to do,' he went on. 'You
can use this, Pricey. Bat baseballs through the windows of a firescraper from a
lower roof across the street, spend – '

'Skyscraper,' said Mrs Lockhorn.

To Price's secret delight his host, after a slow stare at Mrs Lockhorn, repeated with great authority, 'Firescraper.' He winked at Price. 'I want to spend
the night in Ovington's,' he said. 'I want to open a pigeon. All my life I've
wanted to cut a dove open, looking for the goddamnedest omens in the history
of the world. Like the Romans performing the ancient assizes. I want to find
two hearts in one of the sons of bitches and go crying through the night, like
another Whozis, "Repent, ye sinners, repent. The world is coming to an end." '

'George,' said Mrs Lockhorn, 'the newspapers can't print things like that.'

Lockhorn didn't hear her. He picked up the glass and drank the trickle of
ice water in it. 'Go down, ye sinners, to the sea,' he said, with a wide gesture.

'Talk about your book,' said his wife. 'The newspapers want to know about
your book.'

Lockhorn looked at her. 'They are all the same, Pricey,' he said, 'and they
differ as the waves differ. Only in height. The blood of the dove, as they say,
Pricey. I'll tell you about the book, drunk as I unexpectedly am, or get.'

'He's terribly tired,' cut in his wife.

'Spiritual hope!' bawled Lockhorn, so loudly Price started the ice tinkling
in his glass. 'Spiritual hope is my tiny stock in trade, to quote the greatest
master of them all.'

Mrs Lockhorn, observing that the newspaperman looked puzzled, said, 'He
means Henry James,' and then, to her husband, 'I think he spoke of his *small*
trade, George.'

'The greatest master of them all,' said Lockhorn again. 'I always begin with
a picture, a visual picture. Woman standing in the doorway with the evening
sun in her hair, as Hockett would put it.'

'Hockett?' asked Price, realizing, with a small cold feeling in his stomach, that he was not going to have anything to write.

'Your boss,' said Lockhorn.

'Oh, Hammer,' said Price.

'I beg your pardon?' said Mrs Lockhorn.

The author jiggled what was left of the ice in his glass. 'The women write backwards,' he said, 'beginning with their titles – "Never Dies the Dream," "Lonely Is the Hunting Heart." '

'It's "The Heart Is a Lonely Hunter," ' said his wife, but Lockhorn waved her away.

'I'm tired of the adult world seen through the eyes of a little girl,' he said. 'A woman forgets everything that happens to her after she is fourteen. I, too, have lived in Arcady, Pricey, but I'm tired of viewing the adult world through the great solemn eyes of a sensitive – what is that word like nipper?'

'Moppet?' asked Price.

'Sensitive moppet,' said Lockhorn, closing his eyes, and sinking deeper in his chair.

Price attempted to make a surreptitious note on his copy paper.

'You can't use that,' whispered Mrs Lockhorn. 'He's talking about one of his closest women friends.'

The interviewer put his pencil and paper away as his host opened his eyes again and pointed a finger at him. 'Henry James had the soul of an eaves-dropper,' he said. Price gave a laugh that did not sound like his own. 'Every-thing he got, he got from what he overheard somebody say. No visual sense, and if you haven't got visual sense, what have you got?'

Price stood up as if to go, but Lockhorn waved him down again and grinned at his wife. 'Pricey, here, has invented some remarkable game, Martha,' he said. 'Tell Martha about your game, son. It's all we've talked about all after-noon.'

Price swallowed.

'What sort of game is it?' asked Martha.

'It's nothing, really,' gurgled Price. He stood up again. 'I must be running along,' he said.

'Sit down for a moment,' said Mrs Lockhorn. 'George, you better lie down awhile.'

To Price's astonishment, the novelist got meekly to his feet and started for the door into the hall. He stopped in front of Price and stuck an index finger into his ribs, making a skucking sound with his tongue. 'Is love worse living?' he said, and went out into the hall and closed the door behind him. He began to stomp up the carpeted stairs, shouting, 'Dorothy! Nettie! Martha!'

Price, swallowing again, idiotically wondered what ever became of Pauline.

'As you see, he's really worn out,' said Mrs Lockhorn hastily. 'He's not as young as he used to be, of course, and I wish he'd give up writing. After all, he's written eighteen books and he has a comfortable income.'

From far upstairs Price heard a now faint shouting for the lost Pauline.

'Are you sure you won't have another drink?' asked Mrs Lockhorn, not moving from the edge of her chair.

'A quick one, perhaps,' said Price. 'Just half a glass.'

'Surely,' said Mrs Lockhorn with the hint of a sigh, taking his glass. 'Bourbon?'

'Scotch, if you don't mind,' said Price.

She made it very small, and very weak. 'I know that you will use discretion,' she said. 'George has become a little reckless in some of the things he says, and I hope you were able to tell the truth from the things he just makes up.'

Price finished half his drink. 'I'm afraid I really haven't got anything,' he said miserably. 'Perhaps you could tell me something I could use.'

Mrs Lockhorn looked mysterious. 'There are some wonderful things about the book,' she said. 'I mean about the way he wrote it and what had to be done by the publishers. He had actually written, word for word, a chapter from one of his earlier books into the new one. He hadn't copied it, you understand. It was simply there in his memory, word for word.' Price got out his pencil and paper, but his hostess lifted her hand. 'Oh, mercy!' she said. 'You can't possibly print that. He would be furious if he found it out.'

Price looked puzzled. 'If he found it out?' he asked.

She stood up and Price got to his feet. 'Oh, he doesn't remember writing it,' she said. 'It was just stuck in. The publishers had to take it out. But you mustn't mention it. Please don't even tell Mr Hockett.'

Price set his glass down on the table beside his chair. 'I believe my hat and overcoat –' he began.

'I'll get them,' she said. 'They must be in the closet hall.'

They went to the closet. There was no sound from upstairs. Price got into his coat, and Mrs Lockhorn went with him to the front door and opened it. 'I'm sorry,' she said. 'I'm afraid it's been something of a wild-goose chase.'

'I'm afraid it has,' said Price, a little grimly.

Mrs Lockhorn gave him her best hostess smile. 'George gets mixed up when he's tired,' she explained, 'or he wouldn't have said "Is love worse living?"'

Price matched her smile with one just as artificial. 'He was quoting one of the most famous lines ever written by James Joyce,' he said. He went out and got into his car. 'Goodbye, Mrs Lockhorn,' he said.

'Goodbye, Mr Pricey,' she called to him. Her smile was gone. 'I'm sorry you didn't have time to tell me about your game.'

'Some other time, maybe,' said Price, whose smile was also gone, and he started the engine.

Mrs Lockhorn closed the front door.

When Price had driven a few hundred yards from the house, he took the copy paper from his pocket and threw it out of the window. Then, suddenly, he reached for his pencil and threw it out of the window, too.

Lady in a Trap

SOMETIMES THOSE little fillers you see in newspapers are more fascinating and provocative than the major news stories, and one of this kind turned up not long ago in the watchful and sympathetic *New York Times*. It went like this: 'When a female mole is caught in a trap, the male often worries so much that he starves to death.' My wife read this item aloud to me, in a reproachful tone, clearly implying that the male of any species, including mine, would be awkwardly helpless, and just go to pieces, if he came upon his mate caught in a trap, or bound and gagged and locked in the linen closet. I spoke up before she could get off whatever sardonic comment was on the tip of her tongue.

'Devoted little fellow, the ground mole,' I said quickly. 'Note that he does not seize this golden opportunity to run away with the female chipmunk that lives in the oak tree. No, he stands loyally by, thinking of Mama and grieving over her fate.'

'In a tomcat's eye he does,' said my wife. 'The item does not say "grieves," it says "worries." It was obviously written by a male. You would think that the male mole was in a worse dilemma than the female. The trouble with the male is –'

'The trouble with the female is that she is constantly walking into traps,' I cut in. 'I will never forget that awful, cold night on Third Avenue when we couldn't get a cab, and one suddenly drove up from nowhere and stopped, and a man got out of the back seat, held open the door, and said, "Get in." Before I could stop you, you got in and I had to follow. It turned out that we were in a gyp cab and that the gallant gentleman who had offered to share his taxi was, in reality, a burglar.'

'He was not a burglar, he was only a pickpocket,' my wife explained, 'and besides, he dropped us at our apartment building, and he didn't steal anything. You are trying to change the subject.'

'You were just lucky that night. I managed to get between the guy and you, or he would have had your money and mink. The female should always avoid doors that are held invitingly open, especially those that are held open by a small stick, or by a pickpocket.'

'All the male mole thinks about when he finds his mate in a trap,' she went on, oblivious of my warning, 'is where his next meal is coming from. That isn't his loved one he sees in the trap, it is his cook. The male knows that as soon as he finishes the crackers and milk – and the whisky – and is faced with the problem of cooking something, he is a gone male. He will starve to death out of ignorance, and not out of sorrow. You surely remember the time that you –'

507

'I don't want to go through that again,' I said, crisply, knowing full well what she was thinking about. She was thinking about the time I poured some dry Wheatena in the top of a double-boiler, filled the bottom part with water, and set the boiler on a gas jet, getting not cereal for breakfast, but only evaporation. My wife and I can never talk about the ineptitude of any male without bringing his faults and flaws down on my own head, but this, I understand from my men friends, is an unfair trick resorted to, in argument, by all wives.

A few days later, when she had driven over to the hairdresser's in Torrington, I decided to make a secret exploration of our pantry and kitchen, so that I could show an easy surprising familiarity with them the next time she said, 'A man never knows where anything is.' Since it was the cook's day off, I had the house to myself, and I decided to proceed on the assumption that Mama was caught in a trap and that I had to prepare a meal for myself, without help from any female. The experiment proved, to my dismay, that the average husband would be lost in his own kitchen. Let us take not me, but a hypothetical husband named John, whose wife is caught in a trap.

Entering the kitchen, he is instantly surprised by its strangeness, and also by its neatness. He wanders into the pantry and sees a lot of drawers and cupboard doors. The first door he pulls open reveals nothing to eat, but only several shelves containing enough glasses of all kinds, it seems to him, for a family of fifteen – highball glasses, and glasses for sherry, cocktails, wine, and just plain water. The next door opens up to reveal two hundred plates, including the Spode set, and green glass ones for salad. Next he finds himself palely wandering among big, useless platters and formidable tureens. He decides he is up too high and he opens a couple of cupboard doors flush with the floor, and gets tangled up with the things you make onion soup and shirred eggs in, and a lot of iron, copper, and aluminium objects, in a recess that becomes deeper and darker, at the end of which he unearths a waffle iron. He hastily closes these doors and begins pulling out drawers filled with knives and spoons.

At this point, he realizes that he should probably find the refrigerator, which he finally does, peering helplessly inside, getting his forefinger into something cold and sticky, and, at length, removing a head of lettuce wrapped in cheesecloth, and two eggs. He sets these on the kitchen table, but the eggs begin to roll, so he puts them in his pocket.

Coffee is now the thing that comes to mind, but all he can find at first is a shelf holding raisins, cream of wheat, corn meal, noodles, rice, Jello, cake flour, Quaker oats, and baking powder. Not far from these he finds vanilla, spices, tabasco sauce, and a bottle of Worcestershire. He now feels that he is losing ground rapidly. Ten minutes later he finds the coffee in a can marked 'Coffee,' puts it on the kitchen table, takes off the lid, and finds himself, to his astonishment, placing the two eggs in the coffee can, where they will not roll. This, it occurs to him, is somehow wrong, and he remembers Christopher Columbus's solution of the problem of how to keep an egg from rolling. He takes out one of the eggs, strikes one end of it smartly on top of the table, and produces a small pool of yolk and white. The egg does not stand on end, as it should. It leaks. He leaves the other egg in the coffee can and begins to hunt for a percolator. This takes him back to the dark recess with the waffle iron and the other metal objects. There is no percolator, and he realizes why when he sees the Silex and remembers that the old-fashioned percolator is gone for ever.

He knows he cannot work the Silex, so he gives up the idea of making coffee and thinks of opening a can of peaches. Before he can find a can of peaches, he has placed seventeen cans of other things on the floor. Now comes the problem of opening the peaches, and he goes through the drawers looking for a can opener. He can't find one and remembers vaguely having heard something about an electric can opener. He looks around the walls and spots the Mixmaster, but something keeps him from trying to open the can of peaches by putting it in the Mixmaster and starting the thing. He is suddenly no longer hungry.

The project of cooking something is completely abandoned, for he is faced with a much more urgent task: how to get rid of the mess he has created with the egg, and prevent his wife from finding out about it when she comes home. He tries to pick up the spattered egg, with no success, so he looks around for a cloth, and spots one neatly folded over the back of a kitchen chair. On this he wipes his eggy hands and, as the cloth falls open, he sees that what he has hold of is an apron. Panic seizes him now, and he wipes up the broken egg with the apron. This doesn't seem to work too well, so he gets water in a glass and pours it on the table top and then wipes some more.

The dilemma now is what to do with the apron. Many a husband, living in the country, would get the spade and bury the apron outdoors, but John is at heart a city man. The wild idea crosses his mind that he can hide it in the garbage can, but a misty sense of the fitness of things restrains his hand. He hurries into the living room and stuffs the apron in the wastebasket, but even as he does so, the dreadful compulsion is forming at the back of his mind to wash out the evidence of his guilt. He takes the apron from the wastebasket, goes upstairs, runs a tub of hot water, and douses the apron.

What he has now is something so wet that it cannot possibly be dried before his wife gets home. Every husband must work out this quandary in his own way. The more timid men may try to hide the wet apron inside an overcoat hanging in a closet, or under the clean pyjamas in a bureau drawer. The bolder ones, like me, will spread the thing over a radiator, or pin it to the shower curtain.

My own experience has taught me that nothing can be successfully hidden from a woman, unless she hides it from herself. The common housewife knows the whereabouts of everything small, but she has a tendency to mislay waffle irons and the like, and the one you found in that dark recess may cheer her up so that she will forgive the incident of the apron. I would get those seventeen cans off the floor, though, and take that egg out of the coffee and put it back in the refrigerator.

File and Forget

I WANT to thank my secretary, Miss Ellen Bagley, for putting the following letters in order. I was not up to the task myself, for reasons that will, I think, become clear to the reader.   J.T.

WEST CORNWALL, CONN.
NOVEMBER 2, 1949

Miss Alma Winege,
The Charteriss Publishing Co.,
132 East What Street,
New York, N.Y.

DEAR MISS WINEGE:
Your letter of October 25th, which you sent to me in care of The Homestead, Hot Springs, Ark., has been forwarded to my home in West Cornwall, Conn., by The Homestead, Hot Springs, Va. As you know, Mrs Thurber and I sometimes visit this Virginia resort, but we haven't been there for more than a year. Your company, in the great tradition of publishers, has sent so many letters to me at Hot Springs, Ark., that the postmaster there has simply taken to sending them on to the right address, or what would be the right address if I were there. I explained to Mr Cluffman, and also to Miss Lexy, when I last called at your offices, that all mail was to be sent to me at West Cornwall until further notice. If and when I go to The Homestead, I will let you know in advance. Meanwhile, I suggest that you remove from your files all addresses of mine except the West Cornwall one. Another publishing firm recently sent a letter to me at 65 West 11th Street, an address I vacated in the summer of 1930. It would not come as a surprise to me if your firm, or some other publishers, wrote me in care of my mother at 568 Oak Street, Columbus, Ohio. I was thirteen years old when we lived there, back in 1908.
As for the contents of your letter of the 25th, I did not order thirty-six copies of Peggy Peckham's book, 'Grandma Was a Nudist.' I trust that you have not shipped these books to me in care of The Homestead, Hot Springs, Ark., or anywhere else.

Sincerely yours,
J. THURBER

P.S. Margaret Peckham, by the way, is not the author of this book. She is the distinguished New York psychiatrist whose 'The Implications of Nudism' was published a couple of years ago. She never calls herself Peggy.

J.T.

WEST CORNWALL, CONN.
NOVEMBER 3, 1949

Miss Alma Winege,
The Charteriss Publishing Co.,
132 East What Street,
New York, N.Y.

DEAR MISS WINEGE:
In this morning's mail I received a card from the Grand Central branch of the New York Post Office informing me that a package of books had been delivered to me at 410 East 57th Street. The branch office is holding the package for further postage, which runs to a considerable amount. I am enclosing the notification card, since these must be the thirty-six copies of 'Grandma Was a Nudist.' I have not lived at 410 East 57th Street since the fall of 1944. Please see to it that this address is removed from your files, along with The Homestead address.

Whoever ordered those books, if anyone actually did, probably wonders where they are.

Sincerely yours,
J. THURBER

THE CHARTERISS PUBLISHING COMPANY
NEW YORK, N.Y.

NOVEMBER 5, 1949

Mr James M. Thurber,
West Cornwall, Conn.

DEAR MR THURBER:
I am dreadfully sorry about the mix-up over Miss Peckham's book. We have been pretty much upset around here since the departure of Mr Peterson and Mr West, and several new girls came to us with the advent of Mr Jordan. They have not yet got their 'sea legs,' I am afraid, but I still cannot understand from what file our shipping department got your address as 165 West 11th Street. I have removed the 57th Street address from the files and also the Arkansas address and I trust that we will not disturb your tranquillity further up there in Cornwall. It must be lovely this time of year in Virginia and I envy you and Mrs Thurber. Have a lovely time at The Homestead.

Sincerely yours,
ALMA WINEGE

P.S. What you had to say about 'Grandma' amused us all.   A.W.

COLUMBUS, OHIO
NOVEMBER 16, 1949

DEAR MR THURBER:

I have decided to come right out with the little problem that was accidentally dumped in my lap yesterday. I hope you will forgive me for what
happened, and perhaps you can suggest what I should do with the books.
There are three dozen of them and, unfortunately, they arrived when my
little son Donald was alone downstairs. By the time I found out about the
books, he had torn off the wrappings and had built a cute little house out of
them. I have placed them all on a shelf out of his reach while awaiting word as
to where to send them. I presume I could ship them to you C.O.D. if I can get
somebody to wrap them properly.

I heard from old Mrs Winston next door that you and your family once
lived here at 568 Oak Street. She remembers you and your brothers as cute
little tykes who were very noisy and raised rabbits and guinea pigs. She says
your mother was a wonderful cook. I am sorry about Donald opening the
books and I hope you will forgive him.

Sincerely yours,
CLARA EDWARDS
(Mrs J. C.)

WEST CORNWALL, CONN.
NOVEMBER 19, 1949

Mr Leon Charteriss,
The Charteriss Publishing Co.,
132 East What Street,
New York, N.Y.

DEAR MR CHARTERISS:

I am enclosing a letter from a Mrs J. C. Edwards, of Columbus, Ohio, in the
fervent hope that you will do something to stop this insane flux of books. I
never ordered these books. I have not read 'Grandma Was a Nudist.' I do not
intend to read it. I want something done to get these volumes off my trail and
cut out of my consciousness.

I have written Miss Winege about the situation, but I am afraid to take it up
with her again, because she might send them to me in care of the Department
of Journalism at Ohio State University, where I was a student more than
thirty years ago.

Sincerely yours,
J. THURBER

P.S. I never use my middle initial, but your firm seems to think it is 'M.'
It is not.   J.T.

THE CHARTERISS PUBLISHING COMPANY
NEW YORK, N.Y.

Mr James M. Thurber,   November 23, 1949
West Cornwall, Conn.

DEAR MR THURBER:

Mr Charteriss has flown to California on a business trip and will be gone for several weeks. His secretary has turned your letter of the 19th over to me. I have asked Mr Cluffman to write to Miss Clara Edwards in Columbus and arrange for the reshipment of the thirty-six copies of 'Grandma Was a Nudist.'

I find, in consulting the records, that you have three times ordered copies of your own book, 'Thurber's Ark,' to be shipped to you at West Cornwall, at the usual discount rate of forty per cent. I take it that what you really wanted was thirty-six copies of your own book and they are being sent out to you today with our regrets for the discomfit we have caused you. I hope you will be a little patient with us during this so trying period of reorganization.

Cordially yours,
JEANNETTE GAINES
Stock Order Dept.

P.S. You will be happy to know that we have traced down the gentleman who ordered those copies of 'Grandma.'

WEST CORNWALL, CONN.
NOVEMBER 25, 1949

Mr Henry Johnson,
The Charteriss Pub. Co.,
New York, N.Y.

DEAR HARRY:

Since the reorganization at Charteriss, I have the forlorn and depressing feeling that I no longer know anybody down there except you. I know that this immediate problem of mine is not in your field, but I turn to you as a last resource. What I want, or rather what I don't want, is simple enough, Harry. God knows it is simple.

I don't want any more copies of my book. I don't want any more copies of my book. I don't want any more copies of my book.

As ever,
JIM

P.S. It has just occurred to me that I haven't seen you for more than two years. Let's have a drink one of these days. I'll give you a ring the next time I'm in the city.

J.T.

THE CHARTERISS PUBLISHING COMPANY
NEW YORK, N.Y.

NOVEMBER 26, 1949

Mr James Grover Thurber,
Cornwall, Conn.

DEAR JIM THURBER:

I haven't had the pleasure of meeting you since I had the great good luck to join forces with Charteriss, but I look forward to our meeting with a high heart. Please let me know the next time you are in the city, as I should like to wine and dine you and perhaps discuss the new book that I feel confident you have in you. If you don't want to talk shop, we can discuss the record of our mutual football team. You were at Northwestern some years ahead of my time, I believe, but I want you to know that they still talk about Jimmy Thurber out there.

Your letter to Harry Johnson has just come to my attention, and I regret to say that Harry is no longer with us. He went to Simon and Schuster in the summer of 1948. I want you to feel, however, that every single one of us here is your friend, willing and eager to drop everything to do your slightest bidding. All of us feel very deeply about your having turned against your book 'Thurber's Ark.' I note that in your present mood you have the feeling that you never want to see it again. Well, Jim, let me assure you that this is just a passing fancy, derived from a moment of depression. When you put in your last order for thirty-six copies, you must surely have had some definite use in mind for them, and I am banking on twenty years' experience in the book-publishing game when I take the liberty of sending these twenty books off to you today. There is one thing I am something of an expert at, if I do say so myself, and that is the understanding of the 'creative spirit.'

We have a new system here, which is to send our authors not ten free copies, as of old, but fifteen. Therefore, five of the thirty-six copies will reach you with our compliments. The proper deductions will be made on the record.

Don't forget our dinner date.

Cordially,
CLINT JORDAN

P.S. I approve of your decision to resume the use of your middle name. It gives a book dignity and flavour to use all three names. I think it was old Willa Cather who started the new trend, when she dropped the Seibert.   C.J.

THE CHARTERISS PUBLISHING COMPANY
NEW YORK, N.Y.

DECEMBER 13, 1949

DEAR THURBER:

Just back at the old desk after a trip to California and a visit with my mother, who is eighty-nine now but as chipper as ever. She would make a swell Profile. Ask me about her someday.

Need I say I was delighted to hear from the staff when I got back about your keen interest in 'Grandma Was a Nudist'? The book has been moving beautifully and its ceiling has gone sky-high. We're planning a brief new advertising campaign and I'd be tickled pink if you would be good enough to bat out a blurb for us.

Yours,
LEON

THE CHARTERISS PUBLISHING COMPANY
NEW YORK, N.Y.
DECEMBER 15, 1949

Mr James M. Thurber,
West Cornwall, Conn.

DEAR MR THURBER:
I hope you will forgive me – indeed, all of us – for having inexcusably mislaid the address of the lady to whom the thirty-six copies of 'Grandma Was a Nudist' were sent by mistake. I understand that we have already dispatched to you at your home another thirty-six volumes of that book.
My apologies again.

Sincerely yours,
H. F. CLUFFMAN

WEST CORNWALL, CONN.
DECEMBER 19, 1949

Mr H. F. Cluffman,
The Charteriss Publishing Co.,
132 East What Street,
New York, N.Y.

DEAR MR CLUFFMAN:
The lady's name is Mrs J. C. Edwards, and she lives at 568 Oak Street, Columbus, Ohio.

I have explained as clearly as I could in previous letters that I did not order thirty-six copies of 'Grandma Was a Nudist.' If you have actually shipped to me another thirty-six copies of this book, it will make a total of seventy-two copies, none of which I will pay for. The thirty-six copies of 'Thurber's Ark' that Mr Jordan has written me he intends to send to West Cornwall would bring up to one hundred and eight the total number of books that your firm, by a conspiracy of confusion unique even in the case of publishers, has mistakenly charged to my account. You may advise Mr Jordan that I do not wish to receive the five free copies he mentioned in his letter.

If your entire staff of employees went back to *Leslie's Weekly*, where they belong, it would set my mind at rest.

Sincerely yours,
J. THURBER

P.S. I notice that you use only my middle initial, 'M.' Mr Jordan and I – or was it Mr Charteriss? – have decided to resume the use of the full name, which is Murfreesboro.   J. T.

WEST CORNWALL, CONN.
DECEMBER 27, 1949

Mr Leon Charteriss,
The Charteriss Publishing Co.,
132 East What Street,
New York, N.Y.

DEAR MR CHARTERISS:

I am sure you will be sorry to learn that Mr Thurber has had one of his spells as a result of the multiplication of books and misunderstanding that began with Miss Alma Winege's letter of October 25, 1949. Those of us around Mr Thurber are greatly disturbed by the unfortunate circumstances that have caused him to give up writing, at least temporarily, just after he had resumed work following a long fallow period.

Thirty-six copies of Mr Thurber's book and thirty-six copies of 'Grandma Was a Nudist' have arrived at his home here, and he has asked me to advise you that he intends to burn all seventy-two. West Cornwall is scarcely the community for such a demonstration – he proposes to burn them in the middle of U.S. Highway No. 7 – since the town regards with a certain suspicion any writer who has not won a Pulitzer Prize. I am enclosing copies of all the correspondence between your company and Mr Thurber, in the hope that someone connected with your firm will read it with proper care and intelligence and straighten out this deplorable and inexcusable situation.

Mr Thurber wishes me to tell you that he does not want to hear from any of you again.

Sincerely yours,
ELLEN BAGLEY
Secretary to Mr Thurber

THE CHARTERISS PUBLISHING COMPANY
NEW YORK, N.Y.
DECEMBER 28, 1949

Mr James Murfreesboro Thurber,
72 West,
Cornwall, Conn.

DEAR MR THURBER:

I have at hand your letter of December 19th, the opening paragraph of which puzzles me. You send me the following name and address – Mrs J. C. Edwards, 568 Oak Street, Columbus, Ohio – but it is not clear what use you wish me to make of this. I would greatly appreciate it if you would clear up this small matter for me.

Sincerely yours,
H. F. CLUFFMAN

P.S. *Leslie's Weekly* ceased publication many years ago. I could obtain the exact date if you so desire.

H. F. C.

THE CHARTERISS PUBLISHING COMPANY
NEW YORK, N.Y.
DECEMBER 29, 1949

Mr James M. Thurber,
West Cornwall, Conn.

DEAR MR THURBER:

You will be sorry to hear that Mr Charteriss was taken suddenly ill with a virus infection. His doctor believes that he lost his immunity during his visit to the West Coast. He is now in the hospital, but his condition is not serious.

Since the departure of Miss Gaines, who was married last week, I have taken over the Stock Order Department for the time being. I did not take the liberty of reading your enclosures in the letter to Mr Charteriss, but sent them directly to him at the hospital. I am sure that he will be greatly cheered up by them when he is well enough to read. Meanwhile, I want you to know that you can repose all confidence in the Stock Order Department to look after your needs, whatever they may be.

Sincerely yours,
GLADYS MACLEAN

P.S. I learned from Mr Jordan that you were a friend of Willa Cather's. Exciting!

COLUMBUS, OHIO
JANUARY 3, 1950

DEAR JAMIE:

I don't understand the clipping from the Lakeville *Journal* Helen's mother sent me, about someone burning all those books of yours in the street. I never heard of such a thing, and don't understand how they could have taken the books without your knowing it, or what you were doing with so many copies of the novel about the naked grandmother. Imagine, at her age! She couldn't carry on like that in Columbus, let me tell you. Why, when I was a girl, you didn't dare walk with a man after sunset, unless he was your husband, and even then there was talk.

It's a good thing that state policeman came along in time to save most of the books from being completely ruined, and you must be thankful for the note

Mr Jordan put in one of the books, for the policeman would never have known who they belonged to if he hadn't found it.

A Mrs Edwards phoned this morning and said that her son Donald collects your books and wants to send them to you – to be autographed, I suppose. Her son has dozens of your books and I told her you simply wouldn't have time to sign all of them, and she said she didn't care what you did with them. And then she said they weren't your books at all, and so I just hung up on her.

Be sure to bundle up when you go out.

With love,
MOTHER

P.S. This Mrs Edwards says she lives at 568 Oak Street. I told her we used to live there and she said God knows she was aware of that. I don't know what she meant. I was afraid this little boy would send you all those books to sign and so I told his mother that you and Helen were at The Homestead, in Hot Springs. You don't suppose he would send them there, do you?

and here, gentle reader, I know you will be glad to leave all of us.

The Case Book of James Thurber

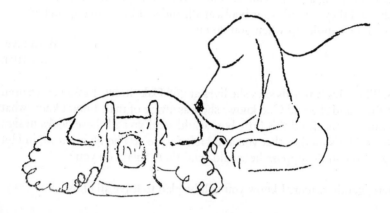

T HE CASE OF the Gloucester Sympathizer was an easy one to crack, once
I had sense enough to stop trying to crack it the hard way. I first heard
about the Sympathizer one day last summer from a friend of mine at
Annisquam, Massachusetts, near Gloucester. He told me he had called the
Gloucester Telephone Company one day, to complain about something, and
the operator had said, 'One moment, please. I'll connect you with the Sympathizer.' 'She must have said "supervisor," ' I said. This annoyed him, since he
is proud of his ear and accuracy. 'Not at all!' he snapped. 'I said, "Connect me
with whom?" and she repeated, "With the Sympathizer." '

I wanted to know what the Sympathizer was like, when he finally connected
with her. 'Did she begin by saying, "Heavens to Betsy, isn't that too bad! I'm
dreadfully sorry." ' He looked disappointed. 'She was courteous, crisp, and
competent,' he said. I reached for my hypodermic needle. 'Was she terribly
solicitous?' I demanded. He frowned. 'No,' he said, 'she wasn't.'

When I got back to my home in Cornwall, Connecticut, I picked up the
phone and asked the Cornwall telephone operator to connect me with the
Sympathizer. 'You're a caution, Mr Thurber,' she said, laughed, and hung
up. Then I called the long-distance operator in Torrington, fifteen miles
away. She said there wasn't any Sympathizer in Torrington, but she was sorry
it had happened, whatever it was. I could tell that she thought I was a caution,
too. I was about to try Hartford, to see if there was a Sympathizer there, when
it occurred to me to write the Gloucester Telephone Company and ask them
about their Sympathizer. I got a prompt and cordial letter from the company,
announcing that there wasn't any Sympathizer, and offering its consolations
and best wishes. I got my violin out of its case and began sawing moodily in

the general direction of 'Chloe,' lost in meditation. Naturally, I deduced at last, no reputable firm or corporation would employ a sympathizer, because the very existence of such a person would lend a note of gloom and insecurity to merchandising and other business transactions. I telephoned my friend and gave him the results of my findings in one sentence. 'There isn't any Sympathizer,' I told him. 'Yes, there is,' he snarled. 'Go to hell,' I said, and hung up.

The Case of the Gloucester Sympathizer was similar to the Case of the Young Woman Named Sherlock Holmes, a problem I solved the easy way a couple of years ago. George Spencer had told me that a guy he knew named Harry Huff was going to marry a girl named Sherlock Holmes. I said this was nonsense, because there isn't any girl named Sherlock Holmes. He said I didn't know anything about it. I said it was dangerous to believe everything one heard, and to go around repeating it. He snapped the leash back on his dog's collar, picked up its throwing stick, and went away.

I got out the phone book. There were two Henry Huffs listed, and I called the first one. 'Nah,' he said, 'I'm living in sin with Dr Watson. I thought everybody knew that.' He was obviously the wrong Henry Huff, and I hung up on him. The second one turned out to be the right one. I asked him to spell out the name of his fiancée. Without hesitation, he said he didn't want to, so I mentioned George Spencer and what he had said about Sherlock Holmes. Huff was annoyed, but he finally told me the name of the girl he was going to marry, one Shirley Combs.

It reminded me of the Curious Adventure of the Oral Surgeons' Mouse, which had taken place thirty years ago when I was a reporter. The city editor answered the phone one day, and then sent for me. 'The oral surgeons in convention here are about to operate on a mouse,' he said. 'Slide over and watch it.' I went away and came right back. 'What's the matter?' snarled the editor. 'Wouldn't the mouse open wide?' 'It wasn't a mouse,' I snarled. 'It was a mouth, it was a guy's mouth.' This was a great blow to the editor, almost as great as that which befell the little boy in Pennsylvania Station who thought the announcer was announcing the Make Believe Train, only to find out it was just the old Maple Leaf Express, on its routine way again.

The Anatomy of Confusion is a large subject, and I have no intention of writing the standard treatise on it, but I offer to whoever does, the most singular of all my cases, the Case of the Cockeyed Spaniard. This remarkable piece of confusion took place in Columbus, Ohio, as long ago as 1922. I lived next door to a young couple named Dan and Janet Henderson at the time. Dan was a well-known reveller of the neighbourhood, given to odd companions and peculiar pranks. One afternoon about six o'clock, Janet phoned me and asked me to come over. Her voice sounded wavy and troubled. 'What's Dan up to now?' I asked. She sighed. 'He's bringing home a cockeyed Spaniard,' she said, 'and I simply won't face them both alone.' I slipped my brass knuckles into my pocket and went over to the Henderson house. 'The only Spaniards I know of in Columbus,' I told Janet, 'are a dozen students at Ohio State, but I doubt that they would be cockeyed as early as six o'clock.'

It transpired that Dan Henderson had phoned his ominous message while Mrs Henderson was in the bath-tub. Their coloured maid Mary had answered the phone. I interviewed Mary in the kitchen. She was pop-eyed and nervous. The physical stature of the Spaniard and the degree of his intoxication had obviously become magnified in her mind. 'I ain't goin' to mess around with no cockeyed Spaniard,' she told me flatly. 'If he mislests me, I'll hit him with a bottle.' While we waited for Dan and his friend to show up, I began to apply my special methods to the case, and before long I had figured it out. No doubt you have, too, since you are probably smarter than I was in 1922.

When Dan came home to his frantic wife, he was carrying the cockeyed Spaniard in his arms, but the fellow was, of course, neither cockeyed nor Spanish. He was sad-eyed, four months old, sleepy, hungry, and definitely sober, as cute a cocker spaniel as you would ever want to see. Mary stubbornly clung to the name she had got over the phone, and her insistence on this pleasant distortion became generally known about town. People would call up the Henderson house and ask for her and say, 'This is the Canine Census Bureau. What kind of dog do you have in your home?' Mary would always reply promptly and brightly, 'He's a cockeyed Spaniard.' I often wonder what ever became of her. I hope she is well and happy.

Do You Want to Make Something out of It?

(Or, if you put an 'o' on 'understo,' you'll ruin my 'thunderstorm'.)

I'M PROBABLY not the oldest word-game player in the country, and I know I'm not the ablest, but my friends will all testify that I'm the doggedest. (We'll come back to the word 'doggedest' later on.) I sometimes keep on playing the game, all by myself, after it is over and I have gone to bed. On a recent night, tossing and spelling, I spent two hours hunting for another word besides 'phlox' that has 'hlo' in it. I finally found seven: 'matchlock,' 'decathlon,' 'pentathlon,' 'hydrochloric,' 'chlorine,' 'chloroform,' and 'monthlong.' There are more than a dozen others, beginning with 'phlo,' but I had to look them up in the dictionary the next morning, and that doesn't count.

By 'the game,' I mean Superghosts, as some of us call it, a difficult variation of the familiar parlour game known as Ghosts. In Ghosts, as everybody knows, one of a group of sedentary players starts with a letter, and the spelling proceeds clockwise around the group until a player spells a word of more than three letters, thus becoming 'a third of a ghost,' or two-thirds, or a whole ghost. The game goes on until everyone but the winner has been eliminated. Superghosts differs from the old game in one small, tricky, and often exacerbating respect: The rules allow a player to *prefix* a letter to the word in progress, thus increasing the flexibility of the indoor sport. If 'business' comes to a player, he does not have to add the final 's'; he can put an 'n' in front, and the player who has to add the 'e' to 'unbusinesslik' becomes part of a ghost. In a recent game in my league, a devious gentleman boldly stuck an 'n' in front of 'sobsiste,' stoutly maintaining the validity of 'unsobsisterlike,' but he was shouted down. There is a lot of shouting in the game, especially when it is played late at night.

Starting words in the middle and spelling them in both directions lifts the pallid pastime of Ghosts out of the realm of children's parties and ladies' sewing circles and makes it a game to test the mettle of the mature adult mind. As long ago as 1930, aficionados began to appear in New York parlours, and then the game waned, to be revived, in my circle, last year. The Superghost aficionado is a moody fellow, given to spelling to himself at table, not listening to his wife, and staring dully at his frightened children, wondering why he didn't detect, in yesterday's game, that 'cklu' is the guts of 'lacklustre,' and priding himself on having stumped everybody with 'nehe,' the middle of 'swineherd.' In this last case, 'bonehead' would have done, since we allow slang if it is in the dictionary, but 'Stonehenge' is out, because we don't allow proper nouns. All compound and hyphenated words are privileged, even 'jack-o'-lantern' and 'love-in-a-mist', but the speller must indicate where a hyphen occurs.

Many people, who don't like word games and just want to sit around and drink and talk, hate Superghosts and wish it were in hell with Knock, Knock, Who's There? The game is also tough on bad spellers, poor visualizers, mediocre concentrators, ladies and gentlemen of small vocabulary, and those who are, to use a word presently popular with the younger drinking set, clobbered. I remember the night a bad speller, female, put an 'm' on 'ale,' thinking, as she later confessed, that 'salamander' is spelled with two 'e's. The next player could have gone to 'alemb' – the word 'alembic' turns up a lot – but he made it 'alema' and was promptly challenged. (You can challenge a player if you think he is bluffing.) What the challenged player had in mind was 'stalemate.' The man who had challenged him got sore, because he hadn't thought of 'stalemate,' and went home. More than one game has ended in hard feelings, but I have never seen players come to blows, or friendships actually broken.

I said we would get back to 'doggedest,' and here we are. This word, if it is a word, caused a lot of trouble during one game, when a lady found 'ogged' in her lap, refused to be bogged, dogged, fogged, jogged, or logged, and added an 'e.' She was challenged and lost, since Webster's unabridged dictionary is accepted as the final judge and authority, and while it gives 'doggedly' and 'doggedness,' it doesn't give 'doggedest'. She could also have got out of 'ogged' with an 'r' in front, for 'frogged' is a good word, and also what might be called a lady's word, but she stuck doggedly to 'doggedest'. Then there was the evening a dangerous and exasperating player named Bert Mitchell challenged somebody's 'dogger.' The challenged man had 'doggerel' in mind, of course, but Mitchell said, in his irritating voice, 'You have spelled a word. "Dogger" is a word,' and he flipped through the unabridged dictionary, which he reads for pleasure and always has on his lap during a game. 'Dogger' is indeed a word, and quite a word. Look it up yourself.

When I looked up 'dogger' the other day, I decided to have a look at 'dog', a word practically nobody ever looks up, because everybody is smugly confident that he knows what a dog is. Here, for your amazement, are some dogs other than the carnivorous mammal:

'The hammer in a gunlock. Any of various devices, usually of simple design, for holding, gripping, or fastening something; as: a Any of various devices consisting essentially of a spike, rod, or bar of metal, as of iron, with a ring, hook, claw, lug, or the like, at the end, used for gripping, clutching, or holding something, as by driving or embedding it in the object, hooking it to the object, etc. See RAFT DOG, TOE DOG. b Specif., either of the hooks or claws of a pair of sling dogs. See CRAMPON. c An iron for holding wood in a fireplace; a firedog; an andiron. d In a lathe, a clamp for gripping the piece of work and for communicating motion to it from the faceplate. A **clamp dog** consists of two parts drawn together by screws. A **bent-tail dog** has an L-shaped projection that enters a slot in the faceplate for communicating motion. A **straight-tail dog** has a projecting part that engages with a stud fastened to or forming part of the faceplate. A **safety dog** is one equipped with safety setscrews. e Any of the jaws in a lathe chuck. f A pair of nippers or forceps. g A wheeled gripping device for drawing the fillet from which coin blanks are stamped through the opening at the head of the draw-bench. h Any of a set of adjusting screws for the bed tool of a punching machine. i A grapple for clutching and raising a pile-driver monkey or a well-boring tool. j A stop or detent; a click or ratchet. k A drag for the wheel of a vehicle. l A steel block attached to a locking bar or tappet of an interlocking machine, by which locking between bars is accomplished. m A short, heavy, sharp-pointed, steel hook with a ring at one end. n A steel toothlike projection on a log carriage or on the endless chain that conveys logs into the sawmill.'

And now, unless you have had enough, we will get back to Superghosts, through the clanging and clatter of all those dogs. The game has a major handicap, or perhaps I should call it blockage. A player rarely gets the chance to stick the others with a truly tough word, because someone is pretty sure to simplify the word under construction. Mitchell tells me that he always hopes he can get around to 'ug-ug' or 'ach-ach' on his way to 'plug-ugly' and 'stomach-ache.' These words are hyphenated in my Webster's, for the old boy was a great hyphenator. (I like his definition of 'plug-ugly': 'A kind of city rowdy, ruffian, or disorderly tough; – a term said to have been originated by a gang of such in Baltimore.') In the case of 'ug,' the simplifiers usually go to 'bug,' trying to catch someone with 'buggies,' or they add an 'l' and the word ends in 'ugliness.' And 'ach' often turns into 'machinery,' although it could go in half-a-dozen directions. Since the simplifiers dull the game by getting into easy words, the experts are fond of a variant that goes like this: Mitchell, for example, will call up a friend and say, 'Get out of "ightf" twenty ways.' Well, I tossed in bed one night and got ten: 'rightful,' 'frightful,' 'delightful,' 'nightfall,' 'lightfoot,' 'straightforward,' 'eightfold,' 'lightfingered,' 'tight-fisted,' and 'tight-fitting.' The next day, I thought of 'lightface,' 'right-footed,' and 'night-flowering,' and came to a stop. 'Right fielder' is neither compounded nor hyphenated by Webster, and I began to wonder about Mitchell's twenty 'ightf''s. I finally figured it out. The old devil was familiar with the ten or more fish and fowl and miscellaneous things that begin with 'nightf.'

It must have been about 1932 that an old player I know figured that nothing could be got out of 'dke' except 'handkerchief,' and then, in a noisy game one night this year, he passed that combination on to the player at his left. This rascal immediately made it 'dkee.' He was challenged by the lady on *his* left and triumphantly announced that his word was 'ground-keeper.' It looked like an ingenious escape from 'handkerchief,' but old Webster let the fellow down. Webster accepts only 'groundman' and 'groundsman,' thus implying that there is no such word as 'groundkeeper.'

Mitchell threw 'abc' at me one night, and I couldn't get anything out of it and challenged him. 'Dabchick,' he said patronizingly, and added blandly, 'It is the little grebe.' Needless to say, it *is* the little grebe.

I went through a hundred permutations in bed that night without getting anything else out of 'abc' except a word I made up, which is 'grabcheck,' one

T

who quickly picks up a tab, a big spender, a generous fellow. I have invented quite a few other words, too, which I modestly bring to the attention of modern lexicographers, if there are any. I think of dictionary-makers as being rigidly conventional gentlemen who are the first to put the new aside. They probably won't even read my list of what I shall call bedwords, but I am going to set it down anyway. A young matron in Bermuda last spring told me to see what I could do with 'sgra,' and what I did with it occupied a whole weekend. Outside of 'disgrace' and its variants, all I could find were 'cross-grained' and 'mis-graff,' which means to misgraft (obsolete). I found this last word while looking, in vain, for 'misgrade' in the dictionary. Maybe you can think of something else, and I wish you luck. Here, then, in no special order, are my bedwords based on 'sgra.'

pussgrapple. A bickering, or minor disturbance; an argument or dispute among effeminate men. Also, less frequently, a physical struggle between, or among, women.

kissgranny. 1. A man who seeks the company of older women, especially older women with money; a designing fellow, a fortune hunter. 2. An overaffectionate old woman, a hugmoppet, a bunny talker.

glassgrabber. 1. A woman who disapproves of, or interferes with, her husband's drinking; a kill-joy, a shush-laugh, a douselight. 2. A man who asks for another drink at a friend's house, or goes out and gets one in the kitchen.

blessgravy. A minister or cleric; the head of a family; one who says grace. Not to be confused with *praisegravy*, one who extols a woman's cooking, especially the cooking of a friend's wife; a gay fellow, a flirt, a seducer. *Colloq.*, a breakvow, a shrugholy.

cussgravy. A husband who complains of his wife's cooking, more especially a husband who complains of his wife's cooking in the presence of guests; an ill-tempered fellow, a curmudgeon. Also, sometimes, a peptic-ulcer case.

messgranter. An untidy housekeeper, a careless housewife. Said of a woman who admits, often proudly, that she has let herself go; a bragdowdy, a frumpess.

hissgrammar. An illiterate fellow, a user of slovenly rhetoric, a father who disapproves of booklearning. Also, more rarely, one who lisps, a twisttongue.

chorusgrable. *Orig.* a young actress, overconfident of her ability and her future; a snippet, a flappertigibbet. *Deriv.* Betty Grable, an American movie actress.

pressgrape. One who presses grapes, a grape presser. Less commonly, a crunch-berry.

pressgrain. 1. A man who tries to make whisky in his own cellar; hence, a secret drinker, a hidebottle, a sneakslug. 2. One who presses grain in a grain presser. *Arch.*

dressgrader. A woman who stares another woman up and down, a starefrock; hence, a rude female, a hobble-dehoyden.

fussgrape. 1. One who diets or toys with his food, a light eater, a person without appetite, a scornmuffin, a shuncabbage. 2. A man, usually American, who boasts of his knowledge of wines, a smugbottle.

bassgrave. 1. Cold-eyed, unemotional, stolid, troutsolemn. 2. The grave of a bass. *Obs.*

lassgraphic. Of, or pertaining to, the vivid description of females; as, the guest was so lassgraphic his host asked him to change the subject or get out. Also said of fathers of daughters, more rarely of mothers.

blissgrey. Aged by marriage. Also, sometimes, discouraged by wedlock, or by the institution of marriage.

glassgrail. A large nocturnal moth. Not to be confused with *smackwindow*, the common June bug, or bangsash.

hossgrace. Innate or native dignity, similar to that of the thoroughbred hoss. *Southern U.S.*

bussgranite. Literally, a stonekisser; a man who persists in trying to win the favour or attention of cold, indifferent, or capricious women. Not to be confused with *snatchkiss*, a kitchen lover.

tossgravel. 1. A male human being who tosses gravel, usually at night, at the window of a female human being's bedroom, usually that of a young virgin; hence, a lover, a male sweetheart, and an eloper. 2. One who is suspected by the father of a daughter of planning an elopement with her, a grablass.

If you should ever get into a game of Superghosts with Mitchell, by the way, don't pass 'bugl' on to him, hoping to send him into 'bugling.' He will simply add an 'o,' making the group 'buglo,' which is five-sevenths of 'bugloss.' The word means 'hawkweed,' and you can see what Mitchell would do if you handed him 'awkw,' expecting to make him continue the spelling of 'awkward.' Tough guy, Mitchell. Tough game, Superghosts. You take it from here. I'm tired.

A Final Note on Chanda Bell

(After reading two or three literary memorials, to this or that lamented talent, written by one critic or another.)

THERE WERE only three of us around Chanda Bell at the end: Charles Vayne, her attorney; Hadley, the butler (if he was a butler); and myself. The others had departed with the beginning of the war, to new dedications, or old hideouts, and the obituaries in the journals after Miss Bell's death were erroneous in claiming that the great, dark house in the East Sixties was, up to the very last, bedlam and carnival. Chanda Bell's famous largess and *laisser-faire* had, naturally enough, attracted the strange and the sublimated from the nooks and crannies of Greenwich Village. I had been particularly pleased to witness the going away of the middle-aged man who rode the tricycle, the schoolteacher who had resigned from the human race to become a bird, and Miss Menta, the disturbingly nude Chilean transcendentalist.

Charles Vayne, as regular and as futile as a clock in an empty house, showed up once a week with important documents that Chanda Bell would never sign. Some of them were dated as far back as 1924. A year of my friendship with the gifted lady had passed (so long ago!) before I could be sure that I knew what she was trying not to say, but Vayne never knew. Her use of the triple negative, in such expressions as 'not unmeaningless,' and her habit of starting sentences in the middle bewildered him, and so did her fondness for surrogate words with ambiguous meanings, like the words in dreams: 'rupture' for 'rapture,' 'centaur' for 'sender,' 'pressure' for 'pleasure,' and 'scorpio' for 'scrofula.' She enjoyed frustrating him and she made the most of his discomfiture. 'Praise me!'

she would say as he handed her a fountain pen and the documents, which she always waved away. 'Praise me!' she would command again. He invariably reacted the same way. It had become a kind of ritual. 'I repeat that I have not read a novel all the way through since "The Crimson Sweater," by Ralph Henry Barbour,' he would say. His expostulations and his entreaties amused her for a while, but then she would poke at him with her cane and drive him off, crying, 'He comes without armour who comes without art!'

Hadley, who ushered the attorney in and out every Wednesday afternoon, had one cold, impassive eye and one that he could cause to twinkle. It gave you the chill sense of being, at one and the same time, in the presence of advocate and adversary. His duties in the final months were sparse, consisting mainly of serving Madeira to Chanda Bell and me, or to Chanda Bell and Vayne and me, in the Grey Room, after four o'clock, when she had had her egg and had dressed and was ready to receive. One always stood in her presence, for it was Chanda Bell's conceit to believe that only the uncomfortable are capable of pure attention.

Chanda Bell was fifty-seven when I first bent over her hand, and her mind seemed so keen and agile it was difficult to believe that she could confuse her guests, even her intimates, with one another. But she did. Charles Vayne was sometimes Lord Rudgate, an Englishman of dim background and cryptic reference, and sometimes Strephon ('a Jung mad I cussed in the Sprig'). I was alternately Dennis, a deceased painter, who had specialized in gun dogs for the calendars of coal companies, and one McKinnon or McKenyon, an advertising executive, who had attempted to deflower Miss Bell in a speeding motorboat during the panic of 1907. This was highly exasperating to such scholarly critics as Hudson van Horne and Dantes Woodrow, and they never came back after their separate agonized hours in the underwater gloom of the echoing Grey Room.

It is not congenial to me, at this time, to expose in detail how I became lost – if lost I became – in the 'brilliant wilderness' of Chanda Bell's prose, or to re-enact the process of equation, synthesis, and integration by means of which I was able to reveal the subtle affirmation compounded of the double negative of her unmeaning and her unmethod. This was ably – if mistakenly, still ably – set forth in my 'A Note on Chanda Bell.'* Upon its publication, she had sent for me, and in the fine years of intellectual intimacy that followed, my faith in her genius was more often reinforced than not. It wasn't until the last few months, when, by design or aberration, she began to discuss herself, between teatime and twilight, as if she were discussing someone else, that the blackest of a critic's ravens, uncertainty of his soundness, came to dwell in my consciousness. It is a terrible thing not to be sure whether one has sought or been sought, not to be able to tell the hunter from the quarry, the sanctuary from the trap.

* *The Neutral Review*, October, 1943.

Chanda Bell had, in fact, commanded me to her salon, but had I not asked for it, had I not commanded the command, by the tribute of my unique and penetrating analysis of her work? She had cause to be grateful, and her summoning me to her side was, in my early opinion, the most natural of acts. Careless and churlish critics, in malice or mischief, had dismissed her bright and tangled intention with such expressions as 'bloom and drool,' 'the amorphous richness of a thrown pie,' 'as dull as Daiquiris with the commodore of a yacht club,' and 'as far to the Right as a soupspoon.' This last was the sheerest nonsense. One might as reasonably have said that she was as far to the Left as a fish fork. The closest she ever came to mentioning politics was one day when, in a rare moment of merriment, she referred to Karl Marx as 'Groucho.' I myself had heard the faint and special obbligato of elfin horns in her work and the laughter in the dusty house, and I alone had seen the swift and single flashing of a naked nymph by moonlight.

It is hard to mark the hour and day when the thunderhead of suspicion first stains the clear horizon of an old admiration, but I came to be drenched, in the horrid mental weather of last autumn, by the downpour of a million doubts and dreads of Chanda Bell. I began to fear that she had perpetrated, in her half-dozen dense, tortured novels, one of the major literary hoaxes of our time, and to suspect that she had drawn me into the glittering web of a monstrous deceit, in order to destroy, by proxy and in effigy, the entire critical profession. We would sit in the Grey Room from four till dark – she had permitted me to sit, at last, with the compassionate concession of a queen – and she would pierce my thin armour of hope and prayer with sharp and studied flicks of her sardonic, allusive intelligence. 'You have the scaffold touch of a brain certain,' she told me one afternoon. This was in the best tradition of her infernal dialectic. I could figure, in accordance with her secret code, that I had the scalpel touch of a brain surgeon, or I could take her to mean, in perverted literalness, that I was doomed to die – and was about to – an awful death for my wrong and sinful certainties.

'You have found the figure, Thurber,' she told me one afternoon, 'but have you found the carpet?' This was accompanied by her shrewd, tiny smile. I could not determine whether she meant there was something to find that I had not found, or nothing to find at all, beneath the gleaming surface of her style. The devil of it was that I could not be sure of anything. I spent that night going over 'The Huanted Yatch' with a fine-tooth comb, searching for esoteric anagrams, feeling for what she had called 'the carpet.' I scrutinized, investigated, explored, took apart, and put back together again the entire fibre and fabric, uncertain of what shape and texture I was looking for. I read the thing backward, and I even tried to read it upside down and in the mirror of my bureau. I copied out one disturbing sentence and carried it about with me for close study: 'Icing mellow moony on a postgate doves snow and love surrender.' Its once perspicuous feel-meaning deserted me, and its cool loveliness became the chatter of a gibbon in my distraught consciousness. I could no longer tell whether it was beauty or balderdash. If it was balderdash, the book degenerated into the vivid cackling of a macaw, and my critique stood as a monument to a fatuous gullibility.

Towards the end, Chanda Bell began to talk about herself in the third person, as if she were not there in the house but on her way to visit us. 'I've asked her to tea,' she would tell me, 'but it will not astonish me if she fails to appear. Nobody has ever been able to pin her down.' And she would study the effect of this upon me with her hooded gaze. She had lapsed into simple, declarative sentences, and this was a comfort, but I was deeply perturbed by the feeling that her outlandish fantasy and her revelations were new and planned inventions of her cruelty.

'Chanda Bell,' she said one evening, 'had an allowance of two hundred dollars a week while she was still in pigtails. Her father, the millionaire industrialist, doted on the awkward, big-eyed little girl. He would bring her curtseying into the library for his cronies to admire. "By God, she'll be the first woman president of Standard Oil!" he exclaimed one night. He had a stroke when he discovered that she proposed to become a writer. "By God!" he roared. "I would sooner see you operate an unsuccessful house of ill repute!" At fourteen, a dreadful thing occurred. The small son of one of her father's gardeners sold two poems to the *Atlantic Monthly*, entitled "Ruffian Dusk" and "The Strangler of Light." Chanda offered him fifty dollars a week to write poems that she should sign and publish. The little boy coldly rejected the proposition, and his father, a stern Presbyterian, informed Chanda's father of the deal and how it had fallen through. "By God!" the old man roared. "At least she's not guilty of integrity, and that's more than I can say for any Bell in four generations except my grandfather and myself".'

Miss Bell let her reminiscence trail off here, and she watched me from her divan with her penetrating eyes. 'Ah,' I said hopefully, 'but she learned that day the high and holy importance of integrity, I trust.' Chanda Bell gave me her sign of dismissal, a languid lift of her left hand. 'You are the critic,' she said. 'I am but the chronicler. Leave me now. You perceive she is not coming.' I rose and bowed. 'Perhaps,' I blurted out, 'there is no Chanda Bell.' But she had closed her eyes and turned away.

The next day, they took her to the hospital. 'I have a panther near my hearth,' she said, the first time they let me call on her. I went to see her twice again, the last time with Charles Vayne, who carried, with polished hopelessness, two bulging briefcases, which the nurse would not permit him to open. Chanda Bell was wandering in a far land, but she contrived a faint smile for each of her visitors. 'Dear Rudgate,' she whispered to Vayne, 'what will become of meaning, thank God, when you are dead?' He tried in silence to make her grip a fountain pen, but she shook her head and turned to me. 'Pretension has no plinth, Dennis,' she said. 'Ah, what a dusty answer . . .' Her voice and her heart failed, and the most remarkable woman I have ever known was dead.

*

That night, I called at her house, in the East Sixties. Hadley let me in. I had suspected him for a long time of being joined in dark conspiracy with Chanda Bell to make an end of me. I wondered, as I glared at the cold eye and then at the warm one, whether he might not be a frustrated writer, a bankrupt publisher, or an editor who had suffered a nervous breakdown. I jumped over the amenities of sorrow. 'Her dying request,' I said, 'was that I should examine her papers.'

The eyebrow over his twinkling eye lifted. 'This evening, sir ?' he asked.

'Take me to her desk and open it,' I demanded.

There was a full second's pause, then 'Certainly, sir,' he said, and led the way into the Grey Room. 'If I knew what you seek . . .' he began.

I turned on him. 'I think you do!' I snapped. 'I am looking for proof of whether I am an egregious ass or a uniquely perceptive individual. The line is sometimes thinly drawn between a tranquil old age in this city and exile, say, in Nassau.' He seemed genuinely bewildered.

There was nothing in the desk except a large manila envelope, which bore my name on the cover. I tore it open with shaking hands. Inside was a single sheet of white typewriter paper on which there were three carefully drawn squares, one inside another. 'What does it mean ?' I asked. 'What is it ?'

'If you will permit me, sir,' said Hadley, and he took the paper and studied it. 'That, sir,' he said, finally, 'is what I should describe as a drawing of a plinth.'

I seized him by the shoulder. 'You *are* in on this!' I cried. 'What does it mean ? What's behind it ? Who are you ? What have you two devils been up to all these years ? Why should you want to destroy *me* ?'

He took a backward step and gaped. He was honestly frightened, or else he was a superb actor. There was no twinkle in his eye. 'I do not understand, sir,' he stammered, or seemed to stammer.

I let go of his shoulder. 'My critical reputation is at stake,' I said. 'Has she ever written an explanation of her writing – perhaps to be sent to some journal or periodical after her death ?'

Hadley appeared to frown. 'That, sir, I could not say,' he brought out.

I turned away from him and then whirled back. 'What is the carpet ?' I shouted.

He put several feet of the shiny floor between us. 'I do not know what you mean,' he said nervously.

'Would there be papers anywhere else ?' I demanded.

He looked about the room. 'Nowhere,' he said hollowly.

I walked over and looked out a window for a long time.

Suddenly, Hadley began to speak. 'She had promised to put me in one of her books,' he said in a tone of sadness, or what came to my ears as a tone of sadness. Then his voice brightened. 'I was to have been the uncharacter of the nonbutler,' he said.

I came back from the window and glared at him.

'Her phrase, sir,' he added hastily.

I lighted a cigarette, inhaled the smoke, and blew it out slowly. 'Didn't you appear in any of her novels?' I asked.

'Oh, but no, sir,' he corrected me proudly. 'I did not appear in *all* of them!'

It was as if Chanda Bell were in the room, her bright, dark eyes taking us both in with a look of veiled amusement. 'It must have made you very happy indeed,' I snarled. 'Not to appear in any of her books was wonderful enough, but not to appear in *all* of them – the final accolade, Hadley, the final accolade.' He acknowledged it with a grave bow. 'What has become of her manuscripts and her letters?' I demanded.

Hadley put on a sad expression. 'She burned them, sir,' he said. 'It was her last act in this house.'

I looked for the last time at the Grey Room – the grey desk, the grey chair, the grey Hadley.

'Perhaps a glass of Madeira, Mr Thurber?' asked the butler. I declined ungraciously and said that I must leave. At the door, with the welcome street so near and desirable, he coughed discreetly. 'Do you wish to take this with you, sir?' It was the drawing of the plinth. I took it without a word. 'If I may say so, sir,' Hadley went on, 'you were the closest of all of them.'

I glared at him, but there was no twinkle. 'How close?' I growled.

'Oh, very close, sir,' he said. 'Very close indeed.' This time, I thought I detected the ghost of the twinkle, but I could not be sure. I could not be sure of anything.

It has been eight months since I found the plinth in Chanda Bell's desk. Nothing has happened, but I expect an editor to ring me up any day. 'We've got a remarkable letter or manuscript here, apparently written by Chanda Bell,' he will say. 'Sent to us by her lawyer, in accordance with a request in her will. It isn't signed, but he says she wrote it, all right. Seems she never signed anything. Sort of laughter from beyond the grave, you might say. The old girl exposes her stuff as the merest junk. Proves her point, too. She takes a hell of a crack at your "Note on Chanda Bell." Thought you might want to read the thing and reply to it – we'll print you and her in the same issue. She calls the piece "The Carpet," for some reason. I'll shoot it along.'

No such call has come as yet, but I keep a bag packed, ready at a moment's notice to fly to Zanzibar, or Mozambique, or East Liverpool, Ohio. Meanwhile, I have hit on a new approach to the works of Chanda Bell. I am trying to read them sideways.

T*

There's a Time for Flags

(Notes of a man who bought a curious Christmas gift.)

Dec. 15 – Yesterday morning at eleven o'clock I bought an American flag, five feet by three, and a white flagpole, eighteen feet high, surmounted by a bright golden ball, and now I am trying to figure out why. The incongruity of buying a flag and a flagpole in the middle of December as a Christmas present for my wife has begun to disturb me. True, the gesture is not so elaborate as that of the man in the madrigal who gave his true love a partridge in a pear tree, two turtledoves, and more than a hundred and twenty other gifts, counting the fifes of the eleven fifers and the drums and drumsticks of the twelve drummers, but it is approximately as hard to explain. When did the idea first come to me? Or was it merely an idea? Could it be that I was seized by the stern hand of Compulsion, that dark, unseasonable Urge that impels women to clean house in the middle of the night and men, or at least me, to buy flags in the dead of winter?

As I write this, twenty-four hours have gone by since I bought the large flag and the enormous pole, but unlike every other purchase I have ever made, including my banjo-mandolin and my Cadillac, the emblem and staff show no signs of dwindling to normal proportions in my consciousness. They occupy the whole landscape of my thought. Last night I woke up and thought about the eighteen-foot pole, realizing sharply the measure and magnitude of what I had done. I had bought, for the yard of my home, a flagstaff designed and intended for the grounds of an institution. Nothing smaller than a boys' school with an enrollment of four hundred would think of ordering a pole of that heroic height. A flag for a private residence is supposed to be hung out of an upper-storey window on a five-foot pole. 'Great God,' I said aloud. 'What is happening?' asked my wife, without waking up. It was a good question, a searching wind, a whisper and a rumour . . . a wink of the eye . . . a shake of the head . . . high as his house, they say . . . O say ain't you seen . . . every heart beats true . . . to the red, white, and blues in the night . . . where there's never a post or flag . . . and forever impede Mayhew Wade . . .

I became furled, at last, in sleep.

Dec. 16 – I woke early this morning from a deep dream of flags, and tried to remember when I first got the idea, or when the Compulsion first got me. Did it go back to the quiet years in Washington, D.C., at the turn of the century, when I was fascinated by the miniature flags that came with packs of Sweet Caporal cigarettes? Have I always had a secret desire to command a battleship, or own an office building, or become headmaster of a boys' school with an enrollment of four hundred? Am I intent on blowing psychological taps over the memory of one of those horrible captains of cadets at Ohio State University thirty-five years ago? If so, why didn't I buy a bugle? Oh, there must be some simpler explanation. Guilt. That's it. That's what it is. Guilt, the most powerful force in the life and psyche of the individual, more durable than love, deeper than fear. But guilt about what? What have I ever done that demands such a vivid and magnificent symbol of regret? I can think of nothing, except that, as a boy, I sympathized with the cause of the Southern Confederacy and once announced, in Miss MacIlvain's Eighth Grade class at Douglas School, that the South would have won the war if Stonewall Jackson hadn't been killed at the Battle of Chancellorsville. But this sin is surely not black enough to call for so large a flag and so long a pole. I continue to ponder the provenance of the purchase.

DEC. 17 – This is exactly what happened. I phoned Jack Howard about three o'clock on the afternoon of December 13th – was it only four days ago? – and asked him if he would go shopping with me. There was a Christmas present I wanted to buy for somebody – a flag. 'A flag?' he asked. 'You mean one of those clips?' 'Not costume jewellery,' I said. 'If I were shopping for that, I'd take a woman with me. I want to buy an American flag. A big flag.' 'Oh?' Jack said, and, after a moment, 'Sure. Fine. Fine. When do you want to go? I can't make it this afternoon.' I arranged for him to pick me up the next morning at ten-thirty at my hotel in the West Forties. I had come to town three days before from my home in Cornwall, Connecticut, to buy a fl— to do my Christmas shopping.

When Jack and I were in a cab the next day, on our way to the famous Annin flag store, at Sixteenth Street and Fifth Avenue, he said, 'They're worried about you at my office – well, not worried exactly, but interested.' I didn't say anything. 'I told Chuck Nelson you were going to buy a flag and he said, "What's he up to?"' Jack laughed. 'All you need to do now,' he went on, 'is to buy a record of "The Stars and Stripes Forever" and they'll have you up before the Un-American Activities Committee.' He was right, and I was frightened. 'I wish you hadn't told everybody,' I said. 'A thing like this can get all over town.' I felt that he was studying my right profile. 'Well, what *are* you up to?' he asked, with a laugh that didn't seem genuine. 'I'm not up to anything,' I said coldly. 'I'm simply going to buy a flag. You don't have to go with me if you don't want to.' 'Forget it,' he said. 'I'll turn up my coat collar and pull down my hat. You call me Joe and and I'll call you Sam.' I leaned back in the cab, trying to indicate that I didn't want to talk about it. He began to whistle George M. Cohan's tribute to Old Glory.

Outside of the employees of the store, there was only one other person in Annin's when we got there. I realize suddenly as I write this that, in retracing my steps, I have come upon the small and simple solution of the case of the man who bought a flag in December. For some years now I have not been able to see to get around as well as I used to, especially in crowded stores at Christmastime. I remember now a rough experience I had last year in a store filled with fragile crystal and china objects, a store in which I had bought Christmas presents over a period of years. The last time I visited it, in December, 1948, I distinctly overheard a clerk say, 'Sweet God, here's that man again!' I retreated from the store without buying anything, and fortunately without breaking anything, but the adventure had left its deep psychic mark. Subconsciously, since that day I had been seeking an easy, a less perilous, way out of my private shopping problems. My unconscious mind had found the answer. Hardly anyone would be shopping for a Christmas present in Annin's in December. I recall now that a line of verse, written by Clinch Calkins twenty years ago, had been running through my thoughts for months: 'The peril streamed through us like flags.' By an easy process of association, the peril of shopping had been linked up with the word 'flags,' and from there it was an even easier step for my mind to pick out the cathedral calm of the Annin store as the perfect place for me to buy my wife's principal Christmas present. The lady who stepped up to wait on us was gracious, competent, and unsuspicious. After all, you must run into all kinds of people in a flag store.

I see now that the flagpole was an afterthought. The five-by-three woollen flag that I decided on came to only five dollars, which didn't seem enough to pay for a gift. 'How about a ten-by-six?' I asked the lady. 'You don't want a ten-by-six flag,' Jack said. 'Not unless you own a skyscraper.' It was then that the idea came to me of buying a pole, halyards and all, to go with the Star-Spangled Banner. 'I would like to look at a flagpole,' I said. 'Certainly,' said the lady, leading the way to the flagpoles. 'Who is this present for?' Jack asked me. 'Eisenhower?' 'It's for my wife; it's for Helen,' I said. I had hold of his left arm and I could feel him shrug, but he didn't say anything. There were flagpoles six feet tall, twelve feet tall, and on up. I finally selected an eighteen-foot pole, which came in three six-foot sections. The price, six times that of the flag, seemed to me suitable for a Christmas gift for one's wife. 'What do you think of it?' I asked Jack. He sighed. 'It's your life,' he said. 'Go ahead. Maybe an eighteen-foot flagpole is what Helen has always wanted.' So I bought the flag and the pole and ordered them to be shipped to Cornwall, Connecticut. When we hailed a cab outside the store, Jack said, 'Let's go somewhere and grab a drink.' 'It's only eleven o'clock,' I told him. 'Let's go somewhere and grab a drink,' he said again, and we did.

DEC. 18. 11 A.M. – Now that I know, or think I know, why I bought the flag and the flagpole, I have begun to worry about the effect they will have on my wife. She is used to getting things from me no larger than a woman's hand. I hope the pole doesn't upset her too much, the way the father in Barrie's 'Mary Rose' was upset when they told him his daughter had suddenly returned after twenty-five years in Fairyland. 'I have been so occupied all my life with little things' was all that he could say. I don't want Helen to be stunned by a bolt from the red, wh— I mustn't go on like this.

2 P.M. – I finally told Ben Tuller, who does everything about my place, from shooting crows to finding the coins I drop when I hang my trousers up, that I had bought a present for my wife that would probably arrive at the express office in four or five parts, three of them six feet long. 'I can get a couple

of my wife's brothers to help me get it over here,' he said, 'and maybe we can stow it in the garage till Christmas without Mrs Thurber finding out, but I wouldn't count on it. Women have a way of knowing there are flags and flag-poles about. One thing I wanted to ask –' 'How did you know it was a flag and a flagpole?' I cut in. He stared at me. 'You told me yesterday,' he said. Maybe I am losing my mind. I didn't remember telling him. 'What do you want to know?' I asked. Before replying he gazed out the window for a moment, and then, 'How do you aim to gift-wrap that pole?' he asked. I hadn't thought about that. I simply hadn't thought about it. And even if I could wrap the three six-foot sections, even if there was that much tissue paper and ribbon in the world, Helen wasn't strong enough to unwrap them. 'I'll have to exchange it,' I said. 'Maybe they haven't shipped it yet. I'll exchange it for something else.' 'At *Annin's*?' asked Ben. 'All you could get in place of it, I should think, would be a six-foot pole and maybe four more flags.' I turned, without a word, and walked out of the room.

11.45 P.M. – I can't go on with it, I'm not getting anything done. I just sit here and make occasional notes. A few minutes ago my wife came into my room and said, 'What are you up to?' There was that question again, that note of suspicion. 'I'm planning to overthrow the government,' I said. 'By force, if necessary.' 'Then you'll need your rest,' she said. 'Come on to bed.' As patriotic as she is, like all persons born in Nebraska, she'd be the first to lob a grenade in-to a congressman's living room, if I gave the word. She has what has been called 'the strong loyalty of the wife.' I'm going to bed now, but that doesn't mean I'll sleep.

DEC. 19 – Well, the cat's out of the bag. This morning I got a letter from Annin & Co., and my wife, who always reads the mail to me, opened it and began to read it aloud. 'No!' I cried, but it was too late. The fat was in the fire. The letter follows, in full, and will serve to authenticate these notes for such of my readers as may have suspected I didn't actually buy a flag and a flagpole but was just making it up:

DEAR SIR:

As per the request of our Miss Tal, we are pleased to inform you that the flag and the flagpole are already on their way to you.

We wish to advise you, however, that we have billed you for an additional $3.00, due to the fact that Miss Tal erroneously charged you for the pole without the 22-C Gold Leaf Copper Ball. This additional charge of $3.00 is for the Gold Leaf Copper Ball.

Miss Tal was of the thought and opinion that you wanted the set-up as displayed in the store, and the Ball is being shipped with the flag and the flagpole.

We trust that what we have done meets with your entire approval, and, hoping to be of further service to you, we are

Very truly yours,

ANNIN & CO.

GEORGE JAMIESON

I told my wife the whole story, beginning with my phone call to Jack Howard. She was wonderful about it. 'I'm really glad to know what it is,' she said. 'Mr Purvis at the express office phoned this morning before you were up and said he had two packages for you, one of them more than six feet long, and heavy. I've thought of everything, from a croquet set to a collapsible dog kennel.' She considered a moment. 'The pole isn't luminous at night, is it?' she asked. 'I don't think so,' I said, 'but we could train a spotlight on the flag at night.' 'No, we couldn't,' she said. 'It's going to be evident enough the way it is, what with that twenty-two carat gold ball.' I began to breathe shallowly. 'Three dollars seems pretty darn reasonable for a twenty-two-carat gold ball,' I said. 'Do you suppose they meant to say three hundred dollars?' My wife sighed. 'Men shouldn't be allowed to shop alone,' she said. 'It's – it's dangerous.' 'No, it isn't,' I protested. 'Well, chaotic, then,' she said. I settled for that.

DEC. 20 – Last night my wife woke me up long after midnight. It turned out she hadn't been able to get the eighteen-foot pole out of her mind. She had been lying there thinking about a lot of other things, too. 'I was just worrying about what the neighbours will think,' she said. 'I can't very well explain to them why you bought the flag and the pole, because it's too complicated. I understand it, but they wouldn't. They would just think you were facetious, or flippant, and you simply can't kid around about the American flag in a quiet, reserved New England community like this.' I got up and lighted a cigarette. 'I'm not kidding around,' I said. 'I love the flag. As garish as it is, it has beauty, dignity, and even grandeur, and that is something of a miracle.' 'For heaven's sake,' she said, 'don't tell people it's garish.' 'What has happened to the time of Man,' I demanded, 'when the possession of your country's flag is looked upon as subversive or something?' Helen sighed. 'Well, anyway,' she said, 'we can't put it up in the snow. You'll have to wait till Flag Day. When is Flag Day?' 'April 14th, I think,' I told her. 'No, it's in June,' she said. 'I'm sure it's in June, but it might be safer if we waited until the Fourth of July.' 'Maybe it would,' I agreed. 'Not even a senator could find fault with a man who flies the American flag on the Fourth.' I got back in bed. Half an hour later I spoke to her in the dark. 'I was just thinking,' I said, 'I was just thinking that everybody will hear about this, and next December Annin's will be just as crowded as every other store on Fifth Avenue. I've killed the goose that laid the golden ball. It's going to be terrible for me.' 'It's going to be wonderful for Annin's,' murmured my wife. I couldn't tell whether she was awake or talking in her sleep.

DEC. 21 – This morning I asked Ben Tuller if he had told his wife's brothers about the flag and the flagpole. 'They didn't have to help me,' he said. 'There were only two boxes, and I handled them myself.' My face must have shown relief. 'I wouldn't tell anybody about this,' he said. 'It's between you and me. You can count on that.' I thought he sounded a little aggrieved. 'I never questioned your loyalty,' I assured him. 'Of course, people are bound to see the flagpole sooner or later,' he said. 'We'll face that problem when we come to it,'

I told him. 'Where is the stuff now?' 'In the attic,' he said. 'Do you want me to wrap the pole for you?' 'No,' I said. 'I've decided just to wrap the flag. I can do that myself.' I started out of the room, but turned at the door. 'I suppose I should have married Barbara Frietchie,' I said. Ben made no comment.

Tonight I hope to sleep all the way through to the dawn's early light.

What Cocktail Party?

'I'M NOT SO STUPID as to believe that the cocktail party in "The Cocktail Party" is actually a cocktail party,' Grace Sheldon told me the other day at a cocktail party that was unquestionably a cocktail party. 'What do *you* think it is?'

I was all wariness in a moment. Ever since the distinguished Mr T. S. Eliot's widely discussed play came to town, I have been cornered at parties by women, and men, who seem intent on making me say what I think 'The Cocktail Party' means, so they can cry 'Great God, how naïve!' and then go around telling people that I probably don't even know the significance of the pumpkin in 'Cinderella.' I have learned to spar for time, with a counter-question of my own. 'Do you believe in the innocence of the innocents in "The Innocents"?' I asked Grace Sheldon.

Grace finished her Martini and looked around for the man in the white coat with the cocktail tray. 'The only thing I am sure of,' she said, 'is the death of the salesman in "Death of a Salesman." I'm sure he dies and is supposed to be dead.'

'You're just an old positivist,' I said.

'The point is whether Eliot was impelled to write the play by forces beyond

543

his control and cognizance,' chimed in Charles Endless, joining us and waving his empty highball glass. 'I presume you're talking about *the* play.' Endless is forever repeating the critical judgments of his psychiatrist, Dr Carl Wix, and embroidering them with the skeins of his own prejudices. 'There is no such thing as the power of conscious selection in the creative writer,' Charles went on. 'I should say that the psychic inspiration of "The Cocktail Party" was the consequence of something Eliot had done, whereas "The Turn of the Screw" – or "The Innocents," if you prefer to call it that – is clear proof of Henry James's conscious unawareness of something he had *not* done.'

'Something important, of course,' I annotated.

'Vastly,' underlined Endless. 'Observe the size of the symbols these two writers have been impelled to select from the stockpile of literary devices and properties: the holy cross and the dark tower.'

'I haven't seen "The Sign of the Screw," and I don't want to talk about it,' said Grace. 'I want to find out what Mr Thurber thinks "The Cocktail Party" is about. I'm not interested in what Dr Wix thinks was the matter with Henry James.'

'Great God!' cried Charles. 'The woman seeks narrative sense in the sheerest mechanism of expiation!'

'I do not,' said Grace, taking another Martini from the hovering cocktail tray.

Endless bowed with what he believed to be eighteenth-century grace, and was about to set off to find more congenial intellectual companionship when Malcolm Codd said something that arrested him. Codd, who had appeared quietly, as usual, from nowhere, wore glasses with flesh-coloured rims and sipped furtively at a glass of milk. 'Yes?' said Charles irritably, turning on him.

'I say,' Codd said, 'that anyone is indiscreet who tells what he thinks the play means. It is clearly one of those projection techniques, like the ink blots that are now all the vogue with psychiatrists. What the spots and the play mean to you is the thumbprint of your persona, the signature of your psyche, a history of your past, a key to your bedroom, a portrait of your ego in Technicolour. I would no more think of telling you what "The Cocktail Party" meant to me last Saturday afternoon than I would think of telling you last night's dream.'

'You should have read either a great deal more or a great deal less than you have,' Charles said.

I decided to colour the dialogue with some rhythms of my own, since they always annoy Charles. 'What makes you think, Codd, that the meaning of the play to you, or last night's dream, is sure to show a sinister significance?' I asked.

Charles stared at me in horror. 'Great God!' he cried. 'Are you looking for the bluebird of happiness? Do you think there are actually hinges on chimneys so the stars can get by? Do you believe Love will slay the dragon and live happily ever after?'

I was as cool as steel. 'I believe in the sudden deep greenness of summer,' I said. In the fifteen years I have known Charles, his scepticism has always shattered against my affirmation, and he knows it.

'Bah!' he said, turning grandly on his heel, and bumping into old Mrs Weaver, who is convinced that Eliot wrote the play in his sleep.

'Goddam it,' she said, 'look where you're going.'

Mrs Codd laughed. Since she never says anything, I hadn't noticed she was there.

'He is lost beyond saving,' Codd said, taking his wife's arm and leading her away.

One always knows Grace Sheldon is there. She began to chew on it again. 'I don't know you well enough to tell you what Dr Wix thinks "Gentlemen Prefer Blondes" is about,' she said, watching Ruth Endless dive out of a cloud of women, strafe her husband briefly, and disappear behind a cliff of laughing men. 'Or rather,' she went on, 'what Charles says Dr Wix thinks it means. But you still haven't told me what *you* think of "The Cocktail Party".'

I laughed a laugh that was not actually a laugh.

'What *don't* you think it means, then?' she put in helpfully.

I circled around this for a moment. 'Do you mean what Eliot is *intentionally* not saying, or what he just *happens* not to have said?' I asked, with enormous tidiness. She looked bewildered and I tried to clear it up for her, and for me. 'Let me put it this way,' I said. 'No playwright has ever deliberately said "Kings wear oysters in their shoes." This line has not been left out, however, in the sense that it has been *rejected*. It is certainly not what Eliot is *not* saying. If we charged him with it, he might quite properly reply, "I would never not say that!"'

Grace Sheldon sighed, and robbed the passing tray of another drink. 'Then what is it he isn't saying?' she wailed. 'What is it he doesn't mean to mean?'

'My dear lady,' I said, 'if we were to discuss what he does not mean, we would find ourselves discussing what some other particular play does mean, since I am persuaded that what he is not saying has been said in some identifiable drama, and just as vehemently as he has not said it, if not so eloquently. The question is – what other play?'

Grace made a desperate stab at it. '"Candida"?' she whispered.

I am afraid I sneered. Grace can be extraordinarily obtuse. 'I am not privy to what Eliot is not saying,' I said coldly, 'but I will stake my sacred honour that he is not not saying what "Candida" says.'

Grace glanced at her watch. 'I wish everybody were as simple as Shaw,' she said. 'I'm going home.' And she went.

Ruth Endless descended on me with Archie Kess in tow. 'Archie has a theory about Peter Quilpe in "The Cocktail Party",' she said. 'Archie thinks Quilpe is not really the wife's lover but the husband's fantasy of the kind of lover she would pick if she picked one.'

'A degradation symbol?' I asked.

'Exactly,' said Archie. 'Eliot has given the word "Quilpe" the same force as our "twerp" or "drip." If he had meant the character to be real, he would have called him Querringhouse, or Quillingham, or Quartermaine.'

I turned this over in my mind. Then Ruth said, 'I happen to know that Quilpe is based on an actual person Eliot can't stand named Sweeney, or Prufrock, or some such name. Just as Julia in the show is Lady Serena Carnarvon, or somebody, who once hit Eliot with a paper dart at a musicale in London.'

Archie kept nodding and grinning, and I snarled at him, 'If it gives you two any satisfaction to find the paper snow of personal retaliation in this magnificent blizzard of poetic thought, I hope all the radiators in your part of Hell go thrump.'

'All the time?' asked Archie.

I walked away from them and joined Betty Logan and Tom Frayne.

'For God's sake, Betty,' Frayne was saying, gesturing with his cigarette, 'say the Psychiatrist is Ambition, or Hope, or God, or Escapism, or Dedication, or the Father Image, or the Death Urge, or the Oedipus Complex, or a snatch of song you can't get out of your mind, but don't stand there and try to tell me he is an actual, carnate, human male psychiatrist. Can you imagine such a well-bred and cultured English psychiatrist – for that is what is what he would be if he were mortal – *crashing* a cocktail party in London?'

'What makes you think it is a cocktail party?' I asked coolly. 'Eliot himself says –'

'I don't care what Eliot himself says,' snapped Tom. 'Eliot has missed a great many of the meanings in his play – wasn't that obvious to you when you saw it?'

'I wouldn't say "obvious",' I said. 'I would say it nagged and nibbled at the rind of my consciousness.'

'What do *you* think the play is about? What do *you* think it means?' asked Betty.

I decided to withdraw down a murky by-pass. 'The identity of the third murderer in "Macbeth" has puzzled Shakespearean scholars for more than three centuries,' I said. 'Would it impair or increase your pleasure in the great tragedy if you found out who he actually is, or was?'

'It wouldn't make any difference to me,' Betty said.

'What are you driving at, Thurber?' asked Tom.

'The Catonian Trium,' I said. ' "The Cocktail Party" is plainly a revaluation of the theory of Cato the Elder that two primary identities can sustain an unidentifiable third. That is, the *duum* differs from the *unum* in that it can absorb, without distortion of meaning, the introduction of an unknown, or mysterious, or debatable third.'

'Naturally,' said Tom with crisp impatience. 'Everybody knows that. But it doesn't apply here. You are adding the Psychiatrist to Julia and Alex when, as a matter of fact, *they* are added to him. You don't seem to understand what identity is being concealed.'

I found myself in the embarrassing position of being routed in an argument involving a theory I had made up. 'He'll debauch you, Betty,' I said, and retreated from the field.

When the Eliot play begins to burn at the edges of a cocktail party, it spreads rapidly through the room, igniting every tongue, including the tongues of those ladies and gentlemen who haven't seen the play and don't intend to, or can hardly wait. On my way to the front hall, after waving goodbye to my hostess, I overheard a young man telling a pretty girl that the play is a hoax, the secret of whose anagrammatic scheme had been figured out by his roommate at Harvard, a brilliant chap named Buzz Walkley. As I passed into the hall, Judge Henneman trotted out of the lavatory, hardly able to breathe, as usual, and seized my arm. 'What's fellow up to?' he wheezed. 'Study of the female element in the human male,' I explained. 'Buncombe,' he wheezed. 'Discipline breaking down all over world.' He stood there, gripping my arm and trying to breathe for a full minute. Then he let go and tottered back to the controversy.

I turned to find Edgeley, the butler, waiting with my hat and coat and stick. 'What do *you* make of it, Edgeley?' I asked.

He helped me on with my coat. 'It's another variant of the prickly-pear theme, I should say,' he ventured, 'if I'm not perhaps being a bit too basic.'

'Not at all,' I said. 'I'm afraid some of us have been much too high in the superstructure to see the fundamentals clearly.' We walked to the door.

'Your point is prettily taken,' he said.

I thanked him.

'There is an ancient Latin saying,' he went on, 'which, freely translated, goes like this: "If my ship burn at sea, then who shall know its destination save the stars and God?"'

'Who indeed?' I said cautiously. I thought I detected a faint whiff of kirsch on his breath.

'My colleague, Huntington,' he continued, 'has hit it off rather sharply, I think – but I am boring you.'

'Not at all,' I told him. 'What does Huntington say?'

'Huntington says, "It is desolater than you think."' He opened the door for me. 'Quite keen, don't you agree?'

'Very,' I said.

I went out and Edgeley closed the door slowly and softly behind me. I stood a moment on the stoop, wondering vaguely about his background. A cab turned the corner and I waved it down. When I got in, I glanced at the driver's identification card and saw that his name was Louis Sandek. He turned around and looked at me thoughtfully. 'You know something?' he said. I took fifty cents out of my pocket, gave it to him, got out of the cab, and slammed the door shut. He shrugged and drove off. It was twelve blocks to my hotel, but I walked. I was in no mood to listen to the Sandek version.

Joyeux Noël Mr Durning

I THINK I would have allowed the illicit merchandise to lapse into forfeiture if it had come from anyone except Maria and Olympy, but I couldn't let them down. I could have written them, of course, saying that I had received their *joli cadeau*, but it is awkward to thank someone for a bottle of liqueur if you don't know what kind of liqueur it is. Thus it was that I replied to Mr Durning's form letter, received ten days before Christmas five years ago.

If you received one of these notifications, and I understand that hundreds, or perhaps thousands, were sent out, you were probably sensible enough to give up the struggle for your bottle by the middle of February, but I am made of a sterner curiosity. Once the game was afoot, I – but let us begin with Mr Durning's first letter:

TREASURY DEPARTMENT
BUREAU OF CUSTOMS
NEW YORK 4, N.Y.

IN REPLY REFER TO:
Seiz. No. 41802
Det. No. 3173-M-48
DECEMBER 14, 1948

Mr and Mrs James Thurber,
The New Yorker,
25 West 43rd Street,
N. Y. City 18, N. Y.

SIR AND MADAM:
There has been placed under seizure the merchandise set forth below which

arrived in the mails from Mr and Mrs Sementzoff; contained in a package addressed to you.

(1) bottle – 1/5 gal. size – Alc. Liqueur.

You are informed that any postal union (regular) mail articles or parcel post package received from abroad which is found to contain spirituous, vinous, malted, fermented, or other intoxicating liquor of any kind, is prohibited importation in the mails and is subject to seizure and forfeiture under the provisions of section 340, title 18, U.S. Code, and section 593 (b) of Tariff Act of 1930.

If you desire to obtain possession of this liquor you must furnish to the Law Division of this office, ROOM 318 CUSTOMHOUSE, BOWLING GREEN, NEW YORK, NEW YORK, a statement setting forth the facts surrounding the importation indicating whether the same is for your personal use or for commercial purposes, that the merchandise, if released, will not be replaced in the mails, and that notification has been given to the shipper that the importation of intoxicating liquors through the mails is prohibited. Upon receipt of such statement you will be advised of the terms upon which the liquor will be released to you.

Unless the liquor in question is taken possession of by you within a reasonable time, the same will be disposed of according to law.

Respectfully,

HARRY M. DURNING,
Collector of Customs
By: J. P. SHARAGHER
Actg. Dep. Coll.

Now, this document smelt to heaven of potential prolixity and proliferation, and my family and friends, knowing my tendency toward querulous impatience in protracted official give-and-take, warned me to ignore it. But I thought of Olympy and Maria. The last time my wife and I saw them was in the troubled spring of 1938, when we waved good-bye to them as we drove away from the Villa Tamisier, in Juan-les-Pins. I later wrote a small memorial to Maria's cooking and character, and to the wild abandon and quiet fortitude of her husband the day he drove my Ford sedan – and me – into a telephone pole. We heard from them during the first year of the Occupation, in a letter addressed to me in care of the New York *Herald*, New York, U.S.A. They were in good health but sad spirits, and somehow deeply concerned about our safety (in that most dangerous of war fronts – Connecticut). We sent them boxes of food from time to time, and our repeated assurances that we were well and safe, but Maria was apparently not convinced. The day the American troops arrived, she wrote us, she ran out into the streets of Juan-les-Pins and demanded *nouvelles de M. et Mme. Thurber* from a passing column of soldiers.

A captain – who didn't know the Thurbers from Adam and Eve – shouted back at her that we were carrying ourselves well, and Maria was at last relieved of her grand anxiety. I have often wished that I could thank that gallant officer for his quick and thoughtful good tidings about Maria's *Monsieur et Madame à New York*.

Yes, thinking about Maria and Olympy, I had to get that bottle. My first brave letter, together with its tangled consequences, follows, for your information and guidance:

WEST CORNWALL, CONN.
DECEMBER 17, 1948

The Law Division,
Office of the Collector,
Room 318, Customhouse,
Bowling Green,
New York, N. Y.

GENTLEMEN:

I am writing in connection with a letter of December 14th from Mr Harry M. Durning, Collector of Customs, sent to Mr and Mrs James Thurber, c/o *The New Yorker* Magazine, 25 West 43rd Street, New York City. Mr Durning's letter asks me to refer to 'Seiz. No. 41802 and Det. No. 3173-M-48.'

The bottle of alcoholic liqueur is intended as a Christmas gift to Mrs Thurber and myself, and was shipped from France by Mr and Mrs Olympy Sementzoff, who worked as our gardener and cook in France some ten years ago. They are obviously not familiar with U.S. customs restrictions on shipments of alcoholic beverages from abroad.

I am advising the shippers of the customs regulations that obtain in this case, and asking them to abide by these regulations in the future.

The bottle is intended for the private use of Mrs Thurber and myself and will be used for no commercial purpose. If and when it is released to us, it will not be replaced in the mails.

I await your further instructions in this matter, and regret the inconvenience it has caused you.

Respectfully yours,
JAMES THURBER

TREASURY DEPARTMENT
BUREAU OF CUSTOMS
NEW YORK 4, N. Y.

IN REPLY REFER TO:
GM/22
Seizure No. 41802
DECEMBER 30, 1948

Mr James Thurber,
West Cornwall, Conn.

SIR:
Addressee: Mr and Mrs James Thurber
    Merchandise: 1 bottle 1/5 gal. Alc. Liqueur
    Sum to be deposited: $3.56 (total)
    Receipt is acknowledged of your letter of December 17, 1948, regarding the merchandise listed above which arrived in the mail and which has been placed under seizure for violation of the customs revenue laws.

To secure the release of this merchandise from Customs we require that there be deposited with us the sum above stated. This payment may be made by certified cheque or postal money order payable to the Collector of Customs. You are also advised that in addition to our terms of release which include the payment of the above listed sum, before the merchandise finally may be released, it will be necessary for you to present to this office a state permit therefor from the Connecticut State Liquor Authority at Hartford. Upon receipt of the permit and the payment above listed, the liqueur will be forwarded to you by express, charges collect.

We request that you act promptly in this matter to secure the release of this merchandise: otherwise, it will be disposed of as provided by law.

Respectfully,
HARRY M. DURNING, COLLECTOR
By: ALFRED H. GOLDEN
Assistant Solicitor

WEST CORNWALL, CONN.
JANUARY 5, 1949

Mr Harry M. Durning,
Collector of Customs,
Bureau of Customs,
New York 4, N. Y.

DEAR MR DURNING:
In reference to GM/22 and Seizure No. 41802, and your letter of December 30, 1948, in reply to my own letter of December 17, I am this day writing for a

permit from the Connecticut State Liquor Authority, which I will forward promptly when received, together with a postal money order for $3.56.

Sincerely yours,

JAMES THURBER

WEST CORNWALL, CONN.
JANUARY 5, 1949

Connecticut Liquor Authority,
Hartford, Connecticut

GENTLEMEN:

I have been advised in a letter just received from Mr Harry M. Durning, Collector of Customs in New York, that I must submit to him a Connecticut permit in order to obtain the release of a 1/5 gallon of alcoholic spirits now under seizure in New York. All other requirements set forth by Mr Durning have been satisfied by me. The bottle under seizure will be forwarded to me by express on submission of the proper permit from your authority.

Thanking you for your prompt consideration in this matter, and with best season's wishes, I am

Sincerely yours,

JAMES THURBER

LIQUOR CONTROL COMMISSION
STATE OF CONNECTICUT
HARTFORD

JANUARY 10, 1949

James Thurber,
West Cornwall, Connecticut

DEAR SIR:

Receipt is acknowledged of your communication of January 5, 1949, with reference to alcoholic liquor for your personal consumption which you desire to import into the State.

With reference to this situation, you are advised that it is necessary to apply for and receive a permit for the importation of this type of merchandise. We are enclosing, herewith, blank forms of application, no one of which may be for more than five gallons.

Before executing these applications, the State Tax Commissioner, Excise Division, State Office Building, Hartford, Connecticut, should be advised as to the type of beverage to be imported; if any wine is included, the alcoholic percentage and whether 'sparkling' or 'still'; and they will immediately advise you as to the amount of tax due. The applications should then be executed and forwarded to the Tax Department with a cheque in the amount of the taxes and, when received, that department will then forward them to us with the certification that the taxes have been paid and we will, in turn, issue an Import

Certificate to you which must be forwarded by you to whatever transportation company is to transport the merchandise into Connecticut. This Import Certificate must accompany the merchandise in transit and must be delivered to the importer at the time of the delivery of the merchandise. Upon receipt of the alcoholic beverages, the Import Certificate must of necessity be returned to this department.

   If there is any further information which you desire on the subject, we shall be very glad to advise you upon request.

Very truly yours,

RICHARD H. PINNEY
Executive Assistant
Liquor Control Commission

P.S. The state tax on whisky is computed as $1.00 per wine gallon.

WEST CORNWALL, CONN.
FEBRUARY 4, 1949

The State Tax Commissioner,
Excise Division,
State Office Building,
Hartford, Connecticut

DEAR SIR:
   On December 30, 1948, I was advised by the New York Customs authorities that they are holding one bottle 1/5 gallon alcoholic liqueur, shipped to me, in ignorance of our laws, by M. and Mme Olympy Sementzoff from France. I was instructed to notify the Connecticut Liquor Authority, which informed me, in enclosing applications for release, that I should describe, as herein-above, the nature and contents of the bottle in question. I have set down all that I know about it. The New York Customs demands $3.56 as their fee for release. I await your advice as to the proper tax due in this state, in full and helpless confidence that the aforementioned Christmas present will be disposed of as contraband before a man of my age can possibly satisfy all the documentary requirements. Nevertheless, I am going to try to get it.

   M. Sementzoff is a White Russian, and I trust that the purity of his loyalty to France need not be established by the F.B.I. or any other organization.

Respectfully yours,
JAMES THURBER

STATE OF CONNECTICUT
TAX DEPARTMENT
470 CAPITOL AVENUE
HARTFORD 15, CONNECTICUT

IN REPLY REFER TO:
Beverage Tax Section
FEBRUARY 8, 1949

Mr James Thurber,
West Cornwall,
Connecticut

DEAR SIR:

Receipt is acknowledged of your letter of the 4th received in this office this morning.

We wish to advise that Connecticut state tax on 1/5 gallon of liqueur is $0.20.

If you will forward your remittance in the amount of $0.20 to cover the tax due on the liqueur that is being held by the New York Customs for you, together with the completed applications sent you by the Liquor Control Commission, we will certify payment of the tax to the Liquor Commission who will then forward you a release.

Respectfully yours,
WILLIAM F. CONNELLY
Tax Commissioner
By: ERNEST S. GOODRICH
Director, Excise Division

THE BRITISH COLONIAL HOTEL,
NASSAU, BAHAMAS,
19 FEBRUARY, 1949

Mr William F. Connelly
Tax Commissioner
Hartford, Conn.
Attn: Mr Ernest S. Goodrich,
    Director, Excise Division

Re: Beverage Tax Section

DEAR MR CONNELLY:

In connection with your letter of February 8th sent by Mr Goodrich, I am enclosing a cheque for twenty cents ($0.20), together with the necessary applications, in accordance with your instructions as to the procedure for gaining the release of the bottle of liqueur now being held by the New York Customs authorities.

I am enclosing an American air-mail stamp in order that the release from the Connecticut State Liquor Control Commission may be expedited and I am taking the liberty of requesting your kindness in sending this stamp along to them, so that the release may be sent air mail to me, c/o The British Colonial, Nassau, the Bahamas. A letter sent by ordinary mail might take weeks in getting here and I am unfamiliar with the period of time regarded as reasonable by the New York Customs officials.

Thanking you for your help in this matter,

Sincerely yours,

JAMES THURBER

LIQUOR CONTROL COMMISSION
STATE OF CONNECTICUT
HARTFORD

FEBRUARY 24, 1949

James G. Thurber,
R.F.D.,
West Cornwall, Conn.

DEAR SIR:

Enclosed herewith is Import Certificate No. 1627 authorizing the importation into the State of Connecticut, for your personal consumption, of LIQUEUR.

The Import Certificate must accompany the merchandise in transit *and be delivered to you with the merchandise.*

Upon receipt of the merchandise, the Import Certificate *enclosed must be returned by you to this department.*

Very truly yours,
RICHARD H. PINNEY
Executive Assistant
Liquor Control Commission

The above certificate mailed to British Colonial Hotel, Nassau, Bahamas, as requested. (Air Mail.)

THE BRITISH COLONIAL HOTEL,
NASSAU, BAHAMAS,
MARCH 3, 1949

Mr Harry M. Durning,
Collector of Customs,
Bureau of Customs,
New York 4, N.Y.

DEAR MR DURNING:

With reference to GM/22 and Seizure No. 41802, and to your letters of December 14 and December 30, 1948, I am, pursuant to your direction, enclosing my cheque for $3.56, together with the Import Certificate just issued to me by the Liquor Control Commission of the State of Connecticut.

The Commission has advised me that the Import Certificate must accompany the shipment of the merchandise so that I may return the Certificate to the Commission when I receive it. It is my desire to conform, in full, with all the requirements of your office and those of the Connecticut authorities concerned.

There has been some unavoidable delay in gathering together all the necessary releases and certificates, but I trust I have not exceeded the time limit placed upon the holding of the merchandise. In the past two and a half months I have developed a profound curiosity as to the actual contents of the merchandise.

I understand from a recent newspaper article that your office has been overburdened by the receipt of illegal shipments of alcoholic spirits from friends of Americans in France and other countries who are unaware that their expressions of good feeling are contrary to statutes of the United States. I regret that I have innocently added to your work and to your problems, and I assure you that I have made every effort to prevent the recurrence of this situation.

Sincerely yours,

JAMES THURBER

P.S. I understand that the merchandise is to be shipped to me at West Cornwall, Conn., but it has occurred to me that it may be receivable only by myself or by Mrs Thurber personally. If this is the case, I will not be in West Cornwall until March 8th. There is, however, always someone at my home to receive the shipment.

WEST CORNWALL, CONN.
APRIL 5, 1949

Mr Harry M. Durning,
Collector of Customs,
Bureau of Customs,
New York 4, N.Y.

DEAR MR DURNING:

In further reference to GM/22 and Seizure No. 41802.

I wrote you on March 3rd, air mail from Nassau, the Bahamas, enclosing my personal cheque for $3.56, in final satisfaction of the stipulations of your own office and of the various Connecticut State authorities involved by law in the transaction regarding the shipment to Mrs Thurber and myself of a Christmas gift from M. and Mme. Olympy Sementzoff in France. I am not yet in receipt of the 1/5 gallon of alcoholic liqueur that is being held under seizure by your office, unless the act of forfeiture has already been consummated.

In the fear that the shipment may have been delayed because of some fault or failure of my own, I have gone back over the voluminous correspondence in this matter, searching for possible error on my part, and I have discovered that you asked for a certified cheque or postal money order and that I had said

I would send the tax in the form of the money order. Circumstances operated to place difficulties in my way, since I was in Nassau, where American money orders are unavailable and the certification of cheques was not easy to arrange.

If the merchandise has not yet been forfeited I shall be glad to substitute a certified cheque in the amount of $3.56 for the cheque I sent you on March 3rd.

When and if the bottle is received by me, I want to write the shippers to thank them again for the gift, and I should like to be able to state the precise brand or type of liqueur. Otherwise they might suspect that I had never actually received the present, and this would add further distress to their present embarrassment, which results from their knowledge that their Christmas gift was shipped in contravention, however innocent, of our statutes and regulations.

The Connecticut State Liquor Control Commission has instructed me to return the Import Certificate when I receive the shipment. If the merchandise has, in fact, been forfeited I do not know how to comply with this particular instruction.

My curiosity as to the actual contents of the bottle has not abated, and I would greatly appreciate it if, no matter how this transaction eventuates, you would identify the liqueur for me.

I fully appreciate the problems you have to deal with in the case of the thousands of such shipments mentioned in the newspaper article I read on the subject. This one bottle has very nearly driven me crazy.

Respectfully yours,
JAMES THURBER

WEST CORNWALL, CONN.
APRIL 6, 1949

Mr Harry M. Durning,
Collector of Customs,
Bureau of Customs,
New York 4, N.Y.

DEAR MR DURNING:
GM/22 and Seizure No. 41802.
In reference to my letter of yesterday, April 5, I regret to say that it was written and mailed during the absence of Mrs Thurber, who, upon her return, explained that you had accepted and put through my cheque of March 3rd in the amount of $3.56, and that the cancelled cheque had arrived in my bank statement on April 2nd. She further pointed out that the delay in shipment of the bottle of liqueur is no doubt due to the railway-express strike, which still obtains at this writing.

Please ignore my letter of yesterday and accept my apologies for adding to the confusion and to the considerable dossier in this matter which I have been at fault in amplifying.

Respectfully yours,
JAMES THURBER

P.S. If the Christmas gift does not arrive before Easter, I will be in Bermuda, but the shipment will be received by my caretaker, Mr Ben Tuller, who has instructions to forward the Import Certificate to the Connecticut Liquor Authority on my behalf.

TREASURY DEPARTMENT
BUREAU OF CUSTOMS
NEW YORK 4, N.Y.

IN REPLY REFER TO:
GJM:z/22
Seizure No. 41802
APRIL 12, 1949

Mr James Thurber,
West Cornwall,
Connecticut

SIR:

Reference is made to previous correspondence with this office relative to a shipment of alcoholic beverage consigned to you through the international mails in violation of the United States Code, title 18, sections 1716 and 545, covered by the above seizure number.

This office is in receipt of your remittance in accordance with the terms imposed for the release of this merchandise to you. However, the present express embargo will undoubtedly result in a delay in the receipt of the shipment by you.

Respectfully,
HARRY M. DURNING, COLLECTOR
By: ALFRED H. GOLDEN
Assistant Solicitor

On April 22nd, six days after I had sailed for Bermuda, and one hundred and twenty-nine days after the original form letter from Mr Durning, the merchandise arrived at West Cornwall, Connecticut, intact, according to Ben Tuller, who wrote me air mail that same day, enclosing the import certificate, which, it turned out, had to be signed by me. There were express charges of ninety-five cents on the merchandise, which Tuller paid. He was afraid that I might not return the import certificate to Hartford within the period of five days after the acceptance of the shipment, as prescribed by statute. I think I managed it, in spite of the unfortunate fact that his letter was first delivered, by mistake, to Waterlot, in Southampton Parish, instead of to Waterville, in Paget East, where I was staying. The import certificate, because of the gravity of its warning and the nobility of its language, deserves to be read into this record, and it follows in full, or almost in full:

This certifies that James G. Thurber of R.F.D., West Cornwall, Conn., having paid the tax prescribed by SUB-SECTION (b) of SECTION 986e, 1939 SUPPLEMENT TO THE

GENERAL STATUTES, AS AMENDED, is authorized to import into the STATE OF CONNECTI-CUT ⅕ Gal. LIQUEUR from Mr and Mrs Olympy Sementzoff, Juan-les-Pins, France, for his own use and consumption and not for resale. This certificate must be re-turned to Liquor Control Commission by person to whom issued within five (5) days after receipt of contents represented.

I will spare you my two letters, in French, to Maria and Olympy, the first thanking them for a gift I had not yet received and cautioning them not to do it again, the second announcing that the *joli cadeau de Noël* had arrived at my home five days after *Paques*. I explained that I would be *en séjour à Bermuda* until late in June, but that I would drink to their health and happiness on the Fourth of July.

Maria and Olympy will understand. After all, the French are by no means inexperienced in the long and labyrinthine processes of officialdom, complete with symbols, seals, signatures, and the satisfaction of statutes and stipulations.

Oh, yes, I almost forgot. It was a bottle of Cointreau.

(Consignee's Note: Shortly after the preceding correspondence appeared in *The New Yorker*, I received a nice letter from Mr Durning, enclosing an official cheque for two dollars. It seems that, somewhere along the line, I was inadvertently over-charged that amount.)

The Pleasure Cruise, and How to Survive It

IT HAS OCCURRED to me that there may be persons here and there, young and inexperienced in the ways of the world, who might profit from my own personal TRAVEL HINTS, compiled after looking back on thirty-odd years of knocking about, or being knocked about, the globe. I don't mean the whole globe, of course. I have never been south of Trinidad, north of Quebec, east of Italy, or west of San Francisco, but within these rather roomy limits, I have been knocked about quite a bit.

My first hint – to the gentleman traveller – is a simple one. Never go anywhere without your wife. If your wife won't go, because the concert or canning season is on, or something of the sort, take your sister or your mother or your cousin. The American woman is indispensable in getting the tickets and reservations, packing and unpacking, mixing Bromo-Seltzers, fending off beautiful ladies who are travelling alone, and making herself useful generally. Hers is also the only sex that can successfully close a wardrobe trunk. If a man closes a wardrobe trunk, there is always a sharp snapping sound, caused by the breaking of something that will not bend, such as the handle of a mirror, or the stem of a Dunhill pipe, or the stopper of a perfume bottle. If a woman is deprived of her Chanel No. 5 during, say, a nineteen-day cruise, she will become irritable, and there is nothing more exasperating on a cruise, or anywhere else, than an irritable female companion.

Now that I have mentioned cruises, let us consider more closely the technique of the sea voyage. After the wife has closed the wardrobe trunk and called a taxi, it is only eight in the morning, and the ship doesn't sail till eleven. The husband will complain that it doesn't take three hours to get to a pier only eight blocks from their hotel. He will point out that they can get to Pier 58 in half an hour, with time to spare. He is right, it turns out, but it also turns out that he doesn't know where Pier 58 is. His wife has unfortunately left this one small detail up to him. He tells the taxi driver to take them to the foot of West 58th Street, but when they get there, it transpires that this is not the point of departure of their ship, the *Santa Maria*. It is the point of departure of the *J. B. Cathcart*, a coastwise fruit steamer bound for French Guiana. The taxi driver suggests that the *Santa Maria* probably sails from Brooklyn or Hoboken. The husband figures there is time to try both places, but his wife's sounder judgment prevails. She asks somebody – always an excellent idea – where Pier 58 is, and is told Pier 58 is at the foot of West 16th Street. It is too.

On the way to the right destination, with time to spare – just as the husband had promised – the taxi driver suddenly has a hunch that the *Santa Maria* sails at 11 p.m., on Tuesdays, and not at 11 a.m., on Thursdays. This throws his male passenger into a panic. The seasoned woman traveller pays no attention to all this unnecessary masculine excitement. She leans back in the cab, closes her eyes and wonders if she forgot to pack her white piqué evening dress. Once aboard the ship, the wife (Ellen) tells her husband (George) that she has to unpack her light things right away or they will crush, and she asks him, for heaven's sake, to get deck chairs on the sunny and windless side of the ship immediately, before they are all gone, and also to make table reservations instantly, so they can have a table for two once in their lives, and not have to sit with a lot of strangers. George wanders away on these important errands and (1) runs into an old classmate from Dartmouth and (2) decides that they ought to find out where the bar is and what time it opens for business. When he returns to his stateroom, an hour later, Ellen is in excellent spirits – she has found the white piqué evening dress – but her amiable mood is not going to last very long. 'Did you reserve the chairs and the table?' she asks. 'Hm?' says George blankly. I will spare you the scene that follows. Suffice it to say that the Kendalls (their name is Kendall) have to settle for deck chairs on the sunless and windy side of the ship, and are put at a table for eight: two women buyers from Cleveland, an embalmer and his bride, a pair of giggling college girls and Mr and Mrs George Kendall. She has the chair with the short right-rear leg.

My private tip here is that the wife should reserve the deck chairs and the table, let the dresses crush where they may, but I have never been able to sell the idea to any woman traveller.

The only woman who doesn't care whether her dresses crush or not is the seasick woman, but I wouldn't recommend seasickness as the way out of anything, not even the way out of sitting next to the embalmer at dinner. Speaking of seasickness, I am unlucky enough to have a stomach of platinum, and I haven't suffered from *mal de mer* since the eastward Atlantic crossing of the *U.S.S. Orizaba*, in November, 1918, but this was a transport that took nine days zigzagging from New York to St Nazaire in heavy weather, and there was an honourable excuse for my condition. I say I am 'unlucky' enough to have a stomach of platinum, because the seasick turn to the unseasick on a ship for succour, sanctuary and salvation that are impossible to give. Once, on the Bermuda run – seventeen of us up and around on the second day, out of a passenger list of three hundred – I came upon a lone woman sprawled on a sofa in the library up forward, where rolling and pitching had flung her prostrate and forlorn. She lay on her hat and her right side; one shoe was off; her handbag was open on the floor, its contents scattered; her lipstick was smudged in such a way that she seemed to have bitten her own left cheek. I was appalled – sympathetic, gallant even, but appalled – and when I am appalled, my nervous system becomes an apparatus that, as the French say, *ne fonctionne pas*.

'Do something,' she said in a faint, awful voice.

'Madam,' I squeaked helplessly. I was unable to say anything, but I did something. I put her things back in her handbag and placed it on a table.

'I put your handbag on the table,' I finally managed to croak.

'Do something,' she said again, in the same voice. For a moment I considered putting her shoe back on, but like any other Ohio State man, I was restrained by the feeling that the act would be both insensitive and foolish. Then I suddenly decided to put the shoe on the table with the handbag.

'Do something,' she said, in a weaker tone. I staggered out of the library, hunted up a deck steward and told him about the lady and her extremity.

'Do something,' I begged him. He just shook his head sadly. I rolled on my way, and came to the elevator that ran from A Deck down to E Deck and back. There was a woman there, frantically pressing the bell button. She was standing, and she had both shoes on, but she looked just as ghastly as the lost lady in the library. She grabbed my arm as I tried to walk by.

'E Deck. Quick!' she gasped.

'The elevator will be up –' I began and caught myself, but not in time. Her face took on a saffron hue.

'I'm sorry,' I mumbled. She looked at me with the eyes of a stepped-on spaniel.

'E Deck,' she said again. 'Please.'

I had to do something. I brushed past her and began pushing the bell button wildly. Then I turned and ran. I have often wondered, in my own low and agonized moments, if she made it.

Just what hint to give to the unseasick passenger who may be faced, during an ocean voyage, with crises and suffering similar to my own that terrible day, I frankly do not know. There are certain tortures that we unseasick passengers simply have to endure, I guess. I would appreciate it, though, if you don't go around saying that, in the emergencies I have described, I just 'got the hell out.' I did what I could. There will, of course, always be two schools of thought about that shoe, the school that contends I should have put it back on, and the school that insists I should have let it lie where I found it. Apparently nobody in the world but me would have put it on the table with the handbag. I can only say that if I had it all to do over again, I would still put the shoe on the table with the handbag.

If you travel much on ships you are bound, sooner or later, to run into Mrs Abigail Pritchard, as I shall call her. She is not just one woman, but many; I have encountered at least fifteen of her. Mrs Pritchard may be forty-five, or she may be seventy, but her average age, I should say, is about fifty-seven. She comes from Boston, Hartford, Germantown, Syracuse, Toledo, Chicago, Louisville, St Louis, Denver, Sacramento, and both Portlands. She is a widow, fairly well off, whose children are happily married and the fathers, or mothers, of the prettiest and brightest youngsters in the world, and she has snapshots and anecdotes to prove it. She takes two Daiquiris before dinner and a highball afterwards, and smokes Players, on the ground that they are made of actual tobacco, whereas American cigarettes, in her opinion, are composed of rum, molasses, shredded cork, and factory sweepings. She prefers domestic Burgundies, however, because the so-called French vintages you find on ships are really only cheap Algerian wine that has been poured into genuine bottles labelled Pommard or Chablis. Mrs Pritchard is full of interesting little anecdotes about the late Sir Harry Oakes, the late Richard Halliburton ('that dear boy'), a Colonel Grosvenor in Penang, the gifted Courtney girls (whoever they are), John Barrymore ('poor old Jack'), Heifetz, Houdini, Nell Brinkley, Anna Eva Fay, Percy Marmont, Maurice Costello ('the king of them all'), Kip Rhinelander, Mrs O. H. P. Belmont, Struthers Burt, Ky Laffoon and anybody else whose name you happen to mention. Mrs Pritchard is certain she saw Judge Crater in the Casino at Cannes in 1937, where he was known as Maltby or Goadby, or some such name. 'How do you do, Judge Crater?' she said to him firmly. He started – there could be no doubt of that. 'My name is Maltby (or Goadby), madam,' the man said, and hurried away.

Mrs Pritchard can invariably spot, aboard ship, professional gamblers, unmarried couples sharing the same stateroom, fugitives from justice, fingermen formerly in the employ of Al Capone, cocaine sniffers, bay-rum drinkers, professional men of dubious integrity, women who are mortally ill but don't know it, unhappy wives and gentlemen with phony foreign accents. It makes you nervous to talk to, or rather listen to, Mrs Pritchard. You twist restlessly in your chair, confident that she has figured you for an absconder, a black-marketeer, or a white-slave trader. Mrs Pritchard spends at least two months of every year on ships, but I often wonder why, since she suspects that there is skulduggery afoot from the chart room to the hold. If the ship is even half an hour late in shoving off, she whispers that 'Uncle Joe is behind this delay.' She never clears this up, though, but merely shakes her head wisely, if you ask her what she means. She is sure the ship is going to put to sea with broken pumps, insufficient lifeboats, and a typhoid carrier among the crew. Two days out, she tells you she doesn't like the look of the saxophone player's complexion – he has something contagious, mark her words. The third day out she declares that the chief steward is secreting fifteen thousand pounds of roast beef, which he intends to sell to a syndicate in Port-au-Prince. It costs ten thousand dollars a day to operate a ship, she read in the *Reader's Digest*, and this ridiculous amount is due to thefts of supplies by the stewards.

Even the captain of the ship is not above her suspicion. She is positive that he forgot to order all those automobiles in the hold lashed down, and she knows they will roll to one side if a storm comes up, causing the ship to list, like the *Vestris*, and sink. Mrs Pritchard loves to tell about the time the master of an ocean liner was seized with a heart attack while steering the boat – she still thinks he was an epileptic – and almost ran into an iceberg. But her favourite story is about the time she was on a West Indies cruise, and caught a glimpse of the captain one day. She recognized him instantly as a Major Quantrell (or Chantress, or some such name) wanted in Rangoon for the shooting of a missionary's daughter in a fashionable gambling house. Mrs Pritchard points out that a captain's cabin is the perfect hide-out for fugitives from justice, since nobody is allowed in the cabin except the officers, and they are probably no better than they ought to be, themselves.

The young traveller will naturally expect old, experienced me to advise him how to avoid, or to deal with, Mrs Pritchard. Well, you can't avoid her. Just dismiss that from your mind. She pops up from everywhere and out from behind everything. Even if you hid in the engine room, she would search you out. As for dealing with the old girl, I have invented a rather nasty game called Back Her in the Corner, which works wonders.

'You know the Hotel l'Aiglon in Roquebrune, of course?' I say to her, casually.

'To be sure,' she replies. 'That perfectly gorgeous view of the Bay of Monte Carlo at night!'

We both look dreamy.

'Ah, yes,' I sigh, 'and those wonderful sardines grilled in triple-sec!'

'Yes, yes,' she sighs, 'those delicious sardines.'

You see, she has to keep up a show of having been every place I have been. And here's where my game gets nasty.

'There isn't any Hotel l'Aiglon in Roquebrune,' I say coldly, 'and there aren't any sardines grilled in triple-sec.'

She is furious. I have tricked her, and hell hath no fury like a woman tricked. She gives me a wide berth after that, not even nodding or smiling when I pass her on deck. I can get away with this little game because I am fifty-six,* but such conduct on the part of the *young* traveller would seem imprudent, disrespectful and ill-bred. You'll have to devise your own method of dealing with Mrs Pritchard. You mustn't expect me to solve *all* your travel problems. And please don't write and ask me what to do in the event that you run into the gifted Courtney sisters. I simply do not know.

A few days out of New York (if you sailed from New York), printed copies of the passenger list are usually distributed, containing such names as Jowes, Qmith, Johnsob, Crazier, Aprker, Sommonx and Spider. It takes years of practice to decipher some passenger-list garbles. The letters of my own name have assumed some twenty different permutations, but I am most often listed simply as Jane Phurber, a winsome six-foot Ohio matron who affects men's clothes. My wife, whose name is Helen Thurber, turned up on one ship under the alias of H. Muriel. In some mysterious manner, our false names (I was Joseph Thacher on this occasion) followed us ashore when we debarked at Naples. My wife indignantly showed our true passport names to one Italian official who had insisted we were one J. Thacher and one H. Muriel. He saw his mistake.

'I am all of regret, *signorina*,' he said, in excellent English, 'and expressing sorrows towards you and Signor Muriel.'

'Come on, H.,' I said, 'let's go.'

'O.K., Joe,' she said, and we got out of there.

You will most likely have been at sea a week before you get around to reading the literature you picked up at your travel agency, or at the offices of the steamship line itself. This company gets out a pamphlet entitled *General Informa-*

* Publisher's note: He's fifty-eight if he's a day.

U*

tion, and you should have read it before you got on the ship. It lists a number of things that should not be carried in a passenger's luggage: 'Dangerous articles, such as fireworks, matches, gunpowder, inflammable liquids, cartridges, inflammable motion-picture films.' If you have a supply of skyrockets and Roman candles, it would be wise to dump them overboard some night when nobody is watching you. Skyrockets shot from decks accidentally or out of a misguided burst of patriotic spirit are certain to be construed as signals of distress by other vessels, and this would vex the commander of your ship, to say the least. So leave your fireworks at home, in a safe, locked place, where the children can't get at them. I don't know why you keep fireworks in your house, anyway, but, of course, that is none of my business.

If you have gone on a cruise to relax, and you don't want to romp, run, race or wrestle, stay away from the sports director, a big, energetic blond young man carrying a medicine ball. The female of this species, the sports directress, is active, alert, athletic, aggressive and capable of throwing your wife, or you, over her shoulder with her left hand. If you are not in training and under twenty-eight, don't monkey around with these two. They will run you ragged. They love squatting exercises, chinning themselves, holding their breath, standing on their hands, and touching the deck two thousand times with their finger tips, without bending their knees. Don't try to keep up with them. Refuse their challenges, ignore their taunts. You can't beat them at anything from squatting to ping-pong, unless you are young Mathias, the decathlon champion, and you probably aren't. The sports directors are supposed to organize group recreational activities. This is both a fact and a warning.

Speaking of ping-pong, I once entered a table-tennis tournament aboard the *S.S. President Garfield*, on a trip from New York through the Canal to Los Angeles. The sports director was determined to get me into the table-tennis tournament, probably because he wanted to see me humiliated in the finals. And he did. I lost two straight games to a pretty, attractive young lady, twenty years* my junior. The table was too short, the net was too high, the rackets were warped, the ship rocked, a small boy among the spectators began riding me and I got something in my eye. I explained to my opponent after the match that, on land and under fair and reasonable conditions, I could have pinned her ears back, the best day she ever saw. She was honest enough to admit this. A very pleasant girl, and the luckiest woman I have ever met on sea or land.

The night before a ship makes home port at the end of a cruise, there is usually a ship's concert, or programme of entertainment, in which the Courtney sisters and other gifted passengers are invited to take part. If you are a singer, violinist, bird caller, soft-shoe dancer, whistler, mimic, monologist, contortionist, juggler, hypnotist, ventriloquist, swami, *diseuse* or zither player, you are likely to be asked to join in the fun and do your act. You may refuse, of course, and you should, if you plan to recite all of *Evangeline* or *Hiawatha*. Your fellow-passengers will resent any act that lasts longer than five minutes.

* Publisher's note: Twenty-two years.

Once, coming back from the West Indies on the *Conte Grande*, I declined to appear on the concert programme, and then suddenly, during a lull at midnight, I grabbed up a lighted megaphone and sang *Who?* and *Bye, Bye Blackbird* with the orchestra. Well, not *with* it, exactly, since in *Blackbird*, I was singing '*Oh, the hard-luck stories they all hand me*' while the orchestra was playing '*No one here can love or understand me*', but we were tied at the finish, I am happy to say. The survivors of that concert will doubtless remember my act, but they will not care to dwell on it any more than I do.

Since my performance that midnight, and possibly because of it, some of the more cautious cruise ships have eliminated passenger participation and turned the programme of the final night over to professionals. The last cruise I was on, a few months ago, had no place for amateurs on the Big Night. The entertainment department of WOR provided a soprano, a baritone (to replace me), a prestidigitator, a couple of 'dance stylists,' an accordionist and several other instrumentalists. Talented passengers who had counted on imitating Tallulah Bankhead or playing *Canadian Capers* on a makeshift xylophone composed of White Rock bottles were somewhat mollified when they were given funny hats to wear, horns to blow, bells to ring, and rattles to rattle at the Gala Farewell Dinner that preceded the Gala Farewell Revue. In charge of these Galas, and such affairs as the Fancy Headdress Ball and other intellectual goings on, are the cruise director and the cruise directress (not to be confused with the sports director and the sports directress). When, on my recent cruise, I returned to my stateroom after the Gala Farewell Revue, I found a cheerful note from the cruise director. It read: 'Rise up in the morning with the will that – smooth or rough – you'll grin!' I decided against this. You never know how a customs man may interpret a grin, especially a fixed grin.

Customs inspection is seldom as trying as you think it's going to be, unless you have a shoeful of diamonds or a trunk full of liqueurs. Just take your place under your proper letter (*Q* for Smith, *E* for Perkins, *P* for Thurber, and so forth) and see that you have assembled all your baggage. You will usually find that your typewriter case is missing and that you have a large grey suitcase that doesn't belong to you. The person who owns the grey suitcase may have your typewriter, and he may not. Don't get excited and rush around accusing people of stealing your Corona, just relax. You have all day, you know, and if you went to bed instead of to the bar after the Gala Revue, you will find yourself taking this ancient formality in your stride. It is important not to get mad at your inspector because he wants to go through your effects. That is his job. A Virginian I know, a man impatient of red tape and fiddle-faddle, as he describes all activities of the United States Government, once addressed a group of three customs inspectors as follows: 'Gentlemen, you are clearly insane.' He was the last man off the dock that day.

No travel hints would be complete without some word of caution about shipboard romances, engagements and marriages. The girl or young man you fell in love with on the ship when it was in Southern waters and the orchestra was playing *Night and Day* is going to be subjected to a cruel and rigorous test standing there by a gloomy pile of baggage in a bleak and chilly ship shed. If the swan suddenly becomes a goose, or the knight a clodhopper, it is what is known as 'undergoing a land change.' If you were married aboard ship and the bride, or bridegroom, now appeals to you about as much as a piece of cold whole-wheat toast, you are in a rather serious jam. In America you cannot have a marriage annulled on the ground that it was contracted while you were under the influence of the Gulf Stream and Cole Porter. If you are a man, I suggest that you treat your inamorata with a gallantry tempered by caution during the voyage out and back, and refrain from proposing until you have caught her on the dock. If she is going to be met by her mother and father, her Aunt Louise and her Uncle Bert, you will want to get a look at them first too. During the cruise try to engage the girl of your dreams in discussions of books or politics if you find yourself with her on the promenade deck in the moonlight, while the band is playing *I Told Every Little Star*. It won't work, but try it. All this, I suppose, is really no more concern of mine than why you keep fireworks in the house, so I will not pursue it further.

I hope that the foregoing helpful hints for a happy holiday will make your future sea voyages a little easier and merrier and safer. You need not, to be sure, take my advice or follow my example, in every situation and contretemps I have described hereinabove. If you want to put the shoe back on the sick lady's foot, or just leave it where you found it, feel free to do so. The reason I put the shoe on the table with the handbag was – but we have been all through that. I am beginning to repeat myself. Bon Voyage!

Lanterns and Lances

TO

ROSE ALGRANT

a lady with a lantern, who lights the
pathways of all of us lucky enough to
live where she lives, this book is dedicated with love, wonder and gratitude

Midnight at Tim's Place

'OLD sundials used to boast, in Latin, and I suppose a few in quiet gardens here and there still do, "*Horas non numero nisi serenas*" – "I count serene hours only".'

'*Et pourquoi pas?*' my wife asked vaguely.

It was our first night home after six months in Europe, and the hour at Tim's was late, and more melancholy than serene. We had just heard of the decline of several friends when the stranger with the empty highball glass and the Latin phrase hopped our table.

'My name is Warren Kirkfield,' he said unconvincingly, holding out a damp right hand.

'I bet his real name is Chase or Psst,' said the pretty young woman on my left. I didn't know who she was, or how she had got there. The newcomer ignored this.

'Sit down,' I said unwarmly. 'Urge up a footstool, loosen your stays, saucer your Scotch.'

'Don't be so cruel,' said my wife, moving over so Kirkfield could sit next to her, across the table from me and the fair unknown. 'Maybe he has a right to be sad – it's a free country. Maybe you can't always be *everything* in it, but you can be that.'

'No politics,' said the young woman, with the faintest of hiccups.

'My name is Keith Maitland,' I lied, 'and this is my wife, the former Geraldine Spinney. The lady on my left is a nameless waif out of the night, a poor windlestraw on the stream of time.'

'Ah thought you-all was Bing Crosby,' said the windlestraw, in a fake Dixie that was not too bad for one in her cups. Fake Dixie always enchants me after midnight. I prayed God to keep my hand off her knee.

'Everybody is in the groove tonight,' my wife explained. 'Everybody is just another Gabriel Heatter.'

Suddenly we all had a fresh drink. 'How are you, Bing?' asked Kirkfield, clinking his glass against mine.

'*Non sum qualis eram sub regno bony Sinatra,*' I said quickly, having waited for years to wedge that line in somewhere.

'You finally made it,' my wife said, for she knows all my lines, wedged and unwedged.

'You're just a goddam kissing bug,' the windlestraw told Kirkfield. 'I saw you.' She turned to me. 'I can't leave him alone a minute but what he's bending some girl over backward. This one had glasses and too much teeth.'

. 'I was being a gentleman,' protested Kirkfield. 'The lady had something in her eye.'

'What was it?' asked Mrs Kirkfield, for it was unquestionably she. 'A roguish twinkle?'

'I came here to tell these charming people a sad story, not to refight the war between the sexes,' Kirkfield said.

'Oh, my God! Not that story again,' said his wife.

I had lost interest in her knee. 'Go ahead, Maitland,' I said.

'Just call me plain Keith,' he murmured.

'The people at the next table must think they are losing their minds,' my wife put in.

'Or ours,' Mrs Kirkfield amended.

'Well, then,' Kirkfield began, 'I was on the edge of a nervous crackup last summer, for the usual variety of reasons – fear of death, fear of life, fear of the inhuman being. Also, I had just become forty-one, and realized that I only had nineteen years to live before I would begin to cackle.'

'I won't be there,' said his wife's voice, from inside her highball glass. 'He'll be bald as a beagle and his back will hurt and he'll babble about his conquex.'

'Quests,' my wife corrected her.

'You can say that again,' said Mrs Kirkfield.

'There was only one person I wanted to see, wanted to talk to,' Kirkfield went on. 'The greatest symbol of security in my life, the man who could pull me back from the doors of Hell, my old philosophy professor, Dr Pensinger. I had not seen him for five years, but for nearly twenty we had exchanged post-cards at Christmas and, because it amused him – you know how professors are – on Nietzsche's birthday.'

'I got to have more whisky to get through this again,' said his wife, and we got more whisky.

'Everybody, in college and afterwards, turned to Dr Pensinger for inspiration and consolation,' her husband went on. 'He had, and still has, some piece of unique philosophy for each special case. "You can keep a stiff upper lip, and smile, too," and "Don't let that chip on your shoulder be your only reason for walking erect." We always left Dr Pensinger's study with a high heart and renewed hope.'

'I just won't be there, that's all,' his wife cut in. 'Let him stomp his cane and yell his head off, for all I care. Give me a man like Gary Cooper or Harpo Marx, who doesn't talk for God's sake all the time.'

I touched her glass with mine, and said, 'Here's something in your eye, I hope.'

'Much he'd care if you did,' she said.

'Well, last summer, when I got the galloping jumps, I decided to call on Dr Pensinger and see if he could pull me out of it,' Kirkfield said. 'He lives in a charming house in Riverdale, and I drove up there one Sunday afternoon. His wife opened the door, and said, "We don't need anything today." Before she could shut the door, I told her who I was and why I was there, and she said

Dr Pensinger was in his study, and I could just go on in, and so I did. It was a terrifying visit. He had not changed a bit. He did not even seem a day older than the last time I had met him and listened to his cheering words. The same thoughtful blue eyes, the same reassuring smile, the same gentle voice.' Kirkfield took a great gulp of his highball.

'Then what was terrifying about the visit?' I asked.

Kirkfield lit a cigarette. 'He was wearing two hats,' he said. There was a long pause.

'In his study?' I asked.

'*Two* hats?' my wife asked, putting her realistic finger on the more incongruous fact.

'Two hats,' Kirkfield repeated. 'They were both grey felt hats, one on top of the other. The terrifying thing was that he didn't say anything about them. He just sat there with two hats on, trying to cheer me up.'

'I always say you can have too much philosophy,' Mrs Kirkfield said. 'It isn't good for you. It's disorganizing. Everybody's got to wake up sometime feeling that everything is terrible, because it is.'

'Couldn't you have said, "Pardon me, but you seem to be wearing two hats"?' my wife wanted to know.

'No, I couldn't,' said Kirkfield. 'I don't even remember how I got out of there. I had the chattering jitters. His wife showed me to the door, and said, "Did he buy anything? If he did, I'll simply send it back when it arrives".'

I thought it was time for another drink. We had all finished our last one very quickly.

'We never know what's going to happen to us,' my wife said.

'I don't care if my husband wears *three* hats,' his wife said. 'I won't be there.'

I had a sudden frightening vision of walking about the city in a few years, wearing only one shoe. Even my best friends, I realized, wouldn't mention it. I thought it was time to go home now, and stood up. My wife and I left the Kirkfields sitting there with four drinks, since we had not touched our new ones.

Tim helped me on with my overcoat, and handed me my hat, and we started to the door. One of the waiters came running after me, and handed me a hat. 'You left this the last time you were here,' he said. 'You went away without a hat that night.'

'Don't you dare!' my wife said, but I put the hat he gave me on top of the one I was wearing, and we went out into the street, and I whistled for a taxi. Pretty soon, one drove up and stopped, but when the driver saw that I was wearing two hats, he said, 'Not in this cab, Jack.' He was about to drive off when my wife opened the door and got in. 'I'll see you at the Algonquin,' she said, 'if you get that far.'

I stood there for a long while, and it began to rain. I walked back to the hotel in the rain.

The Last Clock

A Fable for the Time, such as it is, of Man

IN a country the other side of tomorrow, an ogre who had eaten a clock and had fallen into the habit of eating clocks was eating a clock in the clockroom of his castle when his ogress and their ilk knocked down the locked door and shook their hairy heads at him.

'Wulsa malla?' gurgled the ogre, for too much clock oil had turned all his 't's to 'l's.

'Just look at this room!' exclaimed the ogress, and they all looked at the room, the ogre with eyes as fogged as the headlights of an ancient limousine. The stone floor of the room was littered with fragments of dials, oily coils and springs, broken clock hands, and pieces of pendulums. 'I've brought a doctor to look at you,' the ogress said.

The doctor wore a black beard, carried a black bag, and gave the ogre a black look. 'This case is clearly not in my area,' he said.

The ogre struck three, and the doctor flushed.

'This is a case for a clockman,' the doctor said, 'for the problem is not what clocks have done to the ogre but what the ogre has done to clocks.'

'Wulsa malla?' the ogre gurgled again.

'Eating clocks has turned all his "t"s to "l"s,' the ogress said. 'That's what clocks have done to him.'

'Then your clockman may have to call in consultation a semanticist or a dictionist or an etymologist or a syntaxman,' the non-clock doctor said, and he bowed stiffly and left the room.

The next morning, the ogress brought into the clockroom a beardless man with a box of tools under his arm. 'I've brought a clockman to see you,' she told the ogre.

'No, no, no,' said the beardless man with the box of tools. 'I'm not a clockman. I thought you said clogman. I'm a clogman. I cannot ethically depart from my area, which is clogged drains and gutters. I get mice out of pipes, and bugs out of tubes, and moles out of tiles, and there my area ends.' The clogman bowed and went away.

'Wuld wuzzle?' the ogre wanted to know. He hiccuped, and something went *spong!*

'That was an area man, but the wrong area,' the ogress explained. 'I'll get a general practitioner.' And she went away and came back with a general practitioner.

'This is a waste of time,' he said. 'As a general practitioner, modern style, I treat only generals. This patient is not even a private. He sounds to me like a public place – a clock tower, perhaps, or a belfry.'

576

'What shall I do?' asked the ogress. 'Send for a tower man, or a belfry man?'

'I shall not venture an opinion,' the general practitioner said. 'I am a specialist in generals, one of whom has just lost command of his army and of all his faculties, and doesn't know what time it is. Good day.' And the general practitioner went away.

The ogre cracked a small clock, as if it were a large walnut, and began eating it. 'Wulsy wul?' the ogre asked.

The ogress, who could now talk clocktalk fluently, even oilily, but wouldn't, left the room to look up specialists in an enormous volume entitled 'Who's Who in Areas.' She soon became lost in a list of titles: clockmaker, clocksmith, clockwright, clockmonger, clockician, clockometrist, clockologist, and a hundred others dealing with clockness, clockism, clockship, clockdom, clockation, clockition, and clockhood.

The ogress decided to call on an old inspirationalist who had once advised her father not to worry about a giant he was worrying about. The inspirationalist had said to the ogress's father, 'Don't pay any attention to it, and it will go away.' And the ogress's father had paid no attention to it, and it had gone away, taking him with it, and this had pleased the ogress. The inspirationalist was now a very old man whose inspirationalism had become a jumble of mumble. 'The final experience should not be mummum,' he mumbled.

The ogress said, 'But what is mummum?'

'Mummum,' said the inspirationalist, 'is what the final experience should not be.' And he mumbled to a couch, lay down upon it, and fell asleep.

As the days went on, the ogre ate all the clocks in the town – mantel clocks, grandfather clocks, travelling clocks, stationary clocks, alarm clocks, eight-day clocks, steeple clocks, and tower clocks – sprinkling them with watches, as if the watches were salt and pepper, until there were no more watches. People overslept, and failed to go to work, or to church, or any place else where they had to be on time. Factories closed down, shopkeepers shut up their shops, schools did not open, trains no longer ran, and people stayed at home. The town council held an emergency meeting and its members arrived at all hours, and some did not show up at all.

A psychronologist was called to the witness stand to testify as to what should be done. 'This would appear to be a clear case of clock-eating, but we should not jump so easily to conclusions,' he said. 'We have no scientific data whatever on clock-eating, and hence no controlled observation. All things, as we know, are impossible in this most impossible of all impossible worlds. That being the case, no such thing as we think has happened could have happened. Thus the situation does not fall within the frame of my discipline. Good day, gentlemen.' The psychronologist glanced at where his wristwatch should have been and, not finding it there, was disturbed. 'I have less than no time at all,' he said, 'which means that I am late for my next appointment.' And he hurriedly left the council room.

The Lord Mayor of the town, arriving late to preside over the council meeting, called a clockonomist to the stand. 'What we have here,' said the clock-onomist, 'appears on the surface to be a clockonomic crisis. It is the direct opposite of what is known, in my field, as a glut of clocks. That is, instead of there being more clocks than the consumer needs, so that the price of clocks would decrease, the consumer has consumed all the clocks. This should send up the price of clocks sharply, but we are faced with the unique fact that there are no clocks. Now, as a clockonomist, my concern is the economy of clocks, but where there are no clocks there can be no such economy. The area, in short, has disappeared.'

'What do you suggest, then?' demanded the Lord Mayor.

'I suggest,' said the clockonomist, 'that it is now high time I go into some other line of endeavour, or transfer my clockonomy to a town which has clocks. Good day, gentlemen.' And the clockonomist left the council room.

A clockosopher next took the witness chair. 'If it is high time,' he said, 'then there is still time. The question is this: How high is high time? It means, if it means anything, which I doubt, that it is time to act. I am not an actor, gentle-men, but a clockosopher, whose osophy is based upon clocks, not necessarily upon their physical existence, but upon clocks as a concept. We still have clocks as a concept, but this meeting is concerned solely with clocks as objects. Thus its deliberations fall well outside my range of interest, and I am simply wasting time here, or would be if there were time to waste. Good day, gentle-men.' And the clockosopher left the council room.

The clockmakers of the town, who had been subpoenaed, were then en-joined, in a body, from making more clocks. 'You have been supplying the ogre with clocks,' the Lord Mayor said severely, 'whether intentionally or willy-nilly is irrelevant. You have been working hand in glove, or clock in hand, with the ogre.' The clockmakers left, to look for other work.

'I should like to solve this case by deporting the ogre,' the Lord Mayor said, 'but, as a container of clocks, he would have to be exported, not deported. Un-fortunately, the law is clear on this point: Clocks may not be exported in any save regulation containers, and the human body falls outside that legal definition.'

Three weeks to the day after the ogre had eaten the last clock, he fell ill and took to his bed, and the ogress sent for the chief diagnostician of the Medical Academy, a diagnostician familiar with so many areas that totality itself had become to him only a part of wholeness. 'The trouble is,' said the chief diagno-stician, 'we don't know what the trouble is. Nobody has ever eaten all the clocks before, so it is impossible to tell whether the patient has clockitis, clockosis, clockoma, or clocktheria. We are also faced with the possibility that there may be no such diseases. The patient may have one of the minor clock ailments, if there are any, such as clockets, clockles, clocking cough, ticking pox, or clumps. We shall have to develop area men who will find out about such areas, if such areas exist, which, until we find out that they do, we must assume do not.'

'What if he dies?' demanded the ogress eagerly.

'Then,' said the chief diagnostician, 'we shall bury him.' And the chief diagnostician left the ogre's room and the castle.

The case of the town's clocklessness was carried to the Supreme Council, presided over by the Supreme Magistrate. 'Who is prosecuting whom?' the Supreme Magistrate demanded.

The Supreme Prosecutor stood up. 'Let somebody say something, and I will object,' he said. 'We have to start somewhere, even if we start nowhere.'

A housewife took the witness stand. 'Without a clock,' she said, 'I cannot even boil a three-minute egg.'

'Objection,' said the Supreme Prosecutor. 'One does not *have* to boil a three-minute egg. A three-minute egg, by definition, has already been boiled for three minutes, or it wouldn't be a three-minute egg.'

'Objection sustained,' droned the Supreme Magistrate.

The Leader of the Opposition then took the stand. 'The party in power has caused the mess in the ogre's castle,' he said.

'Objection,' said the Supreme Prosecutor. 'There isn't any party in power. The ogre was the party in power, but he no longer has any power. Furthermore, the mess caused by the party cleaning up the mess caused by the party in power, which is no longer in power, would be worse than the mess left by the party that was in power.'

'Objection sustained,' droned the Supreme Magistrate.

The Secretary of the Status Quo was the next man to take the stand. 'We are not getting anywhere,' he said, 'and therefore we should call a summit conference without agenda. A summit conference without agenda is destined to get even less than nowhere, but its deliberations will impress those who are impressed by deliberations that get less than nowhere. This has unworked in the past, and it will unwork now. If we get less than nowhere fast enough, we shall more than hold our own, for everything is circular and cyclical, and where there are no clocks, clockwise and counterclockwise are the same.'

'Objection,' said the Supreme Prosecutor. 'We are dealing here with a purely internal matter, caused by the consumer's having consumed all the clocks.'

'Objection sustained,' droned the Supreme Magistrate.

The Man in the Street now took the stand. 'Why don't we use sundials?' he demanded.

'I challenge the existence of the witness,' said the Supreme Prosecutor. 'He says he is the Man in the Street, but he is, in fact, the Man in the Supreme Council Room. Furthermore, sundials work only when the sun is shining, and nobody cares what time it is when the sun is shining.'

The Man in the Street left the witness chair, and nobody noticed his going, since the Supreme Prosecutor had established the fact that he had not been there.

There was a long silence in the Supreme Council Room, a silence so deep one could have heard a pin drop, if a pin had been dropped, but nobody dropped a pin. What everybody in the Council Room heard, in the long, deep silence, was the slow tick-tock of a clock, a wall clock, the clock on the wall behind the Supreme Magistrate's bench. The officials and the witnesses and the spectators had grown so used to not hearing clocks it wasn't until the clock struck the hour that they realized there was a wall clock on the wall.

The Supreme Magistrate was the first to speak. 'Unless I am mightily mistaken, and I usually am, we have here the solution to all our problems,' he said, 'namely, a clock. Unless there is an objection and I sustain the objection, which I do not think I shall, we will place this clock in the clock tower of the town, where it can be seen by one and all. Then we shall once again know what time it is. The situation will be cleared up, and the case dismissed.'

'One minute,' said the Supreme Prosecutor, and everybody waited a minute until he spoke again. 'What is to prevent the ogre from eating the clock in the clock tower?'

'If you are asking me,' said the Supreme Magistrate, 'I do not know, but I do not have to confess my ignorance, since affirmations of this sort do not fall within my jurisdiction.'

A bailiff stepped to the bench and handed the Supreme Magistrate a folded note. The Magistrate glanced at it, took off his glasses, and addressed all those present. 'The ogre is dead,' he announced.

'Objection,' said the Supreme Prosecutor.

'Objection overruled,' said the Magistrate, 'if you are objecting to the fact of the ogre's death.'

'I accept the ogre's death as a fact,' said the Prosecutor, 'but we are moving too fast, and I should like to call a specialist to the stand.' And he called a specialist to the stand.

'I am a collector,' said the specialist. 'The clock on the wall is the only clock there is. This makes it not, in fact, a clock but a collector's item, or museum piece. As such, it must be placed in the town museum. One does not spend the coins in a museum. The wineglasses in a museum do not hold wine. The suits of armour in a museum do not contain knights. The clocks in a museum do not tell time. This clock, the last clock there is, must therefore be allowed to run down, and then placed in the museum, with proper ceremonies, addresses, and the like.'

'I move that this be done,' the Prosecutor said.

'I should like to continue to know, as much as everybody else, what time it is,' pronounced the Supreme Magistrate. 'Under the circumstances, however, there is but one thing I can do in conformity with the rule which establishes the inalienable fact that the last clock is a collector's item, or museum piece. I therefore decree that the last clock, the clock here on the wall, be allowed to run down, and then placed in the town museum, with proper ceremonies, addresses, and the like.'

The next day, at nine minutes of twelve o'clock noon, the last clock ran down and stopped. It was then placed in the town museum, as a collector's item, or museum piece, with proper ceremonies, addresses, and the like. Among those who spoke were the Lord Mayor, the Secretary of Status Quo, and the Supreme Magistrate. They all chose the same subjects, without verbs or predicates, and the subjects were these: glorious past, unlimited opportunity, challenging future, dedication, inspired leadership, enlightened followership, rededication, moral fibre, spiritual values, outer space, inner man, higher ideals, lower taxes, unflagging enthusiasm, unswerving devotion, co-ordinated efforts, dedicated rededication, and rededicated dedication.

After that, nobody in the town ever knew what time it was. Factories and schools remained closed, church bells no longer rang, because the bell ringers no longer knew when to ring them, dates and engagements were no longer made, because nobody knew when to keep them. Trains no longer ran, so nobody left town and no strangers arrived in town to tell the people what time it was. Eventually, the sands of a nearby desert moved slowly and inexorably towards the timeless town, and in the end it was buried.

Eras, epochs, and aeons passed before a party of explorers from another planet began digging in the sands above the buried town. They were descendants of people from Earth who had reached Venus a thousand years before and intermarried with Venusians. Among them were a young man and young woman, and it was their fortune to be the first to come upon the ancient library of the old inspirationalist. Among some papers still preserved upon his desk were the last things he had written – bits of poetry from the grand Old Masters and the minor poets. One of these fragments read, 'How goes the night, boy? The moomoon is down. I have not heard the clock.' And the very last words his wavery pen had put on paper:

> We can make our lives sublime,
> And, departing, leave behind us,
> Mummum in the sands of time.

'What is mummum?' the young woman asked.

'I don't know,' the young man said, 'but something tells me we shall find a lot of it.' They went on digging, and, in the end, came upon the last clock in the town museum, so clogged with sand they could not tell what it had once been used for, and so they marked it 'Antique mechanism. Function uncertain. Possibly known to the ancients as mummum.' And they took it back to Venus, in a cargo rocket ship, with other mysterious relics of the Time of Man on Earth.

A Moment with Mandy

'WHY didn't God make bats butterflies?' Mandy suddenly asked me one day. Her questions always demand a grave consideration which her impatience with the slow process of the adult mind will not tolerate. Mandy is eight, but I state her age with reservations because she is sometimes fourteen or older, and sometimes four or younger. 'I want to hang by my heels like a bat,' Mandy said, 'but I want to be a butterfly. Daddy couldn't spank me then because I would be on the ceiling.'

'He could get a stepladder,' I said finally.

'I would push it over,' she said. 'Bang!'

'He could call the fire department, of course,' I suggested.

'I would push that over, too,' Mandy said, adding, 'bang, bang!'

'Butterflies don't hang by their heels,' I told her, but she was off on another tack.

'God didn't have to give turtles shells,' she told me.

Here I thought I had her, but she does not corner easily in debate. 'Turtles are very slow,' I explained, 'and so God gave them shells they could hide in, to protect themselves from their enemies.'

'He could make them faster,' Mandy said. 'Why didn't He make them faster?' She had me there. I realized, for the first time, that if God had made porcupines and skunks faster, they wouldn't need their quills and vitriol, respectively.

'Why didn't God give us wings?' was her next question, and I began to lecture on that point.

'We have developed wings,' I told her, but she cut me off with that topic sentence.

'It took God a million billion years to give us wings,' she said. 'They are no good.' To this she added after a moment's thought, or half a moment's, 'We don't have anything.'

'We have better sight than dogs. People can see better than they can,' I told her.

'Dogs don't bump into things. People bump into things,' she said.

'Dogs are guided by better hearing and a better sense of smell than we have,' I explained.

'They can't see a light way way off,' was her answer to that.

'No, but when the man with the light gets nearer, they can hear him, and then they can smell him,' I told her.

She left me flat-footed with a quick passing shot. '*This* light doesn't get nearer, 'cause it's in a lighthouse.'

That annoyed me, for I am a bad loser. 'All right, all right, then,' I snapped.

'We'll move the dog nearer the lighthouse. Aren't you going to allow me to score a single point in this colloquy?'

Mandy has a standard answer for any questions she doesn't understand. 'No,' she said. 'Why didn't God give dogs glasses?'

For days I had been practising some questions of my own for Mandy, and I served them all at once. 'Why don't foxes wear foxgloves? Why don't cows wear cowslips? What was it Katy did? If cowboys round up cows, why don't bulldogs round up bulls?'

'Katy who?' Mandy asked, her quick feminine instinct for scandal making her ignore all the other questions.

'You're too young to know who she was and what she did, and I'm too old to care,' I said.

'My daddy says the bugs are going to get everybody.' Mandy repeated this prophetic piece of eschatology indifferently, as if it didn't matter.

'Your father was referring to a recent announcement by some scientists that insects are increasing alarmingly on this planet,' I told her. 'It is my opinion that they are increasing because they are alarmed by the steady increase of human beings.'

'I want a swan to get *me*,' Mandy said. 'What do you want to get *you*?'

I had to give this some thought. 'Bear with me,' I said. 'It isn't easy to decide. It would be colourful and exotic to be got by a green mamba in the Taj Mahal, but my friends would say I was just showing off, and such an ending would also be out of character. I shall probably stumble over my grandson's toy train and break my neck.'

Mandy, true to form, lobbed her next question over my head. 'What bear?' she said.

'I didn't say anything about a bear,' I said.

'You said there was a bear with you,' she said, 'but there isn't any.'

I went back over what I had said and found the bear, but ignored it. 'We are getting nowhere faster than usual,' I told her.

'What animal would you rather be?' was her next question. I must have been unconsciously preparing for this one.

'I have been a lot of animals,' I told her, 'but there are also a lot I haven't been. I was never a road hog or a snake in the grass, but I was once a news hound.'

'Once my daddy brought an Elk home to our house for dinner,' she said, 'but he was just a man.' She sighed, with the dark light of an old disenchantment in her eyes.

'Men hate to be called animals, but then they form lodges and luncheon clubs and call themselves animals – Elks, Moose, Eagles, Lions, and so on.' I was all set to go further with this line of attack or defence, but her interest, after her fashion, had wandered back. 'Why don't you want to be a road hog?' she demanded.

'Because they turn turtle, and then the bulls ride up on motor-cycles and arrest them.'

'Make up a nursery rhyme,' Mandy commanded me.

I pretended to be having a hard time making up a nursery rhyme, but my anguish was rigged, for I had made one up long ago for just such an emergency and I recited it:

> 'Half a mile from Haverstraw there lived a halfwit fellow,
> Half his house was brick and red, and half was wood and yellow;
> Half the town knew half his name but only half could spell it.
> If you will sit for half an hour, I've half a mind to tell it.'

'My daddy makes up nursery rhymes, too,' Mandy said. I felt sure her daddy's doggerel would top mine, and it did. 'Tell me one of them,' I said, and she did.

> 'Hi diddle diddle, the cat and the fiddle,
> Moscow jumped over the moon.'

'That isn't a nursery rhyme,' I told her. 'That is political science.'

'No, it isn't,' Mandy said.

'Yes, it is,' I said.

'No, it isn't,' she said.

'Yes, it is,' I said.

'No, it isn't,' she said.

It was at this point, or, to be exact, sword's point, that Mandy's mother and my wife (they are not the same person) entered the room and broke into the debate. 'You mustn't say it is if Mr Thurber says it isn't,' her mother told her.

'Are you two arguing again?' my wife wanted to know.

'No,' I told her. 'I was just explaining to Mandy that she shouldn't get her hopes up if she asks a bull on a motor-cycle the way to the next town, and he says, "Bear left at the church." There won't be any bear there.'

'Yes, there will,' Mandy said.

'No, there won't,' I said.

'Stop it,' my wife said. 'It's time to go.' We broke it up, but, at the door, I said to Mandy, 'Next time I'll explain why the wolf is at the door. It's on account of the stork.'

'There isn't any stork, if you mean babies,' Mandy said. I am sure she would have explained what she meant, in simple, childish dialectic, but my wife doesn't want me to know the facts of life. 'For heaven's sake come on!' she said, and roughly but mercifully dragged me out of there.

Moral: If it's words that you would bandy, never tangle with a Mandy.

The Tyranny of Trivia

AN INTREPID young literary explorer named Otto Friedrich recently stumbled upon the body of my work lying sprawled and unburied on the plain, and was distressed to discover that it had been ravaged by trivia. Mr Friedrich thinks that preoccupation with trivia is unbecoming in a writer who belongs to the Solemn if not, indeed, the Sombre tradition of American letters. (How do you like it now, gentlemen?) The critic, whose findings appeared in a periodical called *Discovery*, detected what he called my need to write trivia, and shrewdly coupled it with 'a constant need to make money.' By trivia, the author meant the minor and the unimportant (unless I misread him, he included sex in this category), and not grammar, logic, and rhetoric, the big trivia of the dictionary definitions of the word.

I could begin by insisting that Mr Friedrich has confused my armour with its chink, but this might lead to an intricate and turgid flow of metaphor. It is simpler to say, in another figure, that Trivia Mundi has always been as dear and as necessary to me as her bigger and more glamorous sister, Gloria. They have both long and amicably inhabited a phrase of Coleridge's, 'All things both great and small,' and I like to think of them taking turns at shooting albatrosses and playing the bassoon.

Some notable trivia, such as the last straw, the lost horseshoe nail, and a piece of string, became involved with larger issues, but my own, I am afraid, never rise to such heights. They consist mainly of a preoccupation, compulsive perhaps, but not obsessive, with words and the alphabet, and most of them never get into print. Their purpose is the side-tracking of worrisome trains of thought. The modern mind has many shuttles and shuntings, the principal one being, I suppose, the reading of mystery novels in bed, to shut out the terrors of the night and the world. Profound thought or plain positive thinking does not conduce to repose. Every man, laying his book aside, still has the night and the world to by-pass. The late Bert Leston Taylor used to find comfort in contemplating Canopus, 'a star that has no parallax to speak of.' I happen to get cold up there in the immeasurable spaces of the outer constellations, and my own system of mental sedation is more mundane.

Some may ward off insomnia by reciting poetry to themselves, such as Tennyson's 'The moan of doves in immemorial elms, and murmuring of innumerable bees.' But this has never worked for me, because I invariably begin to take the lines of a poem apart. A friend of mine, fighting off the bells of Poe and avoiding the thickets of Eliot, manages to doze off after several repetitions of, to set it down in a long ramble, 'In Xanadu did Kubla Khan a stately pleasure dome decree, where Alph the sacred river ran through caverns measureless to man down to a sunless sea.' I tried that several times, discovered the solitary long O in 'dome,' the six consecutive words containing R, and the last seven R-less words. The dome seemed to stick up a mile above the sunless sea, the rolling Rs trickled away, and I was left stranded in a desiccation of '. . . to man down to a sunless sea.'

A mariner so easily marooned in a wasteland of verse finds himself turning away from, say, the lines of Shakespeare that end '. . . . how like a god' and towards the old Ed Wynn gag that begins, 'How would you like to die?' If you don't happen to remember it, a group of murderous gangsters, armed with everything lethal, from a hangman's rope to an enormous bottle of poison, propounded the question to the great comedian. 'In Gloria Swanson's arms' was Mr Wynn's prompt and wistful reply.

I was laughing about that ancient routine a few years ago while lying in a hospital bed, and my alarmed nurse asked me what was the matter. My solitary laughter has always alarmed my nurses, of whom I have had more than twenty since the silent artillery of time began firing at me. I told this particular nurse what I was laughing about, and she thought it over solemnly for a moment. 'Well,' she said finally, 'to me she is every bit as attractive now as she was when I first saw her in a silent film about the French Foreign Legion.' She pronounced the last word as if it were 'lesion.' And here I am again, in the midst of verbal trivia. Nurses' verbal trivia, however, are the very best trivia, and rank high in my collection. I remember a Canadian nurse who read aloud to me from some book or other '. . . that first fine careless rupture,' and another who shook me for several long moments one day in 1940 when, in reading aloud from the 'Books' department of an erudite journal, she paused to remark that there were notices of eight books about Mussolini. She had come upon, it turned out, a list of short reviews headed 'Miscellany.' Nurses are wonderful women and dedicated ministering angels, and they have no time to fritter away on the trivia of spelling and pronunciation.

When a patient is lying at right angles to his nurses and doctors and visitors, and considerably lower – in more ways than one – than all of them, he is in the standard posture for the onset of trivia. I have no doubt that many a dark, serious book has been conceived on a bed, but surely few of them will outlast the wonderful description of wallpaper that was born in the mind of Reginald Gardiner when he lay parallel to the floor and at right angles to everybody. The temper of the supine patient, particularly the post-operative, is capricious and unpredictable, and forms one of the best arguments for the theory and practice of minimum bed rest. My own habit, in bed at home or in the hospital, of exploring words and the alphabet acts to prevent my talking back to the wallpaper, a practice that, except in the case of the upright figure, may be more alarming than amusing.

Most of my hospitalizations were during the war years, when nurses were on twelve-hour shifts – a long time to spend alone with me, especially at night.

Many nurses go on the night shift because it is supposed to be easier, but at least one of mine later asked to be transferred to day duty. Nurses, because of their tight and highly specialized vocabulary, are not very good at word games. When I told one apprehensive nurse, around midnight, that only seven capital letters are wholly or partially enclosed – A, B, D, O, P, Q, and R – she promptly printed the entire alphabet on a sheet of paper and told me that H, K, M, N, W, and X are also partially enclosed. She had, you see, set them down squarely on the lines of a sheet of ruled paper. Nurses live by rule and line, and they cannot think of anything as hanging in the circumambient mental air. Occasionally, when I hung a concept there for one of them, she would tiptoe from the room and bring in the night resident doctor. 'This patient,' as I used to be called with a trace of irritation, was set down as atypical, without significance or syndrome.

One night I asked my nurse if she could think of a seven-letter word in which the letter U appears three times. She sighed and said, 'It's probably unusual.' I told her that it was and it wasn't, and she slipped out of the room, and a short time later Dr Conway came in. My doctors always approach my bedside with an air of bluff insincerity, sometimes humming a tune nervously, in an unsuccessful effort to imitate casualness. I asked Dr Conway if he could find the other six-letter word in suture. 'It's right up your alley, but then again it certainly isn't,' I told him. An hour later he came back to say that he couldn't find it, and I had to spell it out for him.

Before many days I had Dr Conway lying awake trying to find a word in which all five vowels appear in order. Even when I told him that three of the vowels come in direct sequence he couldn't get it. Among such words, to release your own mind for more profitable researches, are 'facetious' and 'abstemious.' Doctors go to bed – when they can, which isn't often – in the fond and sometimes desperate hope that they will be able to sleep, and the letters of the alphabet that visit their overburdened minds are cogent ones in familiar combinations, such as T.B. and E.S.P. It occurred to me that Dr Conway, who had a hard time sleeping, might benefit by thinking dreamily of the letter Y and the soporific words for which it stands – yore and yarrow, youth and yesterday. Doctors, however, traditionally hunt for trouble, and all that Dr Conway got out of Y was its noisy category of yammer and yell, yowl and yelp. This worried me, and I suddenly began thinking of myself as doctor and Conway as patient.

'N is probably the letter for you,' I told him, 'and I'm sorry I didn't prescribe it. But you know how it is; we have to proceed with each subject, or patient, by a process of trial and error. Some persons are nauseated by an injection of codeine – but react well to demerol. N should be fine for doctors of your temperament, because it is the letter of nowhere and never, novocain and nicotine and narcotic. If you drift into nightmare and nightshade instead of nightingale and narcissus, it is significant but not necessarily alarming. I worry about my doctors when they are undergoing alphabetical sedation only if they exhibit a tendency to slip too easily from nocturne and Nepenthe into some such sequelae as ninety naked night nurses.' Dr Conway seemed rather more

v

disturbed than amused by my analysis of his association problems. 'I don't know enough words beginning with N to get very far,' he said.

'N doesn't have very many words,' I said soothingly. 'Practically nothing edible begins with N and there are almost no animals at all to keep you awake. So you won't lie there yearning for something to eat or worrying about beasts on the prowl. The newt and the narwhal cannot be said to prowl, but think of the animals that inhabit both sides of N, in M and O. The first has many creatures, from the mastodon to the mouse, and the second has an oppressively oleaginous company of oozy things, from the octopus to the oyster. But in N your consciousness is nurtured by the letter of Nineveh and Nirvana, No Man's Land and nomad, Nemo and Nod.' Dr Conway didn't say anything, he just went away. I understand that he takes sleeping pills now in order to sleep, and tries to think of nothing, including N.

I was perfectly content with my aimless wanderings in the avenues and lanes of the alphabet until Mr Friedrich brought up the factor of value, or worthwhileness. When Dr Alfred North Whitehead died, the *New York Times* described him as 'a supreme adventurer in the realm of the mind.' And now I am afraid that in its little piece about my own passing that great newspaper may refer to me as 'just another vagabond in the backwoods of the imagination.' This has taken the edge off my supine meanderings and given my dreams a nasty turn. In one of them I was being hunted down like a deer in a wooded wilderness. Men like Bertrand Russell, another supreme adventurer in the realm of the mind, kept firing at me from cover. In something of a panic, I have recently been trying to give my nocturnal thoughts at least the semblance of importance. So far this has merely had the effect of making them a little stuffy. Whereas I used to drop off to sleep while looking for quiet characters in B, I now find myself trying to discover something significant in the curious ambivalence, the antipathy-affinity of C and M.

Most of the characters in B, to get back to them for a moment, murder sleep: the bugler, braggart, blowhard, blatherskite, barber, bowler, barker, booster, bouncer, bruiser, and so on. But their broken-bottle bar-room brawling, bombast, bluster, and blockbusting bombardment of Babel and Bedlam die down when you come upon the subdued figures of the only truly quiet characters in the second letter of the alphabet – the butler, the bridegroom, and the burglar. The first night I came upon them, whispering and tiptoeing in the corridors of B, I fell asleep almost instantly. Now I lie awake for hours, staring at the ceiling, becoming more and more involved in what may easily turn out to be the utterly meaningless relationship of C and M. On the other hand, it is just barely possible that I have got the tips of my fingers on a valid and valuable discovery in the field of alphabetical relativity. I began, simply enough, with the discovery that C and M contain some of the greatest traditional antipathetical entities of fact and fiction – cat and mouse, cobra and mongoose, Capulet and Montague. From there I went on to explore certain other tragic associations of the two letters, Mary Celeste, Morro Castle, McKinley and Czolgosz, and Marat and Corday. I tried to get out of the darker side of the combination by thinking of Madonna and Child, Maurice Chevalier, and Christy Mathewson, but then I became wide awake and a little sweaty with Chamberlain and Munich, and Capitalism and Marxism, from which it was a simple mental journey to Christian and Moslem, civil and military, celibacy and marriage, church and monarchy, classical and modern, chemical and mechanical, mundane and cosmic. My mind had no sooner calmed itself with magic carpet than it leaped even wider awake with the Caine Mutiny and the Caine Mutiny Court Martial. I soon realized, as I turned on the lights and lit a cigarette, that C-M clearly militates against that relaxation of posture and thought which leads to unconsciousness. I got into dozens of conjunctions of the two letters – Mark and Cleopatra, Candida and Marchbanks, malice and charity, cow and moon, moth and cloth, mountain and climber, cadets and midshipmen, Monroe and colonization, and Custer and massacre. I began thinking of Charles Martel, who checked the Moors, but found this unrelaxing and tried to settle back in a cosy mental Morris chair. And suddenly I was in the midst of Martini cocktail, maraschino cherry, cockles and mussels, mutton chop, Château Margaux, mulled cider, Martell cognac, chocolate mousse, and Moët et Chandon. This naturally brought on cholera morbus. (Incidentally, the cholera morbus that killed President Zachary Taylor was caused by a surfeit of milk and cherries.) I don't know how I finally managed sleep; perhaps it was by thinking of the triumphs of the Count of Monte Cristo, or the whirling wheels of Monte Carlo, but my unconsciousness did not last long and my dreams were troubled. In one of them I was suddenly enfiladed by the rifle fire of the Coys and McHatfields. This distortion brought me so wide awake that I had to get up and dress.

A few nights later, having resolutely shaken C-M from my mind, I turned to S and W in the hope that the combination would be soft and winsome, soporific and wistful, but there is definitely a dark basic twist in my mental processes somewhwere, for I abruptly shifted from a momentary contemplation of Sweet Williams to storm warning, sou'wester, windstorm, waterspout, and shipwreck. I made a hasty grab for E, with its ease, ephemera, and evanescence, and then found myself, to my dismay, in the endless, eternal, everlasting, energetic enterprise and endeavour of the most restless letter of all twenty-six. Once you get into the explorations, examinations, excavations, and elaborate edifices of E, a tranquil mind is impossible. If you make the mistake of turning in desperation to D, you are even more disconcerted, for its doves, desires, and dreams give way almost at once to its terrible atmosphere of doubt, dread, decline, derangement, decay, dissolution, degradation, and its dire, dismal disease, doom, and dusty death. If you contemplate the thousand depressing words that begin with D, you will understand why it was necessary to follow delightful and delicious with delovely in the Cole Porter song lyric. There just aren't three genuine three-syllable words that would fit into the mood of ecstasy, so one had to be invented. If from this dark, dolorous, demented, destructive, desperate, and demoniac letter you look for serenity in F, you find yourself in both the frying pan and the fire. F is the letter of falter, foozle, flunk, flop, flaw, feeble, flounder, fall, flat, and failure, of fake, fallacious, flim-flam, fishy, fib, fob, foist, forgery, facsimile, and fabrication. The fox of its fox-fire is not a fox, and the fire is not fire. Even its fleabane is often false. It is the flimsy, fluttery, finicky, frantic, frenetic, feverish headquarters of flibberti-gibbet, fuddyduddy, fogey, fossil, fourflusher, frustrated female, and flabber-gasted fussbudget. To sports it brings foul, fault, footfault, fumble, and for-feit. Its fineness and finesse have a filigree frailty, and a furry fungus blurs its focus, making it filmy, fuzzy, and foggy. When you come upon fame, family, fortune, and faith in these surroundings, they have a faint, furtive, fragile, and almost fictitious feeling. F brings the fingers to butterfingers, the fly to fly-by-night, the flash to flash-in-the-pan, and the forsaken to godforsaken. Its friend is too close to fiend for comfort, and it is not reassuring to realize that our finances and future keep such fearful, fitful, fretful, and fantastic company. F is so flagrantly flagitious and so flamboyantly flexuous that it might easily drive any patient to floccillation, or at least make him want to rush out and flense a whale with a fleam. If its fizzle doesn't get us, its fission may.

G, if you are still with me, is no longer the most gruesome, gloomy, and gory letter; its terrors have become old-fashioned with the passing of the centuries and the development of modern man. The things that go bump in G would no longer frighten even Goldilocks, for who is afraid nowadays of ghouls, ghosts, goblins, giants, gargoyles, griffins, gorgons, or Gargantua and Goliath? If you want to get hell's own heebie-jeebies take H. This Century of Violence has in-vented new words and combinations of words and thrown a greenish light on old ones to point up its hellions and horrors, and most of them begin with H: hoodlum, hooligan, heel, hooch, heroin, hitch-hiker, hot-rod, hijacker, hold-up, hop-head, hipped, hideout, hatchet-man, higher-up, hangover, hooker, homicide, homosexual, hydrogen, halitosis, hysteria, and Hollywood.

I don't know whether or not psychiatry has explored the diagnostic poten-tial of what it would surely call, and perhaps already has, letter stimulus and word response. A simple way to measure the degree of apprehension, or *Angst*, in a patient who keeps looking over his shoulder or glancing into the sky would be the C-test or the T-test. I tried both of them on myself one night, with de-pressing results. All hell broke loose in each of them without warning. C has almost as many words of calm and comfort as of crisis and conflict, and the well-balanced psyche should be able to fall asleep while still in the category of anodyne, before the bells of alarm have begun to ring. I started out plea-santly and restfully one night like this: carillon, caroller, cavalcade, carriages, cobblestone, clip-clop, countryside, chickadee, candytuft, chimney corner, cricket, chessmen, cider, chestnuts. Then the trouble began, for C is the letter of catcall, curse, calumny, and contumely. I suddenly found myself in the midst of a loud-mouthed exchange of epithets and insults, from the old-fashioned cad and cockalorum up to the present-day card-carrying Commu-nist conspirator and cockeyed Congressional-committee chairman. (If you can't fill in forty others, from clodhopper to creep, you are out of touch with your times.) The imprecations I had bumped into in C after such a serene start instantly led to creak, crack, crumple, crumble, collapse, crash, conflagration, consternation, confusion, cyclone, collision, calamity, catastrophe, cataclysm, and chaos. Anybody who can doze off while still thinking of clover, candle, comforter, clock, and chime is living in the alphabetical past, and his state of mind is probably even more indicative of derangement than my own.

There isn't a thing C can do that T cannot equal or surpass. I forget just how I started out in this promising letter of time and truth, but in a flash I was wandering among turtles and toadstools, and then I came to the tiny termite and what happened was far more terrible than the crack-up in the chimney corner of C: tremble, teeter-totter, tower, tremor, trembler, television, telephone, telegraph, transmission, topple, tumble, twist, topsy-turvy, tumult, turbulent, turmoil, thunder, tempest, tornado, tropical, typhoon, terror, tantrum, tirade, tailspin, traffic tie-up, train, taxi, truck, trolley, tram, terminal, trouble, trial, tears, tribulation, torment, torture, triumph. (I don't know how that triumph got in there, but probably my consciousness had taken as much as it could.)

It is my intention to be helpful as possible to my neighbours at the corner of Dread and Jeopardy, and I suggest that they play around in P before venturing into more menacing letters. P is a rather silly letter, given to repeating itself, and to a strange assortment of games: ping-pong, polo, pool, poker, pedro, pinochle, parcheesi, pussy-wants-a-corner, post office, and pillow. The sixteenth letter of the alphabet has many pixies, great and small: Puck, Pan, Pandora, Peter Pan, Pinocchio, Pollyanna, Puss in Boots, and the Pooh. No other letter is quite so addicted to the vice of alliteration, and it is possible that no writer has ever lived who did not think up and mull over in his mind at least one title in the same category as *Pilgrim's Progress*, *Pippa Passes*, *Pied Piper*, *Pickwick Papers*, *Peterkin Papers*, *Pride and Prejudice*, *Prince and Pauper*, *Poet and Peasant*, *Pit and Pendulum*, *Peacock Pie*, *Potash and Perlmutter*, and so on, and on, and on, back through the ages. I once made up a little man named Pendly in the early years of my constant need to make money, and for some reason or other, no longer clear to me, I invented the name of a make of automobile in the same story. Naturally, I fell into the facile trap of repeating the P in the title of the story, which came out 'Mr Pendly and the Poindexter'. It is because of this confounded tendency that our language is spotted with such expressions as pooh-pooh, pitter-patter, pish-posh, pompon, pretty please, post-prandial, party politics, pumpkin papers, pink pills, pale people, pip-pip, pawpaw, papa, and the awful like.

In conclusion – all this thin slicing is getting us nowhere – easily the most fecund and probably the least frightening combination of letters is S-P. I have been working on it for years, off and on, and it has taken me from Stony Point to Seven Pines and from swimming pool to South Pacific, with hundreds of stop-offs along the way. To games, for example, it has given southpaw, screen pass, short putt, set point, shot put, Sunday punch, and 'sorry partner'. Nothing has leaped out of this union to scale my pyjamas off or to keep me awake very long. Right now, however, I am finding it a somnolent experience to wander in W, with its wilderness, Wonderland, wabe, wildwood, and Woodland of Weir. If you're lucky you can stay with nothing worse than witches and warlocks until the sandman gets you.

Pleasant dreams.

The Wings of Henry James

ONE night nearly thirty years ago, in a legendary New York *boîte de nuit et des arts* called Tony's, I was taking part in a running literary gun fight that had begun with a derogatory or complimentary remark somebody made about something, when one of the participants, former Pinkerton man Dashiell Hammett, whose *The Maltese Falcon* had come out a couple of years before, suddenly startled us all by announcing that his writing had been influenced by Henry James's novel *The Wings of the Dove*. Nothing surprises me any more, but I couldn't have been more surprised than if Humphrey Bogart, another frequenter of that old salon of wassail and debate, had proclaimed that his acting bore the deep impress of the histrionic art of Maude Adams.

I was unable, in a recent reinvestigation, to find many feathers of 'The Dove' in the claws of 'The Falcon', but there are a few 'faint, far' (as James used to say) resemblances. In both novels, a fabulous fortune – jewels in 'The Falcon', inherited millions in 'The Dove' – shapes the destinies of the disenchanted central characters; James's designing woman Kate Croy, like Hammett's pistol-packing babe, Brigid O'Shaughnessy, loses her lover, although James's Renunciation Scene is managed, as who should say, rather more exquisitely than Hammett's, in which Sam Spade speaks these sweetly sorrowful parting words: 'You angel! Well, if you get a good break you'll be out of San Quentin in twenty years and you can come back to me then.' Whereupon he turns her over to the cops for the murder of his partner, Miles Archer (a good old Henry James name, that). Some strong young literary excavator may one day dig up other parallels, but I suggest that he avoid trying to relate the character in 'The Falcon' called Cairo to James's early intention to use Cairo, instead of Venice, as the major setting of his novel. That is simply, as who should not say, one of those rococo coincidences.

The Wings of the Dove is now fifty-eight years old, but it still flies on, outward bound for the troubled future. Since 1902, it has become a kind of *femme fatale* of literature, exerting a curiously compelling effect upon authors, critics, playwrights, producers, and publishers. Seemingly, almost every playwright, from hack to first-rate talent, has been burned by the drama that glows within the novel's celebrated triangle, and has taken a swing at adapting it for stage or screen, usually with less than no success. It was James's own original intention to present his plot and characters in play form, but guardian angel or artist's insight caused him wisely to refrain from diverting into the theatre his delicately flowering, slowly proliferating history of fine consciences, which belongs so clearly between covers and not between curtains.

This doesn't keep people from adapting it, though. In 1956, Guy Bolton made a play out of it, *Child of Fortune*, which was produced on Broadway by the usually canny Jed Harris, who had earlier touched with art ('art schmart,' he himself once disdainfully called it) his directing of *The Heiress*, based on Henry James's novel *Washington Square*. The Bolton 'Dove' died miserably after twenty-three performances. That debacle did not deter television's 'Playhouse 90' from having a go at dramatizing the novel just last year. This adaptation, made by a young man named Meade Roberts, seemed to me closer to the James tone and mood, closer to perfection of total production, than any other dramatization I have seen, and I have seen plenty. (The first one I ever encountered was shown to me by a young professor of English in Ohio forty-one years ago.) The success of 'The Dove' on television lay in a discipline that gave it Henry James's key and pitch, if not his depth and range. Because my sight has failed, I could not see Inga Swenson, who played Milly, and this was probably fortunate, since I was told she looked as healthy as one of Thomas Hardy's milkmaids. But her words fell persuasively upon the ear, and she was the dying Milly to me. The direction gave the play a proper unhurried pace ('sluggish,' wrote one restless newspaper critic), and there were moving off-stage effects – the sound of distant bells in one scene, the haunting cry of gondoliers in another.

In my own college years, 1913–17, the literature courses in the modern English novel that were offered west of the Alleghenies included Hardy and Meredith, and sometimes Trollope, Samuel Butler, and Conrad, but rarely James. My own professor in this field, the late Joseph Russell Taylor, of Ohio State, rated James higher than the rest, and assigned *The Wings of the Dove* as required class reading, with this admonition: 'If you can't make anything at all out of the first hundred pages, don't let it worry you.' It was James's method to introduce his principal characters late, or, as John McNulty once put it, 'to creep up on them in his stocking feet.' Since only about one student in every thirty could stand, or understand, Henry James's writing, there were few persons with whom you could discuss the Old Master in those years. It was in 1930 that the Modern Library first introduced Henry James to its readers, with its edition of *The Turn of the Screw*, which has sold to date ninety thousand copies. The so-called Henry James Revival did not take place until the nineteen-forties, and centred on the hundredth anniversary of his birth. In 1946, the Modern Library brought out *The Wings of the Dove*, which has sold more than forty-one thousand copies. In 1958, 'The Dove' lost its American copyright and fell into the public domain, and in January, 1959, Dell's Laurel edition of paperbacks printed seventy-five thousand copies of the novel, a little more than two-thirds of which either were sold or are out on the news-stands or in the bookstores.

The James Revival deserves the capital 'R,' because the increased sales of his books and the rapidly expanding literature on the man and his life and his work began crowding library shelves all over the country. In 1932, I bought the complete 1922 edition of James, issued by Macmillan of London, but it had not been easy to find. It was available in no New York bookstore then, and I finally got my set through a collector. It came from a private library on Park Avenue, which was then being sold, and not a single page of any of the more than thirty volumes had been cut. It was as if the owner of this particular edition had said, 'I want to buy about two and a half or three feet of the works of Henry James.' Interest in the Revival spread from Broadway to Hollywood. For years, David O. Selznick held the movie rights to 'The Dove', but he never produced an adaptation of the novel, unquestionably because of the difficulty of casting the three principal roles and of finding an adapter who could satisfactorily cope with the dramatization.

This seems the right place to describe briefly the 'game', as James called it, that is afoot in his masterpiece.

Kate Croy, then, an ambitious young Englishwoman, emotionally intense and deeply amorous (James dresses her in such words as 'ardour', 'desire', and 'passion'), is eager to marry a struggling young writer and journalist, Merton Densher in the novel but, mercifully, Miles Enshaw in the television play. Having developed, because of a penniless life with a wastrel father, what would now be called a neurosis or psychosis, Kate, with her 'talent for life', is determined to enjoy money and marriage, and neither without the other. Into her predicament and preoccupation drifts the American girl, Milly Theale, attractive, enormously wealthy, naïve, and genuine, but perceptive ('mobile of mind'), in the best Henry James tradition, and dying. She falls in love with Densher, and the possessed, designing Kate perceives how she can use Milly's situation for her own selfish ends. She deliberately throws Milly and Densher together in Venice, and then reveals her scheme to him. He shall marry Milly, thus killing, you might say, two doves with one stone – Milly's final months on earth will be made happy ones, after which Kate and Densher will live happily ever after on the dead bride's millions. But Milly, again true to the James tradition of innocent American girls entangled in European society intrigue, discovers the true situation – that Kate is in love with and secretly engaged to Densher and that Densher is in love with Kate. Milly dies and, in her 'copious will', leaves much of her wealth to the lovers, but they can never be happy with it, or without it. They are shadowed and separated forever by the wings of the dead dove, by the presence of a girl who is gone but everlastingly there.

Lest my oversimplification in this summary cause the ghost of Henry James to pace and mutter, I shall let him insert here a typical elucidation of the 'conspiracy' of Kate and Merton: 'The picture constituted, so far as may be, is that of a pair of natures well-nigh consumed by a sense of their intimate affinity and congruity, the reciprocity of their desire, and thus passionately impatient of barriers and delays, yet with qualities of intelligence and character that they are meanwhile extraordinarily able to draw upon for the enrichment of their relation, the extension of their prospect and the support of their "game".'

There has probably been no other major novelist whose work has been so often criticized not so much for what it is but for what certain critics think it should have been. One critic, whose name I do not know, becoming impatient of the carpers, once said that they criticized Henry James as they might criticize a cat for not being a dog. These carpers are given to attacking, at the same time, the involved James style and his viewpoint on love, sex, women, affairs, and marriage. One reviewer of the 'Playhouse 90' production insisted that no woman as passionately in love as Kate would hand her lover over to another woman, even temporarily, however great the promised compensation. The sensitive novelist never got used to the assaults upon him – understandably enough, for many of them were brutal. He was accused of 'bombinating in a vacuum' and, by H. G. Wells, of labouring like a hippopotamus trying to pick up a pea. It was not a pea but a pearl, a James defender pointed out, and the hippopotamus had unbelievably skilful fingers.

As James's novels everywhere show, and his prefaces repeatedly declaim, he was caught unceasingly between the urge to 'dramatize! dramatize!' and his passion for indirection – an ambivalence that must present both challenge and handicap to the adapter, however ingenious, of his work. In the last chapter of 'The Dove', James observes that walks taken by Kate and Densher were 'more remarkable for what they didn't say than for what they did.' The book ends with a hopeless headshake by Kate and then the final speech, 'We shall never be again as we were!', which is scarcely the way a born dramatist would bring down his third-act curtain. And what can the helpless adapter do when confronted, as he frequently is, by such lines as this: 'The need to bury in the dark blindness of each other's arms the knowledge of each other that they couldn't undo.' Incidentally, few artists with the physical ability to see appreciate the truth known to all those without sight, that there is a dark blindness and a lighted blindness. Henry James was at home in the dark and in the light and in the shadows that lie between.

The theme of 'The Dove' had germinated in what Edmund Wilson has called James's 'marvellous intelligence' (and Wells his 'immensely abundant brain') upon the death of a first cousin extremely dear to him, Minny Temple, who departed his world and our world (they are in many ways distinctly different) at the age of twenty-four. He became so absorbed in his theme that he was moved to prefigure Milly's death as dragging everybody and everything down with it, like a great ship sinking or a big business collapsing. This massive contemplation of effect belongs to the mind and scheme of the novelist, but it can't very well be encompassed in a dramatization, because one can't get stream of consciousness into a three-act play. It is a commonplace of the ordeal of Henry James that the presentation of his work on the stage, to which he devoted many years, has been invariably better managed in the theatre by other hands than his own. A few years ago, *The Turn of the Screw* was turned into *The Innocents*, and much earlier the unfinished novel *The Sense of the Past* shone upon the stage as *Berkeley Square*. Among the failures on Broadway ('It didn't just close, it flew closed,' said Richard Maney) was an adaptation, nearly four years ago, of James's *The Europeans*, called *Eugenia* and starring Tallulah Bankhead, of whom Louis Kronenberger wrote, in a preface to his

Best Plays of 1956–57, 'only Mae West as Snow White could have seemed more unsuited to a part.' Finding an actress, however gifted, who can play a Henry James woman convincingly must be a nightmare to any producer. One such rare lady is Flora Robson, who starred in London as Tina in Sir Michael Redgrave's recent dramatization of *The Aspern Papers*, a substantial hit and, I am told by a man who has seen them all, the finest presentation of a James work ever brought to the stage.

It had always seemed a wonder to me, until I got involved myself, that practically everybody wanted to write about 'The Dove'. In the preface to the new paperback edition, R. P. Blackmur says, 'By great luck I had been introduced simply and directly, and had responded in the same way, to what a vast number of people have thought an impossible novel by an impossible author and a vast number of other people have submitted to the stupefying idolatry of both gross and fine over-interpretation.' Recently, Dr Saul Rosenzweig, a psychologist and student of Henry James, dug up the opinion of the novelist-psychiatrist Dr S. Weir Mitchell: 'I have read his [H.J.'s] last book with bewildered amazement. Since I played cat's cradle as a child, I have seen no tangle like it. To get the threads of his thought off his mind on to mine with the intermediation of his too exasperating style has been too much for me. A friend of mine says his "Wings of a Dove" [*sic*] are unlike any dove she ever saw, for it has neither head nor tail. However, I am too old to learn a new language and still struggle to write my own with clearness.'

Dr Rosenzweig discovered a reply to the Mitchell objections in the correspondence of Owen Wister, creator of *The Virginian* and of the sundown gun duel on the deserted Western main street. 'Henry James is in essence inscrutable,' Wister wrote to Mitchell, 'but one thing of him I know: our language has no artist more serious or austere at this moment. I explain to myself his bewildering style thus: he is attempting the impossible with it – a certain very particular form of the impossible; namely, to produce upon the reader, as a painting produces upon the gazer, a number of superimposed, simultaneous impressions. He would like to put several sentences on top of each other so that you could read them all at once, and get all at once the various shadings and complexities, instead of getting them consecutively as the mechanical nature of his medium compels. This I am sure is the secret of his involved parentheses, his strangely injected adverbs, the whole structure, in short, of his twisted syntax. One grows used to it by persisting. I read *The Ambassadors* twice, and like it amazingly as a prodigy of skill. One other thing of signal importance is a key to his later books. He does not undertake to tell a story but to deal with a situation, a single situation. Beginning (in his scheme) at the centre of this situation, he works outward, intricately and exhaustively, spinning his web around every part of the situation, every little necessary part no matter how slight, until he gradually presents to you the organic whole, worked out. You don't get the organic whole until he wishes you to and that is at the very end. But he never lets the situation go, never digresses for a single instant; and no matter how slow or long his pages may seem as you first read them, when you have at the end grasped the total thing, if you then look back you find that the voluminous texture is woven closely and that every touch bears upon the main issue. I don't say that if I could I would work like this, or that the situations he chooses to weave into such verbal labyrinth are such as I should care to deal with so minutely and laboriously, even if I had the art to do so; but I do say that judged as only any works of art can ever be judged; viz., by *themselves*, by what they undertake to do and how thoroughly they do it, Henry James's later books are the work of a master . . . .'

Wolcott Gibbs, to get back to the Guy Bolton adaptation of 'The Dove', found *Child of Fortune* ineffably tedious and dull, and Louis Kronenberger concluded that 'The Dove' on the stage 'can only succeed as something quite trashy or as something truly tremendous.' It can, that is to say, succeed only on the scale of soap opera – 'Milly Faces Life', 'Death Can Be Bountiful', 'The First Mrs Densher', 'Wings of Riches' – or on that of grand opera, with such arias as 'O gentle dove!', 'This heart to thy swift flight', 'Fold now thy tender wings', 'Ah, passion but an hour!'

Thus, Meade Robert's 'Playhouse 90' dramatization was a unique achievement. I sat before my television set that night last year hoping for the passable, fearing the worst.

The worst is a perverse tendency, exhibited by at least one adapter in the past, to twist the plot into low, ironic comedy by saving the life of Milly Theale. Densher, that is, marries the rich girl only to find, to his dismay, and that of Kate, that Milly becomes a rose, no longer choked in the grass but fresh-sprung in the June of salutary happiness. We are a sentimental, soft-hearted nation, prone to lay violent hands upon death in art by calling in play doctors and heroine specialists of the kind that 'saved' the doomed Lena, of Joseph Conrad's *Victory*, forty years ago, when it was made into a silent movie that was a combination of Pollyanna and Jack Holt. This saving of heroines, for a more recent instance in another sphere, was rudely accomplished by the Andrews Sisters in the case of the old Irish ballad 'Molly Malone'. The ballad has it that 'She died of a fever and no one could save her', but the sympathetic Andrews Sisters did save her by cutting out that line, fitting her up with an artificial husband, and removing 'Now her ghost wheels her barrow' and inserting 'Now they both wheel her barrow', to the sorrow of millions who love Molly Malone not only alive, alive O, but dying and dead. When the resurrected Molly was crying her cockles and mussels over the airwaves a few years ago, I began fearing that the heroine specialists would go on to resurrect Shakespeare's Juliet, Verdi's Violetta, Wordsworth's Lucy, Browning's Evelyn Hope, Tennyson's Elaine, Poe's Annabel Lee, and Hemingway's Catherine Barkley. My fears gave rise to a terrifying nightmare in which I picked up a copy of *A Farewell to Arms* to discover that its title had been changed to 'Over the Fever and Through the *Crise*'. It was during this period of apprehension that I went about muttering, 'I am mending, Egypt, mending.' But 'Playhouse 90', bless its young heart, let Milly Theale die in the beauty of the Henry James lilies.

The profound and lasting effect upon Henry James of Minny Temple's untimely death shows up in many ways and places in his novels and stories. The simple, faintly comic name Minny Temple is reflected not only in Milly Theale but, in varying degrees, in the names of such other James heroines as Maggie Verver; Maisie, of 'What Maisie Knew'; Mamie Pocock; Daisy Miller; May Bartram; Maria Gostrey; and Mary Antrim. Even Madame la Comtesse de Vionnet was named Marie. More than one of the girls in this 'M' category die in the novels and novellas. I have set down the foregoing names from memory, and I am sure a research through the books would turn up many more. Probably dozens of seniors in English literature courses – like one I met at Yale a few years ago – have devoted their theses to a study of the proper names in Henry James. He had something more than a gift, almost an impish perversity, for the invention of plain, even homely feminine names, and by no means all of them were for his American women. The weediest of all is, I think, Fleda Vetch, of *The Spoils of Poynton*. As for his best-known American females, only a few, such as Isabel Archer and Caroline Spencer, do not grate upon the ear. This is partly because the voices of American women, from coast to coast, as he once said, were a torture to his own ear. Some fifty years ago, in *Harper's Bazar* (this was before it became *Harper's Bazaar*), he wrote half a dozen pieces about the speech and manners of the American Woman, which have never been brought together in any book. They might conceivably throw some light upon the James names for women, and upon his complicated, ambivalent attitude towards the ladies themselves. In any case, he usually took them up tenderly, fashioned so slenderly, young and so rich. What feminine reader has not wept over the death of poor dear Daisy Miller? And what sensitive gentleman can read the closing pages of *The Beast in the Jungle* and ever forget the anguish of John Marcher, to whom nothing whatever had happened, who through life had love forgone, quit of scars and tears but bearing the deep, incurable wound of emptiness? This story tells the tale of its author's loss of 'the wings of experience', the burden and beauty and blessing of the love of a woman – something that was denied to Henry James for a complex of reasons, upon which the Freudians, especially during the nineteen-thirties, liked to get their eager fingers. Basically, he deliberately chose a loveless life because of his transfiguring conviction that the high art he practised was not consonant with marriage but demanded the monastic disciplines of celibacy. He loved vicariously, though, and no man more intensely and sensitively.

It has always seemed to me that Henry James plunged into the theatre to escape, perhaps without conscious intention, from the lifelessness of the silent study and the stuffy ivory tower. But no one can simply, or romantically, account for any novelist's taking on the theatre at intervals. There is always the lure of contact with an audience and the immediate response of appreciation, and there is also always what James called 'the lust of a little possible gold.' He supported himself by his writings, and he had the hope of making a killing on the stage for the sake of his budget and coffers. What resulted was an unequal struggle – his 'tussle with the Black Devil of the theatre'. He wrote a dozen plays in all, but only four were produced, and none were outstanding, and none made any money to speak of. And around him, all the time, bloomed, to his envy and usually to his disdain, such successes by his colleagues as *The Second Mrs Tanqueray*, *An Ideal Husband*, and *The Passing of the Third Floor Back*. James's theatre pieces have been collected by Leon Edel, one of the most eminent living Jamesians, in *The Complete Plays of Henry James*.

Edel's swift and fascinating account of what was probably James's most hideous hour, the first night of his play, *Guy Domville*, at the St James's Theatre, in London, one January night in 1895, is itself worth the price of the volume. What happened that terrifying night would take too long to tell, and could not be done by anyone as well as Edel has done it. The evening might have grown out of the conjoined imaginations of Agatha Christie, Ed Wynn, and Robert Benchley. It began with the receipt of a mysterious telegram of bad wishes, and, after a compelling first act, abruptly changed gear and colour in the second, with the entrance of an actress wearing a strange and comical hat. If James had, up to that night, still toyed with the idea of dramatizing the story of Milly Theale, he must have given up all thought of such a venture the moment he was dragged out upon the stage, at the end of the play, to the boos and catcalls that dominated the applause of an audience containing, among its host of celebrities, three comparatively unknown literary men – Arnold Bennett, H. G. Wells, and George Bernard Shaw. Incidentally, there have been few literary feuds so fascinating, and few so voluminously documented, as that between James and Wells, the introvert against the extrovert, the self-conscious artist versus the social-conscious novelist. The history of this long bicker and battle has been done by Edel and Gordon N. Ray in their *Henry James and H. G. Wells*, published, in 1958, by the University of Illinois Press.

Admirers of literature's hippopotamus with the skilful fingers and the sensitive soul must always mourn his having missed *The Heiress* and *The Innocents* and *Berkeley Square*, but their sorrow is compensated for by a sense of relief that he didn't have to experience the rigours and rigidities of Broadway. Anybody can survive editors and publishers, one way or another, but it takes the constitution of a Marine sergeant major to stand up under the bombardment of producers and directors, not to mention actors and actresses. Ellen Terry once promised to appear in a Henry James play in America, but never did, with the result that he called her 'perfidious'. He did manage to get the great Forbes-Robertson to appear in a play of his, but it is a now forgotten *succès d'estime*, a dim footnote to the record of that actor's achievements in the theatre. Once, James decided to turn a long one-act play of his into three acts by 'curtain drops', dividing it into what he called stanzas or cantos. I can see now the faces of Jed Harris, Herman Shumlin, and Kermit Bloomgarden listening to the Old Master's 'polysyllabic ponderosities' about *that*.

I think it is safe to say that television's voracious gobbling up of the literature of the past, which it regurgitates as Westerns, will leave Henry James's works uneaten, and even unbitten. There are now so many Westerns on television that their writers may soon be forced to adapt even the more famous Bible stories, and we may expect before long a bang-bang based on this distorted text: 'Whither thou goest, I will go, God and the Cheyennes willing.'

Until his untimely death, John Lardner, head of *The New Yorker*'s department of television investigation, viewed with sound alarm and insight the Westernizing, among other things, of de Maupassant's sardonic classic *Boule de Suif*, in which the fat French prostitute of the original was transmutilated into a slender and virtuous Apache princess, while quotations from Shakespeare flowered all over the desert till Hell wouldn't have it. That distortion of an indestructible piece of literature alarmed me, too, coming, as it did, only nine days after my happily groundless fears about the debauching of Henry James's 'Dove'. When de Maupassant's famous coach was diverted from its journey between Rouen and Le Havre and re-routed across the Indian country, I began fretting about what might happen to other celebrated coaches of literature – the one in *Vanity Fair*, all those that rumble through Dickens, and even the one that carries Cinderella to the ball. Then I began worrying about Lewis Carroll's coachless Alice. I could see her being driven, behind four horses, from a ladies' finishing school in Boston to California in order to be joined in unholy matrimony with a disturbed ex-haberdasher, one Mat Hadder, now a deranged U.S. marshal. Down from the hills, at the head of his howling tribe, sweeps Big Chief White Rabbit, but out of the West, the Far-fetched West, to the blare of bugle music, rides Captain Marston ('March') Hare, who falls in love with Alice through the gun smoke, and – Ah, the hell with it. (For the sake of the record, it should be noted, in passing, that *Boule de Suif* was once dramatized for Broadway, with reasonable reverence, in a play called *The Channel Road*.)

I keep thinking of other possible – nay, probable – television corruptions: 'Trelawny of the Wells Fargo,' 'Lady Windermere's Gun', 'She Shoots to Conquer', 'Fanny's First Gunplay', and even 'The Sheriff Misses Tanqueray'. This Tanqueray is the fastest draw in English literature, and can outshoot the notorious desperado, Long Gun Silver (and a heigh-ho to you, Long Gun, says I). To get all this frightening phantasmagoria off my mind, I have begun re-reading, and hiding in, Henry James's *The Sacred Fount*, a story that will, I feel sure, forever foil the bang-bang transmutilators. For such small and negative blessings let us thank with brief thanksgiving whatever gods may be.

One thing that I can't yet dismiss from my waking thoughts and dawn dreams is the impish, tongue-in-cheek compulsion of the Western televisionaries to commingle the Bard and the bang-bangs. The other morning, I woke up with this line, from 'Have Gun, Will Shakespeare', chasing through my head: 'How sweet the moonlight sleeps upon this – *bang!*'

Thataway, stranger, lies madness, so let us iris out on a quieter and safer area.

H. G. Wells, long-time friend and finally enemy of Henry James, once

wrote, 'For generations to come a select type of reader will brighten apprecia-
tively to *The Spoils of Poynton*, *The Ambassadors*, *The Tragic Muse*, *The Golden
Bowl* and many other stories.' His prophecy was right, if you change 'type' to
'types', but his list of the stories he apparently liked best himself is uncon-
vincing to me. I doubt, for instance, whether he ever got through *The Golden
Bowl*, but if he did he left me somewhere in the middle of it. It is hard to understand how he could have left out the most controversial of all James's creations,
The Turn of the Screw.

The undiminished power of the great 'ghost story', after more than sixty
years, was proved again, this time on television, when Ingrid Bergman starred
in a dramatization by James Costigan, put on by the Ford 'Startime' series
just last year. I put 'ghost story' in quotes because of the controversy that still
rages, as rage goes in literary and psychological circles, about the true meaning
of the narrative. Critical minds, in practically all known areas of research and
analysis, have got answers, dusty and otherwise, when hot for certainties in
this, one of the greatest of all literary mysteries. Even with a merely competent
cast, it would be hard to mar, or even dilute, the effectiveness of any dramatization, but Miss Bergman brought a memorable performance to a well-
written, well-directed *Turn of the Screw*. She was equalled in every way by the
performances of Alexandra Wager and Hayward Morse, as the two children of
the eerie household.

One New York critic called it an 'honest to God ghost story', and most
viewers must indeed have been haunted and chilled by the strange goings on
in the great house of the wide, circular staircase and the gloomy corridors.
Dramatic and theatrical effectiveness aside, the question that has fascinated
literary critics and psycho-analysts for six decades is this: Were the apparitions
of the dead ex-governess, Miss Jessel, and of the violently dead ex-valet, Peter
Quint, actual visitations from beyond the grave, or were they figments of the
inflamed psyche of the new governess? The literature on the subject is extensive. Watchers of the television show who want to pursue the mystery into the
library could turn to Edmund Wilson's 'The Ambiguity of Henry James' in
his *The Triple Thinkers*, James's own preface, and the narrative itself. Mr
Wilson pays tribute to Edna Kenton, one of the first psychographers to put
forward the theory of hallucination instead of apparition. The James preface,
in the manner of the Master, weaves a glittery web around his intention, at
once brightening and obscuring it. He speaks of fairy tale and witchcraft,
touches lightly on psychic research, and, of course, jumps over Freud completely. He can set so many metaphors and implications dancing at the same
time on the point of his pen that it is hard to make out the pattern in the
fluttering of all the winged words. I myself have never had the slightest doubt
that he was completely aware of almost every latent meaning that has been
read into the famous story. Henry James was not a student of Freud; he was a
sophomore in psychology compared to his distinguished brother William, and
I once read a letter of Henry's in which he somewhat pettishly dismissed the
assumptions of Freud as akin to those of spiritualism. But when it came to

pondering his plots, turning over his characters and incidents the way a squirrel turns over a nut, he was the pure artist, less susceptible than almost any other to unreasoned impulse.

Some years ago, in a little town in Connecticut, I had the pleasure of meeting, at a party, a gracious lady whose mother was the sister of Minny Temple. She told me a wonderful tale of something that happened at twilight in England many, many years ago, when she was a young girl. I like to think that the incident took place at the very time Henry James was working out, in his conscious mind, the tricks and devices of *The Turn of the Screw*. At any rate, the venerable figure of the distinguished novelist, wearing opera hat and cape, stood outside a house, in the fading light, and peered through a window at the young lady and one or two other girls, to give them what he might have called 'the tiniest of thrills'. And so to me, if to no one else, it is clear that this gave him the idea of the apparition, at a window, of the ghostly figure of Peter Quint.

Alas, I am now told that the gracious lady not only has forgotten the incident but does not believe it happened, and cannot recall telling me about it. And so this rambling flight into the past ends, as perhaps it should properly end, on a faint, far note of mystery.

W

The Saving Grace

'I HAVE wanted to argue with you since 1951,' said a woman who sat down next to me, around midnight, at a recent party in Connecticut.

'You have shown remarkable restraint for your impatient sex,' I said. 'Here it is 1961. What is it you want to be wrong about?'

'In 1951, in an interview, you said that humour would be dead within five years. Well, it wasn't,' she said firmly.

'I said it would either be dead or off its rocker,' I told her. 'Perhaps it is both. You may have seen its gibbering ghost.'

'Do you think ghosts are crazy?' she demanded.

'Well,' I said, 'anyone who rejoins our species, after once being quit of it, can scarcely be called bright, can she?'

Here she proved too quick for me. 'It was Banquo who made that awful scene in the dining-room, not Lady Banquo,' she pointed out. I could have observed that Lady Banquo was not dead, but it would have been too easy.

'Lady Banquo sent him there,' I said. 'You know how women ghosts are.'

'I don't want to get into the First Folio, or anything like that,' she said with a touch of irritation. 'What did you think was the matter with humour in 1951?'

'It was suffering from acute hysteria, pernicious fission, recurring nightmare, loose talk, false witness, undulant panic, ingrown suspicion, and occlusion of perception – quite a syndrome,' I said. 'When reason totters and imagination reels, humour loses its balance, too.'

'It is called the saving grace,' she said, making a sharp left jab of the truism. I wasn't off guard, though.

'Grace can't save us unless we save it,' I said.

'It *is* saved,' she insisted. 'It's on all sides of us. You just don't want to see it. What else do you think has happened to humour?'

'It suffers from chronic crippling statistics,' I told her. 'Humour flourishes only as a free single entity. Humour makes its own balances and patterns out of the disorganization of life around it, but disorganization has been wiped out by organization, statistics, surveys, group action, programme, platform, imperatives, and the like. These are good for satire, but they put a strait jacket on humour.'

A man with a highball glass in his hand wavered over to us and said to me, 'You guys give me a pain in the neck. On the other hand, the pain in Twain stays mainly in the brain.'

For such crude intruders I always carry a piece of complicated academic drollery, and I gave it to him: 'If you prefer "I think, therefore I am" to "*Non sum qualis eram*", you are putting Descartes before Horace.'

He hesitated, jiggling the ice in his glass. 'Nuts,' he said, and wove away.

'Who was that feeble-minded son of bombast and confusion?' I asked my companion.

'My husband,' she said. 'My name is Mrs Groper. Alice Groper. Tell me some more about statistics, but not too much.'

'Last Monday,' I said, 'I heard three news broadcasters say, "*Only* two hundred and sixty-two people were killed in automobile accidents in the past two days," and one of them added that nearly a hundred people – eighty-eight, to be exact – were alive that might have been dead. He was basing his statistics on an estimated three hundred and fifty dead, confidently predicted by the Safety Council. In the place of humour, you see, we have grim, or negative, cheerfulness. One statistician not long ago tried to cheer us all with his estimate that only eighteen million people, not fifty million, would be killed here in a nuclear war. This kind of horrifying reassurance is now our main substitute for laughter.'

'I don't want to talk about horrifying reassurance,' said Mrs Groper.

'Take teeth, then,' I told her. 'Last year, in London, somebody asked me why Americans thought teeth were so funny. I explained that it is not teeth, but the absence of teeth, that we regard as funny, and also the absence of hair.'

'But we laugh at paunches, too,' she cut in quickly, 'and that's the presence of something.'

'Not at all,' I told her. 'What we laugh at is the absence of the once flat abdomen. If I am splitting hairs, they are the hairs just above the male ears, as all the others are so hilariously gone.'

'Let's not go into philosophy or definition,' said Mrs Groper. 'They never get you anywhere.'

'They have got us where we are, or, anyway, they have left us there,' I said. 'Now, disorganization must not be confused with disintegration. If the falling apart of the human body is funny, then death should be the biggest laugh of all. I think I saw this concept forming when the edentulous mouth was first deemed to be uproarious. That was a long time ago, and I hoped that the comedy of dentures would disappear along with the jokes about the activities of Mrs Eleanor Roosevelt, but I was wrong. Mike Nichols and Elaine May, and even the English playwright, Graham Greene, regard teeth as highly amusing. The usually very humorous Nichols and May have a protracted, or perhaps I should say extracted, skit about a dentist who falls in love with the decayed molar of a young woman patient, and then with the rest of her. (They call her Reba, but I would prefer Sesame.) Mr Greene's latest comedy success on the London stage concerned a love triangle involving a dentist, a bookseller, and the dentist's wife. In this play the dentist occasionally flashes his electric torch into his rival's mouth and warns him about a certain tooth. The play was a huge success, and I expect any day now to encounter a burlesque called

The Bridgework on the River Kwai. I happen to consider the oral cavity to be about as humorous as a certain canal. Ask me, what canal?'

'What canal?' asked Mrs Groper.

'Alimentary, my dear Watson,' I said. 'Why don't you giggle?'

'Because my name is not Watson, and I don't know what you're talking about,' she said.

'I am talking about the fragmentation of the human organism as the source and subject of dubious fun,' I said. 'One August a weekly magazine I sometimes write for became *avant-garde* in this field of humour and came up with a comic drawing about the virus called *Staphylococcus aureus*. There were no funny drawings in the magazine about people, only about other creatures. The idea that persons, as such, in their entirety may be passing from the American comic scene keeps me awake at night. One dawn I woke up singing, "When you were the fly in the ointment and I was the cat in the bag." Then I worked out the caption for the drawing of a bug in a rug. It is saying to another bug, "I can't get comfortable." '

'But you have done a hundred fables about talking animals and birds,' she reminded me. Having determined not to drink anything that night, I sipped my second highball slowly.

'You have mislaid your discriminator,' I told her brusquely. 'The fable form has immemorially *identified* the behaviour of animals and birds with that of people, to emphasize the foibles and follies of the human race. But talking animals in cartoons are now tending to denigrate man by assuming attitudes of superiority. For example, you find two giraffes staring at a human being and one of them is saying, "There ain't any such animal." Or a cartoon will show half a dozen persons on all fours with their heads buried in the sand, and one ostrich is saying to another, "My God, look who's fallen for *that* old myth." '

'Didn't anything funny at all, in the old-fashioned sense, happen to you while you were in Europe last year?' Mrs Groper wanted to know. 'I think you're just in a depressed mood. You've had too little to drink. I'll get you another highball,' and she did.

'Well, there were the Hugginses,' I said when she came back with the drink.

'Now, *that's* funny.' She laughed merrily.

'Not frightfully,' I said, 'and yet it was frightful, too – what happened to them on the ship coming home, I mean.'

'Did they fall overboard?' she asked.

'No, but they went off the deep end,' I said. 'Here's what happened. Mrs Huggins had bought a new dress in Paris, at the most expensive shop – I'll call it Violetta's. While her husband was out on deck one day, staring at the sea and trying to remember how many people had gone down on the *Titanic*, not how many had been saved, she removed the label from the dress and sewed in the label of what you women call a reasonable shop, a small shop in New York. But it preyed on her mind, and so she later ripped out the label and put the Violetta one back in.'

'That's not so funny,' my companion said. 'We all do things like that. We're all afraid of the customs inspectors.'

'Anyway,' I said, 'my wife and I met the Hugginses for drinks one night after dinner on the ship. They had already had a lot of cocktails and wine, and they were both on the edge of their chairs. She was also on the edge of colitis, and he was threatened with a new ulcer.'

'I don't see why, if she had sewed the real label back in,' said my companion.

'It was this way,' I said. 'Huggins told his wife that any customs inspector would be able to tell that the Violetta label had been sewed into the dress by a nervous and amateur hand – that is, a guilty hand.'

'So what?' demanded Mrs Groper. 'It belonged there.'

'Belonging is a matter of congruity, not of simple fact,' I explained. 'The human mind, or mental state, being what it now is, the inspector would be sure to say, "Madam, this is clearly not a Violetta dress. You have sewed the label of an expensive Paris shop into an inexpensive American-made dress that you obviously took to Europe with you." '

'But why would Mrs Huggins conspire with herself to pay duty on an imported dress when she didn't have to, if it wasn't really imported, even though it actually was?' Mrs Groper asked.

'You're oversimplifying,' I told her sharply. 'The assumption would be that Mrs Huggins was trying to get away with something. I mean, that she was willing to pay a hundred dollars in duty just to prove to her friends that her husband could afford a Violetta dress for her.'

'What finally happened?' asked Mrs Groper.

'Huggins wanted to throw the dress overboard,' I said. 'To save money, you see.'

'Do I?' she asked.

'Certainly,' I said. 'If the case got to the courts as the result of Mrs Huggins's determination to prove that the Violetta dress was in fact a Violetta dress, Violetta herself might have to be flown to New York to testify. Lawyers' fees, court costs, and so on would run into a pretty figure. Well, anyway, over our drinks that night, Mrs Huggins burst into tears. My own wife, returning from the ladies' room at that moment, accused me of having hurt her feelings. That made *me* mad. Then suddenly Huggins smote the table with his right fist, breaking his glasses, which he had forgotten were there. His wife reached over impulsively and cut her right index finger on a fragment of broken lens.'

'I think you're losing me now,' my companion said.

We're all lost,' I said irritably. 'When Mrs Huggins's finger began bleeding, I yelled at her, "Why in the name of God do you have to cut yourself every time your husband breaks his glasses?" You see, I was mad at her now because she had not denied that I had hurt her feelings. Humour had folded its tents like the Arabs and noisily stolen away from a situation that demanded its presence.'

'Goatblather,' said Mr Groper, as he passed my chair, jiggling ice cubes in a fresh highball.

'Your husband has all the charm of a gentleman I shall now tell you about,' I said. 'The story points up the decline of humour in our time and in our species. Recently two couples, entirely unknown to each other, were leaving a Broadway theatre at the end of the play. They were moving slowly and with difficulty up the crowded aisle, when the observant wife of one man whispered in his ear, "You're unzipped!" He hastily zipped and, in so doing, caught in the zipper the fringe of the other woman's stole. The embarrassing predicament soon became uncomfortably obvious to all four. They were huddled together as they reached the kerb, where the husband of the woman with the trapped stole said grimly, "Let us not make a social occasion of this. We shall all get in the same cab and drive to whichever apartment is the nearer." And they did just that, in gloomy silence.'

'But,' said Mrs Groper, 'they could have taken separate cabs, and the stole could have been returned next day.'

'The husband of the stole,' I explained, 'made it clear that he did not want to exchange names with the other couple. When they got to the nearer apartment, the two gentlemen retired to another room, where they finally managed to extricate the stole. Then the two couples separated without so much as a good night.'

'But if they had had a nightcap together, they all would have laughed about it,' said Mrs Groper. 'You just can't be dignified in a situation like that. You need another drink.' And she left to get me one.

'Keep it clean, Mac,' said the peripatetic Groper, passing my chair again.

'Don't you ever sit down, for God's sake?' I yelled after him. His wife brought me the fresh drink, and I added a moral to the tale: 'When dignity does not give, humour cannot live.'

At this point my wife joined Mrs Groper and me and said, 'Why are you shouting?' I started to explain, realized that it couldn't be done, and sulked instead.

'Did Mr Huggins finally throw the dress overboard?' Mrs Groper asked my wife.

'Oh, that,' my wife said. 'Of course not. They were lucky. The customs inspector didn't even look at the dress.'

The party was growing noisy now, and we could hardly hear one another. Someone had put a record on the phonograph, and several couples were dancing.

'If that's all there is to it,' said Mrs Groper, 'it isn't really frightful unless Mrs Huggins got blood poisoning and died.'

'Oh, my God, I didn't know that!' my wife cried.

'We all have to go sometime,' I yelled.

'I was ready to go an hour ago,' my wife said, 'but you were taking something apart, as usual.'

'A woman always assumes that a man is taking something apart when he's trying to put it together,' I said.

'We *must* go,' my wife insisted.

'Not until I save Mrs Huggins's life,' I said. 'It's the least I can do.' But Alice Groper was no longer interested in the plight of the Hugginses.

'Your husband has been officiating at the burial of humour,' she said.

'Oh, he has, has he?' said my wife. 'Well, he defends humour just as often as he buries it. It all depends on whether he, or somebody else, is attacking it. Doesn't it?' she demanded.

'Yes,' I said, grudgingly, pulling myself out of my funereal mood.

'Now you're making sense,' said Mr Groper, holding out his hand. I thought for a moment of biting it, but shook it instead. 'How's about a little old toast to humour?' he asked. The music had stopped and the others in the room gathered around us.

'You do the honours,' Mrs Groper said to me. I stood up, without too much difficulty, and held my glass high.

'Here's to the Queen,' I said. 'The Queen of the graces.' As we were drinking to the hardy survivor of centuries of American life, our hostess, a lady of great charm but small regard for syntax, cried, 'Do not for God's sake break the glasses! Too many glasses are broken already without toasting Queens, so it is enough, and not funny.' Everybody thought it *was* funny, though, and everybody began laughing. My wife and I were leaving the jolly house, good humour all intact, the sound of merriment in our ears, when Groper came up and extended that damned right hand of his. I took it. 'I'm sorry I mentioned your goatblather,' he said. I wanted to throw him over my shoulder, but I am thirty years too old for that gesture in conclusion. 'It is nanny-blibberers like you that are full of goatblather,' I told him.

'Come on!' my wife said, pulling me towards our car as if I were six years old, which, like all American adult males, I sometimes am.

When we were back in our living-room she said, 'Grief-stricken as you are by the death of humour, maybe a nightcap would put you in a better mood.' I nodded, having never rejected a nightcap since 1915.

'I am, *au fond*, a mellow foxy grandpa-type philosopher,' I told her. 'While we finish the nightcap, I shall count your lucky blessings, name them one by one.'

'Then,' she said, 'we'll only need a short drink.' And she made us both a short one.

The Case for Comedy

THE robin in my apple tree sings as cheerily now as if he were living in the Gay 'Nineties, when there never was a cakewalk or a band concert in the park that ended in a knife fight, the throwing of beer cans and bottles, the calling out of the National Guard, and the turning of fire hoses on youthful rioters. Through it all the robin sings, 'Summertime, and the living is easy,' and I wish I could sit down and have a heart-to-heart talk with the merry moron. I would tell him that it is easy enough to be lighthearted if you have not got yourself involved in the Broadway theatre. And if that cued him into 'Give my regards to Broadway,' I should probably make a pass at him with a fly swatter and order him out of the house, or the tree.

Editors, and other busy minds, keep asking me what I think about the future of the American theatre. If they telephone me in the country to ask this question, I always say, with a sigh of relief, 'Then you mean it's still alive!' Naturally, I worry about the fabulous invalid, which has got into a far worse state since the 1920s than I have. In 1928, Philip Barry's *Holiday* opened on Broadway on a Monday night in November, and there were four other openings that night, and twelve in all during the week.

Later the legitimate theatre acquired a slow, wasting ailment. It began to develop the nightmares and matinéemares that now afflict the drama. Once, last summer, when the robin woke me with his Gershwin tune, I lay there retitling certain plays to fit the temper and trend of the present day, and came up with these: *Abie's Irish Neurosis, The Bitter and Ache Man, Ned Macabre's Daughter, I Dismember Mama, They Slew What They Wanted, Toys in the Psychomatic, The Glands Menagerie, Destroy Writes Again, The Manic Who Came to Dinner*, and, a title calculated to pop you out of bed and into a cold tub, *Oklahomosexual.*

It seems to me that this year's extensive arguments and debates about the morbid and decadent state of so-called serious modern drama skim the surface like skipping stones because they fail to take into consideration the dying out of humour and comedy, and the consequent process of dehumanization, both on stage and off. There were literally dozens of comedies to lighten the heart and quicken the step between, say, *The First Year* and *Life With Father*. These were comedies of American life, familial and familiar, but they seem like ancient history now, something to be discussed solemnly by a present-day Aristotle. They could be more cogently and amusingly discussed by a new Robert Benchley, but, alas, there isn't any.

The decline of humour and comedy in our time has had a multiplicity of

610

causes, a principal one being the ideological beating they have taken from both the intellectual left and the political right. The latter came about through the intimidation of writers and playwrights under McCarthyism. The former is more complex. Humour has long been a target of leftist intellectuals, and the reason is simple enough in itself. Humour, as Lord Boothby has said, is the only solvent of terror and tension, and terror and tension are among the chief ideological weapons of Communism. The leftists have made a concerted attack on humour as an anti-social, anti-racial, anti-labour, anti-proletarian stereotype, and they have left no stereotype unused in their attack, from 'no time for comedy' to the grim warnings that humour is a sickness, a sign of inferiority complex, a shield and not a weapon.

The modern morbid playwrights seem to have fallen for the fake argument that only tragedy is serious and has importance, whereas the truth is that comedy is just as important, and often more serious in its approach to truth, and, what few writers seem to realize or to admit, usually more difficult to write.

It is not a curious but a natural thing that arrogant intellectual critics condemn humour and comedy, for while they can write about Greek Old Comedy, Middle Comedy, and New Comedy with all the flourishes of pretension, they avoid a simple truth, succinctly expressed by the *Oxford Classical Dictionary* in its discussion of Middle Comedy. 'Before long the realistic depiction of daily life became the chief aim in Comedy. Ordinary, commonplace life is no easy subject to treat interestingly on the stage; and Antiphanes contrasts the comic poet's more difficult lot with the tragedian's, whose plot is already familiar, and the *deus ex machina* at hand – the comic writer has no such resources.'

The history of stage comedy, in both Greece and Rome, begins with cheap and ludicrous effects. In Greek Old Comedy there were the padded costumes of the grotesque comedian, the paunch and the leather phallus. The Roman Plautus, in freely translating Greek New Comedy, stuck in gags to make his rough and restless audiences guffaw, so that in the beginning comedy was, to use a medical term, exogenous – that is, not arising from within the human being, but dragged in from the outside. The true balance of life and art, the saving of the human mind as well as of the theatre, lies in what has long been known as tragicomedy, for humour and pathos, tears and laughter are, in the highest expression of human character and achievement, inseparable. Many dictionaries, including the *O.E.D.*, wrongly hyphenate tragicomedy, as if the two integral parts were warring elements that must be separated.

I think the first play that ever sent me out of the American theatre in a mood of elation and of high hope for our stage was *What Price Glory?* Amidst all the blood and slaughter there ran the recurring sound of congruous laughter. I still vividly remember the scene in which the outraged French father of an outraged daughter babbles his grievance for a full minute to the bewildered Captain Flagg, who then asks a French-speaking American lieutenant, 'What did he say?'

w*

'Rape,' said the lieutenant.

That scene fairly shines with humanity when compared to an episode in the recent *There Was a Little Girl* in which the raped little girl solemnly asks her seducer if he had enjoyed the experience. And I can still recall the gleams of humour in R. C. Sherriff's *Journey's End*, as bitter a war play as any.

'What kind of soup *is* this, Sergeant?' asks Captain Stanhope.

'Yellow soup, sir,' says the mess sergeant, apologetically.

Screen writers, as well as playwrights, seem reluctant, or unable, to use the devices of comedy out of fear of diluting suspense. A few years ago, in a movie about a bank clerk who stole a million dollars, crammed it into a suitcase, got into a taxi with his unaware and bewildered wife, and headed for an airport to flee the country, there came a scene in which he handed the driver a fifty-dollar bill and told him to 'Step on it.' Now I submit that the wife of an American male of modest income would have gone into a comedy scene at this point, but the writer or writers of the script must have been afraid that such an interlude would ruin the terror and tension, and terror and tension must be preserved nowadays, even at the expense of truth.

Katharine Hepburn recently said that our playwrights should 'rise above their time,' but if they tried that, they would simply sink below themselves, or sit there staring at the blank paper in their typewriters. Separate moulds turn out unvarying shapes. You can't make a Tennessee Ernie out of a Tennessee Williams any more than you can turn a callin' back into a trough cleanin'. A callin' back, if you don't know, is a gatherin' of folks at the bedside of a dyin' man, to call him back. I hope this doesn't inspire one of the morbid playmakers to make a play in which the dyin' man drags all the other folks down with him.

It will be said, I suppose, that I couldn't write such a tragedy because of the limitation of my tools and the nature of my outlook. (Writers of comedy have outlook, whereas writers of tragedy have, according to them, insight.) It is true, I confess, that if a male character of my invention started across the stage to disrobe a virgin criminally (ah, euphemism to end euphemisms!), he would probably catch his foot in the piano stool and end up playing 'Button Up Your Overcoat' on the black keys. There are more ways than one, including, if you will, a Freudian stumble, to get from tragedy into tragicomedy. Several years ago a book reviewer in the *New York Sunday Times* wrote: 'The tragedy of age is not that a man grows old, but that he stays young,' and, indeed, there is the basis of a good tragedy in that half-truth. The other half might be stated, in a reverse Shavian paraphrase, 'The trouble with youth is that it is wasted on the old.' There is where the comedy would come in to form a genuine tragicomedy. At sixty-five, going on sixty-six, I think I can speak with a touch of authority.

Miss Hepburn (to get back to her) is devoted to the great plays of Shakespeare, who didn't rise above his time, but merely above the ability of his contemporaries. He often wrote about a time worse than his own, such as the period of Macbeth. In that drama he could proclaim that life is a tale told by an idiot, full of sound and fury, signifying nothing, but say it in a play told by a genius, full of soundness and fury, signifying many things. The distinguished Mr Williams and his contemporaries are not so much expressers of their time as expressions of it, and, for that matter, aren't we all? The playwright of today likes to believe that he is throwing light upon his time, or upon some part of it, when his time is actually throwing light upon him. This, it seems to me, has always been the case, but it happens more intensely now, perhaps, than ever before. Moreover, there are two kinds of light, the glow that illumines and the glare that obscures, and the former seems to be dimming.

The American family, in spite of all its jitters and its loss of cohesion, still remains in most of its manifestations as familiar as ever, and it is our jumpy fancy to believe that all fathers are drunkards, all mothers kookies, and all children knife wielders planning to knock off their parents. Our loss of form in literature is, in large part, the result of an Oral Culture into which we began descending quite a while back. This is the age of the dragged-out interview, the endless discussion panels on television; an age in which photographers, calling on writers in their homes, stay around the house as long as the paper hanger or the roofer. Everything is tending to get longer and longer, and more and more shapeless. Telephone calls last as long as half an hour, or even forty minutes by my own count; women, saying good-bye at front doors, linger longer than ever, saying, 'Now I *must* go,' and, eventually, 'Now, I *really* must go.' But nothing is accomplished simply any more. Writers of letters finish what they have to say on page two and then keep on going. Khrushchev talks for five hours at press conferences, and may even have got it up to ten by the time this survey appears. (Moral: Great oafs from little icons grow.)

As brevity is the soul of wit, form, it seems to me, is the heart of humour and the salvation of comedy. 'You are a putter in, and I am a taker out,' Scott Fitzgerald once wrote to Thomas Wolfe. Fitzgerald was not a master of comedy, but in his dedication to taking out, he stated the case for form as against flow. It is up to our writers, in this era of Oral Culture, to bring back respect for form and for the innate stature and dignity of comedy. We cannot, to be sure, evoke humorists, or writers of comedy, by prayer or pleading or argument, but we can, and must, hope for a renascence of recognizable American comedy. The trend of the modern temper is toward gloom, resignation, and even surrender, and there is a great wailing of the word 'Decadence!' on all sides. But for twenty-five hundred years decadence has come and decadence has gone. Reading Webster on the subject might make a newly arrived visitor from Mars believe that everything in art and literature came to a morose end as the nineteenth century closed out. It was a period of Decadence and of the Decadents, led by Baudelaire, Verlaine, and Mallarmé in France. Writes old Noah: 'They cultivated the abnormal, artificial, and neurotic in subject and treatment, tending to the morbid or eccentric, and to the mystically sensuous and symbolic.'

Well, we are still going on, and we have four decades left in this battered and bloody century. Walter Lippmann said last summer, in his first television appearance, that he did not believe the world is coming apart. It is heartening to know that he selected as the foremost leader of our time Sir Winston Churchill, a man also respected for his wit and humour. It is high time that we came of age and realized that, like Emily Dickinson's hope, humour is a feathered thing that perches in the soul.

How the Kooks Crumble

I AM now convinced that American radio, or what is left of it, is unconsciously intent (I hope it's unconsciously) upon driving such of its listeners as are not already kooky, kooky. Before we proceed with the indictment, let's examine the slang noun 'kook,' from which the adjective 'kooky' is derived. The newest Dictionary of American Slang has this to say about kook: 'n. An odd, eccentric, disliked person; a "drip"; a nut. Teenage use since 1958; rapidly becoming a pop. fad word. Kooky, adj. crazy, nuts; odd, eccentric; having the attributes of a "drip".'

It seems to me that the Dictionary of American Slang is a little odd or eccentric (I don't say crazy or nuts) when it fails to trace 'kook' and 'kooky' to the much older slang word 'cuckoo' or 'coo-coo'. It might also have pointed out the possibility that the new word derives from Kukla of the old Kukla, Fran and Ollie television programme. According to the slang dictionary, the female European cuckoo is the bird that lays its eggs in another bird's nest, which may be odd or eccentric, but, as any mother will tell you, is by no means crazy or nuts. The American female cuckoo, by the way, hatches its own eggs in its own nest – but let's not get so deeply into this that we can't get out.

My indictment of radio, to return to that, is aimed specifically at most of the news reporters, or reporters of bad news, to be exact. These men seem to revel in news items of horror, terror, catastrophe and calamity. I have forced myself to listen, during the past few months, to an assortment of these voices of doom which are heard all day long, on the hour or half-hour, over almost all radio stations. It is something in the nature of a God's blessing to cut them off and turn to the intelligent programmes on WNYC and music of WQXR. It is wonderful to get away from the yelling and howling of what might be called the present-day Creepy Time melodies and lyrics (and I apologize to both of those fine words). One of these gibberings poses the question, 'What is love?' and answers it with 'Five feet of heaven in a pony tail.'

But let's get back to those reporters of disaster and death. Most of them seem to have been taught diction, phrasing and monotone in two separate schools for announcers. One group of these men presents the horror of fires, automobile accidents, and multiple family murders in a tone of incongruous and chilling, matter-of-fact calm. The other group leaps upon items of daily terror in a mindless tone of almost eager elation. Let us glance, for as long as we can stand it, at the formula of one of these broadcasts of daily American hell. This kind of programme usually lasts fifteen minutes, begins on a high note of cataclysm, and ends with a report of 'stocks and the weather.' In

between, there are often as many as five or six commercials, and in many in-
stances these are read by the reporters themselves in exactly the same tone as
the calamities, thus giving the listener the spooky feeling that the deaths of
scores of persons in an aircrash are no more important than a new candy bar or
brand of coffee. But let me set down a mild paraphrase of the broadcasts I am
indicting:

'Thirty-seven persons were killed today, and more than one hundred others
critically injured, in a chain collision of some twenty-five pleasure cars and
trucks on a fog-bound New Jersey highway. Mrs Marcia Kook, who yesterday
shot down eleven members of her family with two double-barrelled shotguns,
was killed today by her estranged husband, who also took the lives of the couple
next door, a mortician out walking his dog, two school teachers, and a nun.
Police say that they found two million dollars' worth of heroin fastened to her
underclothing. Do you know the true glory of gracious modern living? You
don't unless you have tried Becker's Butternut Coffee with that serene,
heavenly flavour that you have never tasted before. Try it today and you will
try it always. Arthur Kookman, sought by the police of Long Island for having
blown up two churches and a nurses' home, was arrested today on a charge of
filing a false income tax return. While being arraigned in court, he fired two
shots at the judge, one of them killing Sergeant Jeremiah Kookberg in whose
apartment police later found seventy-six shotguns, thirty-seven vacuum
cleaners, forty-two washing machines, one hundred and fifty refrigerators and
three million dollars' worth of heroin. You will think you're in heaven when
you taste Tiddly-Bits, the wonderful new chocolate-covered candy mints, as
sweet as an angel's kiss.'

My long Spooky Time session with the babble box in my living-room revealed still another source of what appears to me to be a desire, or compulsion,
to drive the nation crazy. This is radio's apparently incurable addiction to
frightening statistics. Many of these grow out of a basically worthy attempt to
interest listeners in contributing money to various campaigns on behalf of
research in heart disease, cancer, muscular dystrophy, and the like. Whoever
writes most of these appeals seems invariably constrained to say something
like this: 'Every eleven seconds in America some man, woman or child is
stricken with Googleman's disease' or 'There are more than eleven million
people in the United States who suffer from unilateral mentalitis or allied ailments.' Among the statistics that I gathered in the course of one afternoon
were these consoling figures: there are nineteen million accidents every year
in our nation; more than fourteen million Americans have, or have had, some
serious mental derangement; fifty-two million dollars' worth of merchandise,
comprising all forms of food, is stolen every year from American super-
markets.

It may be that radio, in flooding the day-time and night-time air with horrible news and distressing statistics, banks on the well-established psychological truth that a person is not so much shocked by what happens to somebody
else as relieved by the realization that he is, at least for the time being,

unstricken and undead. The vast accumulation of all this twisted relief, how-ever, is bound to take its toll of the American mass mind. One afternoon I was joined in front of my radio by three friends who had expressed doubt that so much hell and horror was calmly, or blithely, broadcast to the people of this jumpy republic. They ended up with the admission that I was by no means exaggerating, but even playing the situation down a bit. 'Well,' said one of them, with a heavy sigh, '*we* are still here.' To which another replied, 'As the fellow said at the Alamo.'

There is, believe it or not, good news about the United States of America easily available to every radio press department if the gloomy gentlemen would care to look for it. Medical research, for instance, is continually turning up new devices and techniques for the cure, or alleviation, of almost all ailments. These are usually reported only in medical journals, but, alas, they do not have the impact of death, derangement and disaster. I do not, of course, re-commend sweetness and light or censorship, but merely the application of that now most uncommon of human qualities, common sense. The latest statistics that I have heard over the air, announced calmly by one school of reporters and gleefully by the other, asserted that a careful examination of some thousands of Americans proved that only eighteen per cent of them were mentally well. Just think of it, folks – if there were a hundred guests at the New Year's Eve party you attended, only eighty-two of them were kooky, cuckoo, crazy, or nuts. Incidentally, the prevalent use of the word 'disturbed' to take in all forms and degrees of mental aberration serves only to intensify the en-circling gloom. For example, if one says, 'She is disturbed by her husband's drinking,' it implies that the wife has been driven crazy by it.

Not long ago a woman who was trapped in a New York subway fire, but managed to fight her way to safety, said, 'It was wonderful to see people and light.' An excellent combination, people and light. We ought to try to bring them together more often.

My Senegalese Birds and Siamese Cats

I HAVE been going through some yellowing recollections and old dusty whereabouts of mine, with the vague idea of setting down my memoirs now that I am past sixty, and it comes to me with no special surprise that none of them is stained with blood or bright with danger, in the active, or Hemingway, sense of the word. My experiences, like those of most sedentary men fond of creature comforts such as steam heat and room service, have been distinguished by an average unremarkableness, touched with grotesquerie, discomfort, and humiliation, but definitely lacking in genuine ·50-calibre peril. I have never 'met the tiger face to face,' as Kipling once put it, or climbed anything higher and colder than half a dozen flights of stairs, or struggled all afternoon to land a fish that outweighed me by three hundred pounds. It occurs to me, however, that some of the most memorable adventures of any man's life are those that have had to be endured in a mood of quiet desperation. I am reminded, for specific example, of a quietly desperate night I spent more than twenty-five years ago on the Blue Train running from Paris to Nice.

After my wife and I had become comfortably ensconced in our sleeping quarters on the train (you can't become ensconced any other way, come to think of it) we discovered, to our dismay, that our Couchette, or Sleepette, or whatever it was called, was to be shared by a short, middle-aged Frenchman, who scowled all the time, occasionally muttered to himself, and didn't even look at us. My wife had bought, in a Paris flower market, God knows why, two Senegalese love-birds which hated each other's guts, and she had insisted on bringing them along. Before we all retired, practically at the same moment – and don't ask me how we managed it – our unexpected companion had kept glancing nervously at the bird cage, which my wife had suspended from something. We had had the two birds for about three weeks and the male had never burst into song, although we had been told that he would. We had gradually come to the conclusion that he couldn't stand his mate, had had no say in her selection, and did not intend to serenade her, or even admit that she was there. They would sit side by side all day long on their little wooden swing, not swinging or ruffling a feather, or even looking at each other, just staring into some happier past. In our hotel room in Paris they had slept all night long, motionless and indifferent to each other, and to us. On the train to Nice they decided, out of some atavistic impulse, to fan out their wings all night long, with intervals of only a few seconds between their rufflings. In such cramped lodgings, about eight by five, the noise they made was the noise of half a dozen Pullman porters busy with whisk brooms. I can still hear clearly their continual *flut, flut,*

flut. It began to get me, it began to get my wife, and it began to get the Frenchman.

Our room-mate had gone to bed, composed himself on his back, and pulled on a pair of black cotton gloves. He had then closed his eyes and gone quietly to sleep in a facile way that we envied. He wasn't to sleep long, however, for the flutting began about fifteen minutes after the light had been turned out. The male would flut, and then the female would flut, and then they would flut together. For birds who had never flutted a single flut in three weeks, they turned out to be surprisingly good at it, deeply interested in it, and utterly tireless. After about twenty minutes of the flutting, the Frenchman snarled, 'It is necessary to cover those birds.' My wife, who spoke excellent French, told him that the birds had been covered, and he suggested that she put something else over their cage. This, she explained to him after groping for the word, would cause them to suffocate. The Frenchman said something in a threatening tone that I didn't get, but which was later translated by my wife as, 'It is as well to suffocate as to be strangled.' I got up and put my coat over the cage, but the flutting came through as clearly as ever. All night long the three of us would doze off, wake up, and doze off again. Each time the Frenchman woke up he had a different expression, and he ran through everything from '*zut alors*' to what might be roughly translated as, 'If a merciful Providence does not silence those birds, I shall throw them off the train and myself after them.' (My wife assured me in a whisper that he had said 'myself' and not 'you.')

Two weeks after we got to our hotel in Nice, we were awakened at dawn one morning by the sound of a bird singing. The sound came, astonishingly enough, from our bird cage, and the song was loud, gay, and full-throated. We got out of bed to explore this incredible phenomenon and discovered that the female was lying dead on the floor of the cage. Whether she had died of boredom, or heartbreak, or had been slain by her hitherto mute 'mate,' we never, of course, found out. A few days later, we decided to give the male away, cage and all, to an old woman who was selling birds in the flower market of the old town. She was suspicious at first of two Americans who had only one love-bird and who wanted to get rid of it for nothing. 'Does he sing?' she asked us doubtfully. My wife didn't have an answer ready for that, but I did. 'He sings,' I told her, 'at funerals.' This was literally true. I had decided to bury the dead bird in the garden of the hotel, but I had not known how to get it out to the garden without arousing the suspicion of the French proprietress, a suspicion than which there is none stronger or more durable in the world. Finally, in a kind of elaborate panic, which is customary with me, I had put the unfortunate creature in my pocket and had taken along the cage with the other bird in it. 'What in the name of God for?' my wife had asked me, reasonably. 'To divert suspicion,' I told her. 'I will say I am taking him out for an airing. You come too.' To this she replied firmly, 'No.' I managed to bury the dead bird – it was night and the garden was deserted – without attracting onlookers, although I recall that the proprietress seemed relieved later on when we finally checked out of the hotel. The bird in the cage had sung at the funeral not a dirge but an unmistakable roundelay or madrigal, probably a Senegalese version of 'She is gone, let her go, God bless her.'

The old woman at the flower market stared at me coldly when I mentioned funerals. Experience had doubtless taught her that the line is thinly drawn between American comedy and American insanity. My wife turned away to examine some flowers, with the air of a woman who has become disillusioned and is planning to vanish. I made the mistake, as I always do, of elaborating, and my elaboration in French is something to hear. I think I used the phrase '*gouette de tristesse*', which literally means 'drop of sorrow' and had, as you can see, only the faintest bearing on the situation. Thinking I might be arrested if she allowed me to proceed in my reckless French, my wife rejoined us and came out with the true story of the short, unhappy life of the diminutive parrots, ending with a brief account of the mysterious death of one of them. The old woman's eyes lighted with understanding, and she pointed out that the other bird had probably been a male too. This, she added, took the case out of the realm of *crime passionnel* and into the realm of *sang-froid*. Since the case was plainly not going to be taken to court, the theory, however sound, seemed immaterial and academic. My wife suddenly broke the silence by demanding twenty-five francs for the survivor. This put the old woman on familiar ground. We began to haggle and compromise. She agreed, in the end, to take the bird for nothing, but her tone was aggrieved. She wanted us to know that she had come off badly, for, as she pointed out, where in the world would she get a Senegalese love-bird as a companion for this solitary male?

Love-birds, now out of style, and parakeets, now all the rage, belong to the parrot family, but are cousins and not siblings. Love-birds are found in Africa and South America and parakeets come from Asia, Africa, Australia and Polynesia. Webster's Unabridged says that love-birds are 'largely green or delicate grey', and their name derives from their habit of perching shoulder to shoulder or, as in the case of my own two, cold shoulder to cold shoulder. Senegal is in French West Africa, an area in which Webster obviously never hunted for small parrots, for he makes no reference to the blue Senegalese love-bird. Mine were blue, all right, and if my memory serves after all this time, each of them had a narrow red ring around its neck, but one ring was narrower and fainter in colour than the other, and I had figured this was the mark of the female. I was probably wrong. I don't know any more about love-birds now than I did then, but my knowledge of females has increased somewhat, and I doubt that I could be fooled again. To be sure, I can be fooled about a female's motives, moods or intentions, and by her fast ball, change of pace and cross fire, but not by the mere fact of her sex.

It was on a later trip to France that my wife bought two female Siamese cats, at the same Paris flower market, the one near the Madeleine. She had come upon the cats one early morning in April and couldn't resist buying them and bringing them back to our hotel. Siamese cats, with their unearthly colour scheme and their medieval grace, are as handsome as Florentine daggers or exotic jungle orchids, and Circe and Jezzie – short, of course, for Jezebel –

were no exception. Now I am not a cat man, but a dog man, and all felines can tell this at a glance – a sharp, vindictive glance. I was all for taking the Siamese cats back to the flower market and, after a good look at me, they were all for going. We were sailing back to New York in a week and I said I had heard somewhere that Siamese cats, like some wines and certain poisons, do not travel well. I went on to invent the theory that this strange Asiatic breed is fragile, possessed of a curious death wish, and inclined to die of seasickness. But when women or children buy cats, they keep cats. If you ever see a Siamese cat thumbing a ride by the side of a lonely road, you can be sure it was surreptitiously put out of a car by a dog man and not by a cat woman. Incidentally, for the guidance of such dog husbands as may have cat wives, it is practically impossible to lose a cat. I have records of cats that have been abandoned as far as 585 miles from home and have managed to find their way back, through traffic and across streams, and against all other odds.

Circe and Jezzie did not enjoy the sea voyage, but they survived it, although there were moments when they seemed to be planning to throw themselves overboard, with the idea in mind, I am sure, of returning to earth later in the guise of spirochetes, or loose cellar steps, or United States Senators with voluminous, unevaluated rumours about my un-Siamese activities. The relations between me and the two female felines deteriorated, gradually but surely, all the way from the Hotel Grand Condé on the Rue Saint Sulpice to my home in Silvermine, Connecticut. My friends began to notice the tension between me and the cats, which consisted largely of rigid immobility on the part of all three of us, and a habit of trying to outstare one another.

'You don't understand cats,' one of my friends, Dick Conway, a notorious cat man, told me during a tense week-end at my house. Dick was a writer who found it convenient to explain human and cat problems in terms of eloquent but bewildering metaphors. 'You keep showing them your badge,' he would tell me. 'You pull open a drawer looking for a pistol, not catnip. Siamese cats are full of bells, each with its own sensitive frequency, highly modulated, too, but you insist on tuning in the alarm and not the tinkle.'

I would sit back and try to make sense out of this cipher code while Dick and the cats observed me closely. All three of them had eyes of the same shade of blue, six little blue gun barrels trained on me. I tried, somewhat hysterically, I must confess, to maintain a foothold on Dick's idiom. 'I do not propose to approach these pets,' I said once, 'as if I were going to translate them from the Sanskrit.' Dick cut in quickly with, 'There you go again! You unconsciously put the word "pets" in quotation marks, and the cats know it. They sense the sardonic instantly.'

This was too much for me. 'All right, I'll talk to them in upper case from now on!' I yelled. 'Or would that sound too much like italics? Italics are smug and pretentious, and I suppose they know that.' Dick italicized his superior smile. 'Of course they know it,' he said quietly. I looked at them and they looked at me. They knew it, all right.

I think that Circe and her confederate – Circe had the darker mask and the

blacker silence and the steadier gaze – planned at first to put an end to my life
and dispose of my body. What they plotted was a fatal sprawling fall ending in
grotesque stillness. One evening I almost stepped on a curiously shaped blue
vase the cats had placed on the next to the top step of the stairs going up from
the living-room, or, as they must have thought of it, coming down from the
second floor. A few inches to the left and my foot would have caught the side
of the vase, and I would have plunged all the way down the steps. The cats
were nowhere around at the time, of course, for the purposes of alibi. I took
the vase to my wife, who was in the kitchen, and explained what had almost
happened.

'The darlings couldn't possibly lift a thing like that,' she said. 'You must
have put it there yourself. You know how you absently pick up things when
you are thinking and put them down where they don't belong.' It is true that
I had once put a skillet on top of a phonograph, while trying to straighten out
a paragraph in my mind, and a loaf of bread I had bought at the grocery turned
up, on another occasion, in my bathroom, but the cats were aware of this and
their cunning minds had figured out that I would have been held responsible
for my own demise if their vase trick had worked. 'I hope you won't tell anybody about this,' my wife said in conclusion. 'They would think something is
the matter.' Wives have various ways of saying 'Something is the matter', and
she gave it the inflection that implies the trouble is mental. I decided to tell
about the plot anyway at the next party we attended, but I simply didn't know
how to begin. If a woman companion says over cocktails, 'Have you seen the
movies of any good books recently?' you can't very well reply, 'No, but my
wife's Siamese cats are trying to kill me.' If you say it grimly it sounds as if
you were drunk, and if you say it flippantly it sounds as if you were drunk. So
I simply said, 'No, but I read the books,' and joined a knot of men who were
discussing whatever men discussed that many years ago.

My wife had decided to raise and sell Siamese kittens, and so Circe and
Jezzie were introduced to various Siamese males. These meetings invariably
resulted in nothing more productive than Oriental imprecations, insults and
curses. This was just as well, since, in addition to the two cats, we also had a
kennelful of French poodles – a mother poodle and her eleven puppies – and a
screened-in porchful of Scottish terriers – a mother dog named Jeannie and
her six puppies. The puppies of both breeds had just reached the saleable age
of three months when the Depression occurred and you couldn't give pets
away, let alone sell them. Everybody was trying to unload everything, including saddle horses, but nobody wanted to take them.

I think it was in February, 1930, that we gave up the Silvermine house and
the kennel venture and moved to New York. Five of the young poodles and all
of the Scottie pups had somehow been disposed of – left in cute baskets on
strangers' doorsteps, perhaps, or forced upon relatives and friends at the
point of a gun or a prayer. Jeannie didn't like New York, or poodles, or cats, or
anybody else, so she had been parked with my wife's sister in Westport. I had
nothing to do with getting the mother poodle and her six remaining offspring

to the city – it was mysteriously managed one morning by my wife and an acquaintance of ours who had agreed to go along and help, and who soon thereafter drifted or, to be precise, jumped out of our life. Since nobody else volunteered to help transport the cats to town, it was up to me. I found myself in the back seat of our car with the two cats, a checker-board, an alarm clock, a stack of books, and a heavy cardboard mailing tube, three feet long and four inches in diameter, suitable for carrying drawings – if you're not carrying anything else. My wife drove the car, and our destination was a brownstone in West Fiftieth Street. We had rented an apartment on the top floor where the mother poodle and her six pups, now six months old and full of restlessness and destructive ingenuity, awaited us. We could hear them loudly debating something when the car stopped in front of the brownstone.

I made the mistake of trying to carry the cats and the rest of the stuff in the back seat in one armload, to my wife's dismay and to the cats' delight. They had decided by this time, it soon transpired, not to destroy me, but to humiliate me beyond rehabilitation. All this was a long time ago, but it remains sharply in my tortured memory that I had a cat and the checker-board under one arm, and a cat and the mailing tube under the other, with the index finger of my right hand inserted in the metal ring surmounting the bell on the alarm clock. The books were somehow wedged between my chin and my crossed wrists. The metal ring fitted perfectly; that is, it was easy to get on but almost impossible to get off. Now, nothing has such an unwrapped look outdoors as an unwrapped alarm clock. There is something naked about it, something calculated to make bystanders out of passers-by, especially if it begins to ring, and this one began to ring. Uninterested passers-by suddenly became fascinated bystanders, but nobody offered to help. One or two, fearful of becoming involved in some complex racket common to the streets of New York, hastened away. My wife, half-way up the front steps when the alarm sounded, gave one quick look over her shoulder, ran the rest of the way to the front door, hastily opened it with her key, and disappeared inside. Two or three of the books I was carrying slithered to the pavement, and since the checker-board had no latch, there was a slow, dismal leakage of black and red checkers. It was at this moment that the cats decided it was time for them to dominate the shambles. One of them – Circe, I think – reached up a long graceful front leg, deftly inserted her claws into the brim of my felt hat, and slowly began to draw it down over my eyes. None of the male bystanders did anything except stare, probably figuring that this was the tertiary stage of an incurable dissolution, but a woman decided to help by picking up the books and some of the checkers and trying to pack them back on to me and my parcels of cats and still life. I didn't dare drop the cats, and I couldn't get the ringing clock off my finger, but I let everything else go, and managed somehow or other to get up the steps and reach the door, which I began kicking.

When my wife finally opened the door a few inches and peered out, she beheld a trail of books and checkers leading down to the car. The hat was in the awful pattern somewhere and the mailing tube had rolled into the gutter. The clock had mercifully stopped ringing, but the cats had begun screaming, and there is nothing this side of hell to match the screaming of Siamese cats. I think my wife and the woman Samaritan helped collect the stuff. I think I remember a cop shouting, 'Break it up, now! Break it up!' When my wife and I got inside and closed the door, she took the cats away from me. I was bleeding a little from various scratches. 'It isn't so good upstairs,' she said. I could hear the gleeful yelping of the poodles, who seemed to think it was wonderful upstairs. My wife took the cats and left me to struggle with the clock and to reassemble the litter, some of which was inside and some of which was still out in the vestibule. The kindly woman was in the vestibule too. 'Just what is it?' she asked in the tone of one who simply has to describe what she has been through when she gets home but hasn't the vaguest idea what it actually was. She gave me two checkers and I thanked her and she went away, taking my copy of *The Modern Temper* by Joseph Wood Krutch. Anyway, I hope she is the one that got it. It explains all the predicaments of modern Man except the one I got into that day, and nobody could explain that, or what was still to come.

Historicity lies so close to legend in my world that I often walk with one foot in each area, with side trips, or so my critics declare, into fantasy. This is because of my unenviable talent for stumbling from one confusion into another. Never have my confusions lain so close together, however, as the cat confusion and the dog confusion on that February day nearly twenty-five years ago. It seems that the six young poodles in our apartment had become bored and decided to take everything apart. If you imagine that half a dozen six-month-old poodles raise only a little more than half as much deviltry as eleven would, you don't know poodles. What wasn't so good upstairs, it turned out, was the front room of the apartment where the dogs had been confined, with the hope that their mother would maintain some semblance of order in the temporary absence of human beings. She hadn't. Mother dogs lose interest in their young after they are weaned and disclaim all responsibility for what may happen, indoors or out. The young dogs had taken the phonograph apart, for one thing, and had scattered hundreds of records about the room, as if they had been frantically looking for 'Moonlight Bay' and couldn't find it. Poodles do not like lettuce, mustard and records, so the latter had not been chewed, just scattered. The phonograph had been chewed, though, wood and fabric and metal. The ping-pong table had lost one leg to the onslaught of teeth and collapsed. The collapse would have been something to see and hear, since the table, while still upright, had held three or four paddles, a box containing a dozen balls, thirty or forty books, and an assortment of glass ashtrays, all of which had been added to the jumble of records and pieces of phonograph on the floor. Poodles always listen attentively while being scolded, looking innocent, bewildered and misunderstood. As soon as the lecture was over, they wanted to know if they could take the Siamese cats apart to see what made them scream. I was all for this, but we were outvoted. I can't recall with any clarity what happened after that. Some process of defence mechanism has erased the rest of that ungainly afternoon and evening, except for the protests of a nervously dishevelled gentleman who lived in the apartment below. He came up and knocked on the door and demanded to know what in the name of Heaven we were harbouring and abetting. (Some people merely own dogs, but I harbour them.) 'They are in transit,' I said weakly. He mentioned Federal statutes, state laws, city ordinances, Christianity, common decency, the American Way of Life, and friends of his in high official positions. The young poodles and I listened attentively, all seven of us trembling slightly. The mother dog was asleep, the Siamese cats were profoundly oblivious, and my wife was indignant. What happened after that my memory refuses to divulge. I suppose I slipped away to a speakeasy, in the immemorial manner of the American husband when his household suddenly falls, or is taken, apart. I suppose the bartender who served me drinks that evening thought I was crazy when he asked me, 'What do you know?' and I told him. I still wonder now and then about the husband of the woman who came home with *The Modern Temper* that evening. 'Where d'you get this book?' he must have asked her, and she must have told him.

I don't know what happened to Jezzie finally, but Circe came to a violent end the following year when she sauntered too near a basket containing Jeannie's second litter of Scottish terrier pups. There was no apparent provocation and no warning, just a flash of black and a gleam of teeth, and Circe was no more. I don't think it was assault with intent to kill, but just a maternal reflex, one of the millions of incidents in the bloody pattern of prowl and pounce by means of which Nature maintains its precarious and improbable balance of survival. I am a dog man, as I have confessed, and not a cat man, and as such I have always felt a curious taint of guilt about the unfortunate affair. Dick Conway never actually said so, but I think he considered me a kind of accessory before the fact. I don't know how he came to this morbid conclusion, if he did, but it worried me, and I used to lie awake thinking about Circe until, in the end, I convinced myself that she would come back to earth as a revenant and pounce on me when I was just sauntering along, unprotected and unaware. Once, during such a saunter, I banged my head against the low iron bar of a store awning and was knocked down and dazed. A passer-by helped me to my feet and I mumbled, 'Did you see her? Did you see the cat?' He gave me a concerned look. 'Take it easy, buddy,' he said. 'There wasn't any cat. You banged into that awning.' He thought a moment and added, 'Take a good-sized cat to knock a man down.' I couldn't very well tell him, without being turned over to a cop, that I lived in fear of a Siamese cat that had passed away long ago, so I just muttered something and sauntered on, turning quickly every now and then to see if Something was following me, Something that moved swiftly and made no sound.

Then one day, about five years after Jeannie's fatal pounce, I happened to re-read Clarence Day's wonderful little book called *The Simian World*. This satire on the descent of Man speculates, as almost everybody knows, on the hypothetical nature of the human being if he had descended from other creatures than the anthropoid. The funniest and sharpest chapter of this brilliant exploration deals with the human male and the human female as Cat People. As I read it I realized with a shudder what form my stealthy doom was going to take. In his cat chapter, Mr Day imagines us all at a big party of some kind in a room with thick carpets and heavy draperies. 'Someone is entering! Hush!' writes Mr Day, and he goes on to describe a typical 'lithe silken' female cat human: 'Languorous, slender and passionate. Sleepy eyes that see everything. An indolent, purposeful step. An unimaginable grace. If you were *her* lover, my boy, you would learn how fierce love can be, how capricious and sudden, how hostile, how ecstatic, how violent!' I put down the book and got up and mixed myself a strong whisky-and-soda. At least, I thought shakily, the late Circe, in contriving to bring the chapter to my attention again, had had the unimaginable grace, or perhaps merely the malicious deviltry, to forewarn me of my doom.

Several months after this dreadful revelation Jeannie died of a surfeit of candy, a box of assorted chocolates which, I was confident, had been deliberately placed within her reach by some lithe, silken lady who walked with an indolent, purposeful step. Of course, Jeannie was a very old dog then, but she had probably spent her last years sleeping with one eye open, keeping a sharp lookout for a cat the size of a Saint Bernard, little suspecting that Circe was a woman now, dressed like other women, but a little faster of hand and foot, with slippers as soundless as velvet. They are all Pavlowas, Mr Day had written of female cat humans, and I became wary of women dancers and of dancing in general. Once, though, off guard on a summer evening, I found myself dancing with a woman of exceedingly light step and unimaginable grace and I commented on her ability. 'Oh, I'm a real Pavlowa,' she said in a voice that seemed like a purr. She had sleepy eyes. I almost yelled, 'Cut in on me, for God's sake, somebody! I'm dancing with Circe! I'm dancing with the cat that has sworn to kill me!' I was restrained by the sudden horrible sense that I would be seized and put away, and so I trembled through the dance until the music ended. I had not caught my partner's name, but when I demanded of my startled hostess, 'Who is that Siamese cat I was dancing with?' she reassured me by saying, 'You mean Betty Schwartz? She's Charley Schwartz's wife. Why?' I laughed idiotically and sighed with relief. The final irony could never be *quite* that grotesque. I was never going to be finished off by anybody named Betty. A cat human named Betty would be the reincarnation of a tabby cat, and I am only moderately afraid of tabby cats.

Clarence Day's female cat humans began to prowl my nightmares and to turn up on the corners and in the parlours of my daily life. Looking back from this distance, I can't always distinguish between the reality and the dream, the cat substance and the cat shadow. Most of the ladies, in nightmare or actuality, were possessed of strange feline agilities. One of them, although only five feet two inches tall, got a book down from a shelf too high for me to reach, and I am almost six feet two. Another wanted to discuss Carl Van Vechten and James Mason, two celebrated admirers of cats, and left me abruptly when I brought up the subject of Albert Payson Terhune. A third – oh, I must have met *her* in a dream – said, at five o'clock one afternoon in her drawing-room, 'Do you like tea in your cream?' I never met a Miss Graymalkin, or a Mrs Thomas Katz who lived in a place called The Mews and tried to lure me there on the pretence of showing me her falcons. (Mews, Webster tells me, are cages for hawks.) I really did know a lady, though, who owned a Scottish terrier named Duncan and a bold female cat named Lady, whose name was lengthened to Lady Macbeth after the mysterious and violent death of Duncan. I don't know what became of this woman, but she probably knows where I am. Female cat humans, as I interpret Mr Day, would not phone or send telegrams, since they would not believe in swift means of communication. Their swiftness lies in sudden and unexpected personal appearances.

The last, or the latest, lady of my acquaintance that I genuinely suspected of being Circe in disguise materialized in the chair next to mine about seven years ago in Bermuda at a cocktail party which had reached midnight and was still rolling. This lady began urging me to stop arguing and to start singing, and I asked her what she wanted me to sing. My repertory consists of 'Who', 'Bye-Bye Blackbird', 'Linger Awhile', 'Do You Ever Think of Me?' and 'Manhattan', but what the lady wanted was a song, popular at the time, called 'The Girl That I Marry'. To anybody except me this song is as bland and innocuous as the satins and laces, the cologne and the gardenia with which it gently deals, and so my host and hostess and all the guests except Circe, if it was Circe, were bewildered when I leaped to my feet in the midst of the song, grabbed my hat and coat and wife, and left the party. You have probably figured what had alarmed me, now that you know all about my phobia. It was, of course, the line that goes: 'I'll be sittin' next to her, and she'll purr like a kitten.' After I had jammed my wife into a cab, I explained, 'Maybe her purr is worse than her scratch, but she was definitely purring.' My wife sighed and said simply, 'We stayed too late.'

At my present age, I have begun to feel that I am comparatively safe, and there are so many things besides cats and women to worry about: taxes, fission, fusion, more taxes, subversion, sub-committees, flying saucers (without cream), human beings descended from anthropoids, that persistent pain in my left shoulder, those funny sounds in the attic and in the engine of my car, my increasing blood pressure, my decreasing inventiveness, and the vast Category of Catastrophes. There I go again! This brings me right back where I started, always a good place to stop. A note of warning, however, in conclusion: if you are a dog man who has offended a cat woman, beware of boxes of assorted chocolates that appear suddenly at your elbow without explanation. Have the chocolates analysed by a chemist, and be sure it is a male dog chemist, and not a female cat chemist.

The Duchess and the Bugs

IT is a great moment for an Ohio writer living far from home when he realizes he has not been forgotten by the state he can't forget. He is especially happy to be so signally honoured by a distinguished organization devoted to putting books on shelves instead of taking them off. The writer of humorous pieces has so much fun producing his output that he doesn't always regard it as work, and he is likely to be surprised if it is singled out for an award. He is used to being laughed at, he hopes to be laughed with, but he doesn't expect to be taken seriously, although he likes to believe Booth Tarkington was exaggerating when he said, 'Sobersides looks at humour the way a duchess looks at bugs.' At the same time he is proud of his trade, in spite of his moments of depression when he is convinced that he is read only by duchesses. I have heard from duchesses who suggest that I quit harping on the imaginary flaws of the American Woman and start writing a novel about her true power and glory. I reply that I may try to write such a novel – when my spirit has been broken by the American Woman's power, or transfigured by her glory.

Meanwhile, as my publishers know, I couldn't do without her. Somebody has said that Woman's place is in the wrong. That's fine. What the wrong needs is a woman's presence and a woman's touch. She is far better equipped than men to set it right. The condescending male, in his pride of strength, likes to think of the female as being 'soft, soft as snow', but just wait till he gets hit by the snowball. Almost any century now Woman may lose her patience with black politics and red war and let fly. I wish I could be on earth then to witness the saving of our self-destructive species by its greatest force. If I have sometimes seemed to make fun of Woman, I assure you it has only been for the purpose of egging her on.

A woman practitioner of humour announced a few years ago, in an hour of despair, that humour is a shield and not a weapon. Well, the world has plenty of weapons and it can use a few shields. There used to be men among us who could brandish the shield of humour with telling effect in the now sensitive area of politics and government, giving certain Senators and Congressmen of their time a pretty good banging around. I mean such men, to name only a few, as the H. L. Mencken of an earlier and bolder day, and Finley Peter Dunne, and William Allen White, and old Ed Howe, and Ohio's unforgettable Bob Ryder. The gentle heart, thank God, is often armoured in toughness, courage, and strength. The tradition of rugged and unafraid humour perpetuated by these men must not be allowed to pass into legend and limbo, out of fear and trembling. They did not invent the tradition, of course. It came over in the *Mayflower*, it flourished in the free American soil, it was carried westward in covered wagons, it was borne upon our battlefields as bright and inspiring as regimental colours. It has been seasick, wagon-weary, and shot full of holes, but it has always managed to keep on going.

As a matter of fact, comedy, in all its forms, including the rusty art of political satire, is used to surviving eras of stress and strain, even of fear and trembling, but it sickens in the weather of intimidation and suppression, and such a sickness could infect a whole nation. The only rules comedy can tolerate are those of taste, and the only limitations those of libel. It should be as free and respected as Lincoln's humour or Churchill's wit. It must not be mistaken for, or identified with, a man's political views, or punished for his political past. It will not bear up long under mindless picketing. We must not have guilt by talent, or guilt by profession. There has been so much banning and burning and branding that timorous writers have begun to think of writing as somehow akin to counterfeiting or forgery. One distinguished writer of comedy is reported to have promised a sub-committee of Congress that, to make up for past associations, he was going to write an anti-Communist musical comedy. Humour should never take the form of penance or of penitence. Since the nature of humour is anti-communistic, just as the nature of Communism is anti-humour, such a project would amount, in effect, to an anti-humorous musical comedy. This would be too dull and awful to contemplate, let alone to attend. I would have to be dragged to it. Our comedy should deal, in its own immemorial manner, with the American scene and the American people, without fear or favour, without guilt or grovelling. There is no other form up with which, to paraphrase Sir Winston, we will ever put. Most professional writers, by the way, are happy that the Nobel Prize has gone to a professional writer who says things any damned way he wants to. The thunder of his prose and the lightning of his wit have done much to clear the air for us and to illumine the way.

Let us not forget the uses of laughter or store them away in the attic. If a thing cannot endure laughter, Professor Joseph Russell Taylor used to say, it is not a good thing. He made us understand that laughter is never out of date or out of place. Dangerous men, he once said, are nourished as much by attack as they are by praise. It magnifies their importance, builds them a stately mansion on the front page, and dignifies their meanest motives and their merest shenanigans. Laughter, on the other hand, is often their undoing. It shows them up in a clear and honest light, and drives away the big distorted shadows in which they love to lurk. Many of the perils they flaunt in the shadows are real perils, but they can be dealt with better in the light. Laughter could bring many things out into the open including, I should like to put in here, the true shape and purpose of our Bill of Rights. It was designed as a fortress and a sanctuary, not as a hideout.

I have no doubt that there have been a few conspiratorial writers around, but all the writers I know personally would make very incompetent conspirators. They like to do things in public, not in secret. They want everybody to know what they are up to. The night that Alexander Woollcott was fatally stricken with a heart attack he was engaged in what E. B. White described as a 'public brawl', by which he meant a radio discussion panel over a nation-wide network. An elderly writer I know, a man about ten years older than I am, recently entered a New York hospital for a check-up under an assumed name. The day after he came in he asked his nurse why nobody had telephoned or sent wires, and she reminded him that he had quietly entered the hospital under a pseudonym. 'I know that,' he said irritably, 'but I thought everybody would find it out.'

Some frightened sponsors and radio stations and other well-known pussy-cats have shown, from time to time, a phobia against anyone who has become what is known as a 'controversial figure'. This stupidity has struck at writers who, in this controversial country, have always been controversial persons. A controversial figure is apparently a controversial person who is not afraid to let his views be known outside his own living-room. Discussion in America means dissent. We love to disagree with persons whose opinions we value, for how else are we going to make them value ours? One writer I know and admire was told by his doctors to give up coffee and controversy. He replied that he couldn't live without coffee and couldn't make a living without controversy. He might have said, with equal truth, that he couldn't live without coffee, and wouldn't want to live without controversy. It is possible that this strange and unbecoming hush-hush which seems to have overtaken us is in some way responsible for the decline of humour in America. At any rate, humour flourished in the free and untrammelled 'twenties when, as Harold Ross once put it, humorists were a dime a dozen. There are not many left, alas, and only a handful coming up. I hope that literary humour, by which I mean humour written for newspaper, magazine and book publication, is not dying out in the United States. It has a long and honourable tradition, but it is hanging on by ageing fingertips and it needs new recruits. E. B. White once wrote, '. . . humorous writing, like poetical writing, has an extra content. It plays, like an active child, close to the big, hot fire which is Truth.' The devoted writer of humour will continue to try to come as close to truth as he can, even if he gets burned in the process, but I don't think he will get too badly burned. His faith in the good will, the soundness, and the sense of humour of his countrymen will always serve as his asbestos curtain.